ALCOHOL AND CIVILIZATION

This symposium was designed, organized,
and chaired by the editor,
who was appointed General Program Chairman
by the Department of Continuing Education in Medicine,
University of California School of Medicine,
San Francisco.

ALCOHOL AND CIVILIZATION

Edited by

SALVATORE PABLO LUCIA, M.D., SC.D.

Professor of Medicine and Preventive Medicine;
Chairman of the Department of Preventive Medicine;
Lecturer in Medical History and Bibliography;
Consulting Physician in Oncology;
University of California School of Medicine,
San Francisco, California

McGRAW-HILL
BOOK COMPANY, INC.

New York
San Francisco
Toronto
London

ALCOHOL AND CIVILIZATION

CONTRIBUTORS AND PARTICIPANTS

Franz Alexander, M.D.   Director, Psychiatric and Psychosomatic Research Institute, Mount Sinai Hospital, Los Angeles, California.

Claudia Balboni, M.D.   International Center for Psychodietetics, Rome, Italy.

Karl M. Bowman, M.D.   Professor of Psychiatry, Emeritus, University of California School of Medicine, San Francisco, California.

Kettil Bruun, Ph.D.   Chief, The Finnish Foundation for Alcohol Studies, Helsinki, Finland.

J. Anthony Deutsch, D.Phil.   Associate Professor of Psychiatry and Psychology, Stanford University, Stanford, California.

William Dock, M.D.   Professor of Medicine, State University of New York Downstate Medical Center, Brooklyn, New York.

George C. Drew, M.A.   Professor of Psychology, University College, London, England.

Olof A. Forsander, Ph.D.   Chief, Department of Physiology, Research Laboratories of the State Alcohol Monopoly, Helsinki, Finland.

Leonard Goldberg, M.D.   Professor and Chairman, Department of Alcohol Research, Karolinska Institutet, Stockholm, Sweden.

Leon A. Greenberg, Ph.D.   Professor of Physiology and Biochemistry, Rutgers University, New Brunswick, New Jersey.

Chauncey D. Leake, Ph.D.   Professor of Pharmacology, Ohio State University, Columbus, Ohio

Giorgio Lolli, M.D.   President, International Center for Psychodietetics, Rome, Italy, and New York City, New York.

Salvatore P. Lucia, M.D., Sc.D.   Professor of Medicine and Preventive Medicine, Chairman of the Department of Preventive Medicine; Lecturer in Medical History and Bibliography; and Consulting Physician in Oncology, University of California School of Medicine, San Francisco, California.

David G. Mandelbaum, Ph.D.   Professor of Anthropology and Curator of Ethnology, University of California, Berkeley, California.

Jules H. Masserman, M.D.   Professor of Psychiatry and Neurology, Northwestern University, Evanston, Illinois; and Director of Training, Illinois State Psychiatric Institute, Chicago, Illinois.

v

The Honorable John M. Murtagh, Chief Justice, Court of Special Sessions, New York City, New York.

Nello Pace, Ph.D. Professor of Physiology, Department of Anatomy and Physiology, University of California, Berkeley, California.

Karl H. Pribram, M.D. Associate Professor of Psychiatry and Psychology, Stanford University, Stanford, California.

Berton Roueché, Author, New York City, New York.

John B. deC. M. Saunders, M.D., Ch.B., F.R.C.S. (Edin.) Provost, University of California Medical Center; Dean, School of Medicine; Professor of Anatomy, and Lecturer in Medical History and Bibliography, San Francisco, California.

Robert Straus, Ph.D. Professor and Chairman, Department of Behavioral Sciences, University of Kentucky Medical Center, Lexington, Kentucky.

Alcohol and Civilization, like the symposium on which it is based, is designed to discuss alcohol and its interaction with contemporary civilization; to recapitulate the fascinating story of fermented dietary beverage; to allow us new insight into its ancient uses and offer an opportunity to interpret its significance; and to provide a suitable medium for both scientists working in this field and for an interested audience to learn more about the experimental work dealing with alcohol now being carried out in institutes and university laboratories in many places in the world.

The age in which we live, filled with fear and guilt, anxiety and frustrations, has led us to accept certain dicta as unchallengeable; we have become warped into a pattern of society, rigid in many of its concepts and institutions, and in defense of our selections most of us have spun a protective cocoon as an insulation against our plight and prejudice. Often, when we disagree with a forcefully stated opinion, we may find the effort to contradict it too much for our delicately adjusted emotional equilibrium. Through conditioning, and by conformity, we have come to accept certain acts as sinful—the judgment, often, of a vocal minority—though these acts might in effect prove harmful only to a few.

Toward the end of the last century and during the early part of this century, an intensive campaign was waged against the abuse of alcohol. But in our time alcohol has a negative influence on a minority only. Yet, so strongly has the sense of wrong been inculcated in us with regard to alcohol that one rarely discusses the great mass of people who have derived benefits from its use. So intent are we on rooting out this "evil" that we are willing to throw out the baby with the bathwater. We forget, or blot out from our memories, that fermented beverages have been used as a dietary supplement since the time of the most ancient civilizations.

Fermented dietary beverages, whether of grapes, grains, or other plants or fruits, have been important throughout the history of man. The cultural patterns of many civilizations were woven around the artful use of such beverages. We do not know when in the history of mankind fermentation was discovered, but from the available data it is evident that it has been known and used by man since before re-corded history. In the varieties and elaborations of its uses we en-counter evidence of progressively advanced sophistication. A fer-mented beverage became the all-encompassing symbol of survival, coequal with bread; it was prerequisite in religious and libational ceremonies, affording a closer communion with the gods—its mysteri-ous powers having been accepted as divine manifestations; and man soon learned that it was a useful tool for the healing of the sick—as a medicine and as a vehicle for the many plant substances of the materia medica. In this latter sphere, long tracts have been written on the artful uses of fermented dietary beverages, most notably wine.

In the twentieth century there has been a revival of interest in the value of fermented dietary beverages, and scientists the world over are testing some of the empirical observations of ancient healers. This search has brought to light many interesting facts—facts rarely men-tioned in discussions on alcohol, since the latter usually implies the ogre, alcoholism. But it is only by presenting all the facts to scientists as well as to an interested audience that we can hope to learn in what way an agent or a substance may be used best to alleviate human suffering.

In *Alcohol and Civilization* we have attempted to present the subject from an interdisciplinary viewpoint. Our search for contribu-tors has transcended the usual boundaries of geography and scientific disciplines, and we are fortunate in being able to assemble eminent authorities in the pharmacological, physiological, sociopsychological, psychiatric, and legal fields. We are thus, for the first time, we be-lieve, presenting the subject of alcohol in the broad perspective it deserves. We have reviewed the historic data and learned from them man's needs for an agent which would offer him tranquility and a sense of completeness, and which would, at the same time, afford him relief from fear, anxiety, and pain. In the course of compiling, we have developed new respect for the ancient healers whose observa-tions on the uses of wine in a variety of diseases were so acute that many of their empirical conclusions are only now being scientifically documented in our laboratories. We have brought unprejudiced in-formation on the use of alcohol in civilizations and have had re-emphasized that "in the fruit of the vine, therein lies healing for mankind" [Koran].

One of the few sociocultural elements which has survived the corrosion of time is fermented dietary beverage—the most common exemplar being wine. This alone would suggest that its value and significance must be acknowledged; that instead of discarding it as a "demon," we should have the courage to investigate it further, to discuss it, and to use it for its potential beneficial effects in alleviating the too frequent frustrations of confused living.

The editor wishes to thank the contributors for their excellent and thought-provoking presentations and Dr. Seymour Farber and the Department of Continuing Education, University of California School of Medicine, for constructive suggestions, cooperation, and the opportunity to present this conference on "Alcohol and Civilization." In addition, thanks are proffered to the California Wine Advisory Board, State Department of Agriculture, for support without restriction.

Salvatore P. Lucia, M.D.

John B. deC. M. Saunders, M.D.
Provost, University of California Medical Center, San Francisco
Dean, School of Medicine, University of California, San Francisco

INTRODUCTION

In extending a welcome to a symposium entitled Alcohol and Civilization, it is appropriate to reflect that in its Greek derivation, a symposium had reference to the after dinner drinking party of boon companions. The Greeks in Homeric times saw in the effects of wine the production of a state of mind, a bewildering of consciousness which they called *atē* (ἄτη). This state they regarded as a partial or temporary insanity due not to physiological or psychological causes but to an external daemonic agency or supernatural being residing in the wine itself and hence its spirit or life. As Professor Dodds, the Oxford classicist, pointed out in the Sather Lectures given at this University a dozen years ago, this Greek concept of *atē* in the epic tradition stood for "irrational as distinct from rationally purposive behavior."

Later, as an Ionic importation, *atē* became associated with the Babylonian and Judaic sense of guilt which related to concepts of punishments for moral evils. The greatest of those evils was wanton violence, insolence and riotousness, commonly referred to as *hubris*, and "*hubris* is the primal evil" (υβρις πρῶτον κακόν). Consequently, at Athens, the hubristic law (νόμος ὕβρεως) was very important and comprehended all the more serious injuries done to the person from malicious assault as when under the influence of wine. The concept of *atē* then changed, and the evil debt might be visited upon the children or lead to utter ruin. It became personified as Ate (Ἄτη), the goddess of mischief and the author of all blind, rash actions and their results. The precise theological interpretation, says Dodds, "makes of *atē* not merely a punishment leading to physical disasters, but a deliberate deception which draws the victim on to fresh error, intellectual or moral, whereby he hastens his own ruin—the grim doctrine that *quem deus vult perdere, prius dementat* (whom God wishes to destroy, he first makes mad)." Or, as the Book of Proverbs proclaims, "Give strong drink unto him that is ready to perish. . . ."

But there were other products of these drinking parties. Here arose the refinements of civilization, the symposial songs and the literary tradition of poetry as stated by Cratinos and echoed by Horace that the best poets have sought and found inspiration in drink. Here, under the mellow influence of wine, came social and intellectual entertainment to inspire Plato, Xenophon, and Plutarch to label their famous dialogues "symposia."

The relevance of those ancient Greek views to the topic at hand is obvious since we promptly recognize them like fossils buried in the breccia or matrix of Western culture. Here we see the source, perhaps, of that emotionalism which, owing to the primitiveness of the behavioral sciences, has so beset, in its lack of objectivity and partisanship, the subject of alcohol.

The development of a biological perspective on the alcohol problem has come to us very late. Reasoning by analogy and in the clinical traditions of Hippocrates and Sydenham rather than in terms of the new science, Thomas Trotter submitted his doctoral thesis to the University of Edinburgh, in 1788, contending that inebriety was "a disease produced by a remote cause." But it would require the evolution of a sophisticated chemistry and the suppression of vitalistic theory before Justus von Liebig could establish the manner in which alcohol is metabolized by oxidation. With the addition of an organic and cellular pathology came that enormous preoccupation with the toxic effects of alcohol which proved so stultifying to the development of a deeper understanding of metabolic and psychological correlations.

From the extremes of a self-centered biological position, and in recognition of the complexities of the alcohol problem, we are now constrained to take a more holistic view; to recognize that undue concentration on single factors, be they medical, psychological, social, religious, educational, or legal, tends to distort rather than to offer understanding of the subject. Consequently, this symposium brings together many experts and authorities from differing fields who, we hope, through their discussions will provide us with that comprehensive overview which will both mutually illuminate and yet exhibit the gaps in our understanding.

CONTENTS

xiii

Contents

1

THE EFFECTS OF ALCOHOL ON THE BODY

Dr. Leake   *Alcohol is probably the most widely used drug in the world, and certainly it is the drug with which humanity has had the longest experience.*

Dr. Dock   *There has developed a great gap between the pharmacologic effect or the therapeutic usefulness of alcohol and the use of alcohol by physicians in the management of disease. As a result, most of the clinical value of alcohol has been lost to our patients.*

Dr. Pace   *We ought to change our views on the patron god of drinkers, from Bacchus to Janus. I think we are dealing with a two-faced problem.*

Chauncey D. Leake

Former President, American Association for the Advancement of Science
Professor of Pharmacology, Ohio State University, Columbus, Ohio

GOOD-WILLED JUDGMENT ON ALCOHOL

Editor's Note   *Dr. Leake's address was delivered in the evening of the first day of the symposium, as a dinner talk. In conformity with the symposial character of his statement, he entitled it, in Greek,* Eudaemonic Methophronesis—*aptly translated into English as "Good-willed Judgment on Alcohol." For two reasons, it seems appropriate to place this address at the beginning rather than at the conclusion of the present section. First, it presents a historical background of the uses of alcoholic beverages—a brief outline of man's drinking history, with special reference to the development of a drinking culture in the United States—which naturally takes precedence over such topics as the metabolism of alcohol and effects of alcohol metabolism on the body. Further, Dr. Leake reviews, in nontechnical language, some of the common effects of alcohol; and this broad overview can serve as an introduction to the more formal presentations which follow, facilitating their comprehension by the reader untrained in biochemistry and physiology. Dr. Leake's classical allusions and perspective, moreover, aptly sound the keynote for the symposium as a whole.*

In the late summer of 1960, the Twentieth International Congress on the History of Medicine met in Athens and Cos. One of the delightful features of the conference was a symposium—a genuine symposium, built around wine, which, with beer, was the first great civilizing way in which "alcohol" was used. The symposium was held in a fragrant pine grove on a hillside by the vale of Daphni. This is about halfway on the old Sacred Road, along which festive throngs danced for centuries from Athens to Eleusis for the ancient annual rites of the great Mother Goddess.

At Daphni there had long been a shrine to Apollo, the sportive sun-god, whose darts could kill and whose caress could cure. It was here that the beautiful nymph who gave her name to the place eluded Apollo by changing herself to a laurel or bay tree. In suppressing the pagan miracle cults of Apollo and his healing son, Aesculapius, the early Christians built one of their most ornately decorated churches at Daphni. The splendid mosaics in this building testify to the religious skill and art of the Byzantines.

Apollo's son, Aesculapius, became revered as the god of miraculous healing. After his early cult had flourished at Tricca and Epidaurus, he was honored with resplendent temples for his curative rites at every major community in the classical Greek world. Votive offerings at these temples testify to his miraculous cures following a ritualistic incubation sleep and a visit from the sacred serpents. The ritualistic sleep may well have been aided by wine, and the miraculous cures may well have been furthered by the skill of such lay physicians associated with the Asclepieum as Hippocrates at Cos and Euphyron at Cnidus.

At Daphni, however, the healing cult remained Apollonian until the Byzantine Christians took over. It is highly probable that there was a sacred grove nearby at which festive rites involving wine were conducted. It is intriguing to imagine that these rites still continue in part.

For a dozen weeks toward the end of summer the beautiful pine grove is alive each evening with happy visitors. On entering the gates, one pays a small admission fee and receives a half-liter jug and small glass. One then proceeds along the gravel paths in the grove to a series of pavilions which are scattered at pleasant distances from each other. There are some eighty of these pavilions at which casks of wine are maintained, presided over by dark-haired Greek girls in sparkling native raiment. Each pavilion represents some special winegrowing district in Greece. The visitor may sample any wine desired and after rinsing the cup at the nearby spring may proceed to the next pavilion. When a visitor finds the wine of choice, the half-liter jug may be filled with it, and the visitor may then proceed to the feast.

Scattered through the grove are some three eating and dancing areas. Here, slow-turning hand spits carry lamb, goat, and chickens, any one or all of which may be piled on a platter, along with fragrant cheeses, good breads, honey, and fresh fruits. Small tables cluster around a large dancing floor, where old Greek dances are performed by gaily dressed participants to the accompaniment of pipes, flutes, and drums.

It may be appreciated that the tasting of the various wines produces a gradual feeling of pleasant relaxation, and the soft lights, the green pine boughs, and the gay music make one feel very happy indeed. The evening goes rapidly. The lights dim slowly, and before midnight all have departed and the grove is quiet.

Here is truly a civilizing experience. The groups with which one may mingle are friendly, interested, and given to cheerful reflection and gay comment on the local scene and the joys of good friendship. There seems always to be respect for the ancient Greek ideal of moderation. The Greek maxim, "nothing to excess," may indeed have been a recognition of the importance of self-discipline among a people given naturally to extremes.

One may learn many interesting things about wine at the Daphni festival. For example, scholars have long been intrigued by a phrase used so often in the Homeric poems about the "wine-dark sea." To anyone who has rejoiced in the deep rich sparkling blue of the seas around Greece, the phrase becomes immediately clear when one sees Corinthian wines. These are a deep rich sparkling blue, almost purplish black, and do indeed look like the seas described by Homer. One learns also how the pine resins added to wines in Greece are supposed to confer increased medicinal value to the wine and also to help preserve it. One learns further how varied are the preferences that different people have for different qualities of wine.

An evening at the Daphni wine festival is a rewarding experience. How pleasant it might be if we could develop something of the same sort in our own country! There is also something nostalgically pleasant about the old German outdoor beer gardens; why not revive them, along with the annual wine festival in each of our major communities? Here might be a pleasant civilizing influence which those very ancient beverages, beer and wine, could promote, if taken in moderation.

THE USES OF ALCOHOLIC BEVERAGES

Local groups of people in all parts of the earth learned very early that if wet grain mashes or fruit juices are allowed to stand in the warmth, they would change and, if drunk thereafter, would produce rather pleasing effects. It was quickly found also, as the story of Noah and his sons indicates, that if too much were drunk, there would come confusion, peculiar behavior, and sleep. The beverages made from fermented grains were the early beers, and the drinks made from fermented fruit juices were the wines.

Generally, the use of these strange drinks, which were thought to have magical powers, became socially and ritually controlled. Under these circumstances, whatever excesses might occur were indulged in by all the group, so that there remained a sense of social unity. The ritualistic use was often part of the organized religious services which tended always to bring the group closer together in a common experience and to relate the group more satisfactorily to its environment and its members to each other.

Wine drinking may have early become a feature of the formalities associated with any sort of negotiation or discussion between rival individuals or groups, as in arranging marriages or places to live for migrating families or groups. If so, wine may well have become slowly recognized as a relaxing factor, helpful in easing social tensions. Allusion was made to this in my *Letheon:*[1]

> What Bacchic genius first found joy in fruit juice
> worked upon by warming sun?
> Each tribe preserved the mythic hints
> of earthy Dionysean secrets,
> which suggested peace from frenzied want.
> Peace came with wines and human sympathy.

In the Mediterranean area, the grapes grew on the northeast and northern shores, and here wines became prevalent. Along much of the Nile Valley it was too hot for grapes, so the more common beverage was beer. Many rock carvings and paintings exist from as early as the fourth millennium B.C., showing workmen going through the procedures of fermenting grains and making beers for storage in large jars. Indeed, beer seems to have been so commonly used in old Egypt that it was frequently employed as a vehicle for the prescriptions recommended in such medical papyri as Ebers, Hearst, London, and Berlin, which in their present form date from around 1700 B.C., although they seem to have been copies from much earlier originals. The quantity of beer recommended as a vehicle for the drugs to be used would often have been sufficient in itself to have produced some relaxing and comfortable feeling.

[1] C. D. Leake, *Letheon: The Cadenced Story of Anesthesia,* Austin, University of Texas Press, 1947.

Wines were more generally used among the Semitic peoples of the eastern Mediterranean and among those groups which successively populated the Greek mainland and islands as well as Sicily and Italy. These wines were early used as beverages with meals. Indeed, it may very early have been found that wines and beers were safer to drink than ordinary water. The common pollution of water in ancient times must have contributed to the frequent dysenteries and worm infestations. Slowly the knowledge must have grown that if diarrheas or worm infestations were to be avoided, it would be wise to drink beer and wine.

In more northern European areas, honey fermented, and the resulting potent mead became the socially acceptable beverage. Here, also, the fermented drink was used ritualistically, and often it was employed to raise the emotions in connection with warfare. It is interesting that although beers and wines have remained with us from remote antiquity, mead has practically disappeared from current use.

Among the ancient Greeks there was much respect for wines. In the older matriarchal era wines must have been extensively used ritualistically. The annual sacrifice of the king of the group was probably readily accomplished by getting him well drunk. At the same time the ritualistic use of wine encouraged the orgiastic ceremonies of such women as the maenads, with raving and prophecy until exhaustion occurred. It may well have been that in those ancient days the men, who counted for so little in the tribal organization, were the first to deplore the excessive drinking of wine. It may very well have been the recognition of the tendency of the Greeks themselves to go to excesses that led them to adopt the general admonition of "moderation in all things."

During the second millennium B.C. two groups of Scythian peoples came into the eastern Mediterranean: the Danaan into Greece, and the Gaels along the coast of Asia Minor to Palestine and Crete. These peoples were totem worshipers of the bull and goat, and their antagonisms were reflected in the Mycenaean wars. Their religious beliefs, which were essentially matriarchal, followed them later into Ireland. In Greece their gods survived as Zagreus, the son of Zeus who was reborn as Dionysus. The latter gradually became associated with intense religious rituals revolving around the use of wine, and their socially scandalous excesses were not effectively curbed until well into the Roman era.

During Roman and Byzantine times wines remained the chief table beverage for use in the cities, while beers and mead were extensively drunk in rural areas. As monasteries grew, following the decline of the Roman Empire, winemaking became an essential feature of their economy. This tradition has long persisted.

Meanwhile, with the rise of the Muslim world, a highly sophisticated culture developed, utilizing the ideas and information transmitted from the Greco-Roman period. An extremely important innovation in handling wines occurred under Arabic influence. This was, as customary for the time, an interesting combination of technology and philosophical speculation.

It was generally recognized that there was something rather potent in wine, which could make people feel better, more vigorous, and indeed younger. This was believed to be the "spirit" of wine. Ways and means were considered for isolating this spirit, or at least for getting it in more concentrated form.

The technical procedure developed around a way of heating wine, then preventing the spirit from escaping, and then cooling it so that it would, as we say, condense. Thus, the technique and art of distillation were discovered.

Since the spirit of wine came off in such a finely divided condition as to be invisible, it was called "al-kohl," an Arabic word which means "finely divided spirit," and has become our word alcohol. Certainly, such of this spirit as was captured by distillation was more potent and rapid in its effects than it had been when diluted in the original wine.

At first these distilled spirits were used medicinally. They were found to produce the same kinds of effects, but much more quickly, than when relatively large amounts of wine were drunk. Many attempts were made to explore further the principles of distillation in order to obtain the "elixir of life," that essential spirit of wine which would really make people feel young and keep them so. It is remarkable that this pathetic search has not ceased.

Distillation brought in many delectable "liqueurs," which were flavored by the fermented fruit juices from which they were obtained. At the monasteries many such liqueurs were developed with intricate combinations of health-giving herbs, in a further effort to obtain desired medicinal effect.

As the drinking of alcoholic beverages passed, in the course of history, from ritualistic and other strict forms of social control, drinking to satisfy individual desire became increasingly possible. Excessive drinking thus made its appearance in numerous places among a great many peoples throughout the world. This development and its accompanying problems usually evoked in reaction a variety of attempts at control, sometimes in the form of prohibition. A great body of literature critical of excessive drinking was another by-product of this development. In Europe, the appearance and increasing availability of distilled spirits during the present millennium, which made it so much easier to achieve inebriety, ultimately coincided with increasing population and intensified social pressures, and thus troubles with alcohol came more and more sharply to the fore.

The social disturbances occasioned by the Industrial Revolution toward the end of the eighteenth century, especially in England, brought a renewed intensification of these difficulties with alcohol. The displacement of large numbers of people from quiet rural environments to the factory slums of large cities resulted in appalling misery. Crowded together under filthy conditions, with long working hours and with wholly inadequate pay, the workers lived under pitiable and deplorable conditions. The new class of manufacturers did little to ameliorate the situation; labor was simply a commodity to be bought, and the devil take the hindmost.

Apparently in reaction to their misery, the poor classes had recourse increasingly to cheap and potent alcoholic drinks. The cheapest was "gin," which originally was prepared in Holland, with juniper berries as flavoring. It could be made very cheaply from grain or potatoes, allowing huge profits. The gin mills of London and other big English cities became a national disgrace.

This situation merely increased the social stratification already well under way in England and other industrializing countries. The wealthy continued to use wines in a dignified and appropriate way for enhancing social intercourse, while the poor people and workers swilled beer and gin to forget their miseries.

It was indeed during the eighteenth century period of "enlightenment" that many of the refined conventions regarding alcoholic beverages became established, at least for the socially elite. These evolved from long experience in the use of alcoholic drinks. Thus a "dry" fortified wine, such as sherry, was recognized as appropriate to stimulate appetite before a meal, but one small glass would be adequate and the meal should begin within fifteen to twenty minutes after the *apéritif*. Highly sophisticated tastes developed regarding the appropriateness of various wines to be used as beverages during the meal. Thus light white wines were considered appropriate with fish, poultry, and other such light foods, whereas full-bodied red wines seemed appropriate with meats and heavier foods. Special areas in France, Germany, Italy, and Spain became renowned for the special varieties of wines which they produced, and a sophisticated knowledge of the differences between wines came to be recognized as a cultural asset and still remains a status symbol.

In order to help sleep, after the evening meal it seemed that stronger liquors, such as brandies distilled from wines, were efficacious; in England, particularly, a fortified wine such as port was found useful and pleasant to induce a night's good repose.

Beer drinking extended widely in the Germanic areas and became an essential part of the social conviviality during the long nights. By and large, during the eighteenth and nineteenth centuries, the general civilizing influence of beers and wines became apparent. The beers seemed to promote the *gemütlichkeit* which made everyone in the group feel so good, and the wines gave an air of social grace to family dinners as well as formal banquets.

When one examines carefully the socially approved use of alcoholic beverages during the eighteenth century Age of Enlightenment, as typified by the conventions among the gentlemen and ladies of England and France, one cannot help but be impressed by the good judgment shown socially in utilizing advantageously the now-known actions of alcohol for social benefit. Consider, for example, the merits of the "snifter," that exquisite bit of glassware in which the volatility of alcohol is condensed invisibly to the spirit which is inhaled, thus assuring the rapid absorption, by the tremendous absorbing area of the lungs, of the delectable fragrance of the brandy distilled from grape wine.

IN THE NEW WORLD

It is interesting to consider the growth of the use of alcoholic beverages in the New World. Not all the New World natives used fermented drinks. Some of them had other methods of ritualistic and social exaltation, including tobacco smoking and mushroom and peyote eating. In Latin America, the Spanish and Portuguese overlords followed the civilized amenities of European culture with the use of sherries as appetizers, wines with meals, and liqueurs for after-dinner relaxation or for presumed health effects. Neither the Spaniards nor the Portuguese seem to have made any effort to debauch the natives with cheap alcoholic drinks. It would seem that the French in Canada and through the Mississippi Valley used comparatively few alcoholic beverages, whereas the English invaders of North America preserved in part the cultural amenities of appropriate use of alcoholic beverages. The Puritans in New England brought a general disapproving attitude toward any pleasurable activity, but they did not despise the "good creature," commonly in the form of spirits. The Dutch in New York and the Swedes in Delaware kept to the civilized amenities with alcoholic beverages, and so did the Cavaliers in Maryland.

The rapid expansion of the frontier introduced new conditions of life which gradually led to an uncivilized and unsatisfactory misuse of alcoholic drinks. The long distances to be covered, together with the continuous tension of the frontier, made the use of beers and wines difficult: they were bulky to carry in proportion to the amount of alcoholic effect involved, and comparatively costly. Maize was plentiful and grew abundantly; grain mashes from it would ferment and could be distilled into a potent "corn liquor."

As the frontiersmen pushed West, they found that they could readily produce a powerful alcoholic effect in little bulk by simple distillation for their own needs. They could also ship these goods back home. Thus the nineteenth century in America was marked by an intensification of the trend, already begun in the eighteenth century, to rely increasingly on distilled spirits.[2]

With the increasing tensions before, during, and after the terrible Civil War, the decent social amenities long associated with the use of beers and wines declined. A notable exception, however, was the German immigrants who came to such centers as Cincinnati, Milwaukee, and St. Louis. Here, rather pathetic efforts were made to preserve the *gemütlichkeit* which was so socially civilizing in the south German areas. Beer gardens flourished for a while, and indeed during the latter half of the nineteenth century, the popularity of beer competed effectively with that of whiskey. But as social pressure developed against the excesses of "hard liquor," the "foreign" aspect

[2] The reader is referred to the more detailed history of these developments in the presentation by Berton Roueché.

of the beer gardens, with some of the political corruption associated with the saloon, slowly produced an attitude of social disapproval against the use of alcoholic beverages generally. The beer gardens totally and unfortunately succumbed to the bitter anti-German attitude during World War I.

Nearly a hundred years of history set the picture for the very significant social experiment in the total prohibition of alcoholic beverages in the United States. With mounting drunkenness in American cities and towns, the movement began slowly early in the nineteenth century when the temperance organizations sought to combat local abuses by discouraging the consumption of distilled spirits. That the town drunkard might be a fit subject for medical study was not suspected; instead he was socially ostracized. Toward the middle of the nineteenth century the temperance movement yielded to extremist leadership, adopted a policy of opposing all alcoholic beverages, and then went to its own logical extreme in the demand for total prohibition.

With prohibition as a national policy written into the United States Constitution, the situation really deteriorated. Apart from social demoralization, there were serious economic losses. In most of the large cities in the East and Middle West the great breweries closed, and all the possibility for social relaxation through the group use of beer was lost. The wine industry in New York State and in Ohio closed.

Serious indeed was the disturbance of the carefully developing wine industry in California. Here, wine grapes had been introduced from Austria by Count Haraszthy in 1849. The eighteenth-century Franciscan missions had encouraged the preparation of wines from the native "mission grape," but gradually the more carefully selected French and German wine stocks became popular. At the beginning of this century California, like New York State and Ohio, was producing quality wines which appealed to the discriminating Americans who clung to the cultural standards of the Old World. The light wines from the Sonoma, Napa, and Livermore Valleys, and from the Santa Cruz hillsides, were beginning to be favorably known even among Europeans.

There had indeed been scientific background in connection with the development of these wines. James Blake (1815–1893), that amazing English chemist and clinician who came to California during the Gold Rush, had already helped in the control of phylloxera, the parasitic pest which ruined the French vineyards, and he had also examined the soils of California for their fitness for growing wine, recommending especially the Napa and Sonoma Valleys. He had also analyzed wines for their alcohol, aldehyde, and organic acid content and had related these findings to the character of the grapes grown in the vineyards.

All this development closed with prohibition. However, in California—as in some other places—there was a cheerful disregard for what were considered to be unjust legal restrictions, and many Italian-American citizens, who cherished Old World traditions, made and shared their own wines. California was fortunate in escaping much of the very disturbing and serious antisocial and anticultural aspects of prohibition. Now, it is the most important area for the scientific study of the technology of wines, and its great University supports an honored chair of enology.

Almost every aspect of the prohibition era was unfortunate, insofar as antisocial and anticultural tendencies are concerned. The history of the United States early featured strong opposition among the independent American frontier people to the taxation of their distilled alcoholic products. Taxation was sometimes related to an effort to reduce the consumption of alcoholic drinks, but this was wholly unsuccessful and resulted largely in provoking disrespect for law and law-enforcement officers. With prohibition this disrespect increased, and all the evils of the bootleg era came into the picture, with gangsterism, murder, and total breakdown of law enforcement as far as alcoholic beverages were concerned.

If there was one clear lesson from the prohibition experiment, it was that the American people in large part desired alcoholic beverages for their socializing effect. Another important outcome of the prohibition experiment, which was to become manifest in the era of repeal, was the recognition that there is the possibility of addiction to alcohol on the part of insecure and psychologically disturbed people; and also that there might be metabolic conditions in some people which cause them on the one hand to crave alcohol and on the other hand to be totally unable to handle it without harmful effects. "Alcoholism" was to become widely recognized as a disease, probably capable of effective treatment, rather than perverse antisocial individualism.

The unfortunate aspect of the whole prohibition experiment was that, when it was concluded, the gangsterism which it had spawned persisted and went into the undermining of American morale through the exploitation of addicting drugs, prostitution, and gambling.

Since it took a relatively long time for vineyards to come back into effective culture, winemaking was slow in recovery following prohibition. The breweries were able to get back into business more rapidly, and so were the distillers. These circumstances again reinforced the cultural pattern with regard to alcoholic beverages in the United States, with some slanting toward distilled products. Scotch whiskey had become popular during prohibition, but "bourbon" distilled from corn mash became the common American alcoholic drink.

A social pattern developed of having elaborate cocktail parties before dinner. The cocktail became popular as women participated actively in social affairs where alcoholic beverages were served. These cocktails were usually dilutions of gin, rye, bourbon, or rum, with all sorts of flavorings so as to be more palatable, and this often resulted in more drinking.

It is debatable whether or not the typical American cultural ritual followed at a cocktail party is civilizing or not. It is ordinarily a time of great confusion, not only with the large number of people jammed together in a relatively small place, but also with high emotional excitement. While intellectual affairs often become quite the vogue in connection with cocktail parties, it is doubtful that they result in anything more significant than the boring and often pitiful spectacles caricatured in many movies. Their main function, however, has a certain civilizing influence in bringing people together to share a common experience and find a relief from loneliness, a grudging tolerance for other points of view, and, following the affair, some degree of relaxation.

The unfortunate aspect of cocktail parties is that they are overdone, prolonged for too long a period, and thus destroy any excuse they may originally have had for promoting appetite for pleasant meals together. The ideals and standards of civilized social intercourse in the eighteenth century were centered around the meal, the enjoyment of which might be enhanced by an appetizer, or *apéritif*, served rather formally ten minutes or so before starting the meal. This may have been the original purpose of a cocktail, but in the development of the characteristic American cocktail party, the purpose of the cocktail as an appetizer seems almost fully to have been lost.

It is high time that people generally should begin to understand something about the physiological effects of alcohol, so that it might be used beneficially for individual and social welfare. This certainly is possible, as was clearly enough shown in the social conventions regarding alcoholic beverages which emerged during the eighteenth and nineteenth centuries. It is interesting that the applications of modern scientific information about the biological effects of alcohol support the socially acceptable conventions about the use of alcoholic drinks as these conventions evolved during the eighteenth and nine-teenth centuries.

SCIENTIFIC ASPECTS OF ALCOHOL

In changing the pace of my discussion, in order to consider the biological, and thus human, effects of alcohol as determined scientifically, and especially pharmacologically, I do not feel as full of my subject as I should like to be. A story might be appropriate to illustrate the essence of the scientific spirit in skepticism. Stories about alcohol are legion, but the one I shall tell is supposed to be true.

The law in the state of Wisconsin, as in most of the states, required that all public schools teachers should teach their students "the harmful effects of alcohol." A grammar school teacher in Madison, the home of the University, was doing her duty. She said, "Children, a great scientist took a litter of puppies and divided it into two parts. To one group of little puppies he gave a few teaspoons of alcohol each day in the food, while the other group of puppies had the same food and lived in the same way but received no alcohol. At the end of a couple of weeks, those puppies that had received alcohol were in miserable condition. They had lost weight, their hair was falling out, and they were drooping and very weak. On the other hand, those puppies that had not received alcohol were frisky; their fur was thick and glossy, and they seemed to be happy and in good health. Now children, what does this teach us?" A little girl at the back of the room, the daughter of one of the University professors, and now the distinguished president of Radcliffe College, is said to have answered, "This teaches us that alcohol is bad—for puppies."

It is interesting that the first comprehensive detailed study of the physiological, psychological, and sociological aspects of alcoholic drinks was published, at the beginning of the present century, under the auspices of a New York reform group. The study was made by the best scientists in the United States at that time. The report, in two volumes, was published by Houghton Mifflin, of Boston, and entitled *Physiological Aspects of the Liquor Problem*. It was edited by John Shaw Billings, the remarkable Ohioan, who had so superbly developed the library of the Surgeon General's Office and had started the systematic management of the rapidly accumulating biological, medical, and other scientific reports. He later became the foremost librarian in the United States, and through the example he set at the New York Public Library, he profoundly influenced library service throughout our country.

Many other scientific reports on alcohol have appeared since that time, but it is still fruitful to review the findings and conclusions of Howell, Abel, Chittenden, and other great biological scientists of that period.

Immediate effects Alcohol is remarkable in a physical-chemical sense: it mixes in all proportions with water and is in itself an admirable solvent of many substances that are not so easily dissolved in water. It was this property of alcohol that made it so useful in the developing art of pharmacy, especially in the preparation of tinctures in which many pharmacologically active crude drugs were dispensed. These preparations were introduced during the Renaissance. Alcohol owes its remarkable solvent properties on one hand to its terminal hydroxyl group, which can carry the molecule of alcohol into water, and on the other hand to its hydrocarbon chain, which can carry it into fatty material. Ordinary alcohol, of course, is ethyl alcohol, or ethanol, and is one of many related compounds which have similar actions, but which do not ordinarily occur naturally. Alcohol evaporates readily, and its vapor also condenses easily. These are the properties which were so skillfuly utilized in developing the art of distillation.

Alcohol is rapidly absorbed and distributed into living material. When ingested by mouth by humans, a small portion is absorbed rapidly from the upper part of the alimentary tract, the stomach, into the blood stream. Of course, its absorption from the stomach may be delayed by mucous or protein material in the stomach, which will be precipitated in part by the alcohol, and thus bind it. This is one of the effects of the canapes served with cocktails. Most of the alcohol passes from the stomach to the lower alimentary tract and is absorbed thence.

After absorption into the body, alcohol is uniformly distributed in accordance with the water content of the various parts of the body. This uniform distribution is why an estimation of the alcohol in blood or in freshly secreted urine can serve so readily as an index of the concentration of alcohol in the brain.

As soon as it is in contact with living material, alcohol begins to go to pieces. This metabolism is facilitated by appropriate enzyme systems, so that alcohol is oxidized to acetaldehyde, then to acetic acid, and finally to carbon dioxide and water. This metabolic process provides energy, and in this sense, alcohol has some food value. It provides calories.

Difficulties arise if the enzyme systems are not working properly. Sometimes the oxidation of acetaldehyde to acetic acid may be interrupted; the aldehyde then accumulates, with resulting toxic effects. Some of the unpleasant features of a "hangover" may be due to faulty metabolism of alcohol.

The rate at which alcohol is destroyed in the body is important. If the enzyme systems are functioning smoothly, the rate probably proceeds in a uniform manner. Without being very accurate about it, it would seem that the overall rate is about ⅓ oz of absolute alcohol per hour in a person of average weight. This is an important point in learning how to handle alcoholic beverages in a civilized and sensible manner. In other words, scientific studies confirm long experience that alcoholic drinks should be taken very slowly, if one is not to get drunk. The point is that as soon as one feels that one is reasonably comfortable as a result of the alcohol taken in so far, one should drink no more in each succeeding hour than a small fraction of what has been drunk so far. Then one will not go to excess!

Alcohol has an irritating effect on mucous membranes with which it comes in contact. If the content of alcohol in the beverage is more than 20 per cent, it is likely to cause precipitation of protein, and thus to give some degree of injury to mucous membranes. This is why one should not drink straight distilled liquors, since their alcohol strength is usually 40 to 50 per cent. It is much better to dilute them to about 20 per cent alcohol, which is the customary strength of the fortified wines, such as sherry, which so many centuries of experience have approved for use as an "appetizer." One should never insult one's stomach by putting a higher concentration than 20 per cent alcohol into it. Otherwise, there may result excessive mucous excretion, thickening of the mucous coats, and other harmful effects.

This mild irritant action of alcohol on the stomach mucosa is probably what stimulates the flow of gastric juice, promotes the feeling of hunger, and so helps to induce appetite for the enjoyment of a good meal. The irritant action of alcohol on mucous membranes is associated with its antiseptic action and depends on its power to coagulate protein. It is useful in skin massage, or for "tightening" the skin with face lotions, to try again, pathetically, to look young by preventing the kindly wrinkles of age. The optimum strength of ethanol for sterilizing effect, however, whether on skin or instruments, is 70 per cent. This permits some penetration into germs and thus assures antiseptic action: higher concentrations precipitate surface proteins and prevent penetration, so some germs may survive, whereas lower concentrations are not strong enough to cause the death of the germs.

The most important effects of alcohol are on the nervous system. Nevertheless, it is probable that alcohol acts on all cells, perhaps in disturbing in some way the manifold enzyme systems which characterize the integration of cellular activity. In the central nervous system these enzyme patterns are particularly sensitive to chemicals of all sorts. Alcohol has been shown to make nerve endings draw back a bit at synapses, the places where nerves meet. If the spaces between connecting nerves are increased, there may be disturbance in overall nerve conduction, with some degree of dissociation of ordinary nerve pathways. This seems to be the case when large quantities of alcohol are ingested by mammals, including humans.

Alcohol may also interfere with some of the porphyrin organic complexes in the brain, which, since they may bind various metallic atoms, could act as semiconductors, thus making the analogy between the brain and computers even more appropriate. If alcohol disturbs the semiconducting properties of these porphyrin compounds there might well be considerable disturbance in the overall integration of brain activity and of nerve function.

Dose-effect relations always apply in connection with chemicals that act on living material. The general relationships between the behavior of individuals and the alcohol concentration in the body were amusingly expressed by Emil Bogen of California years ago. He pointed out that if a person has less than 0.05 per cent alcohol concentration in the blood, that person is apt to be dull and dignified. If, however, the concentration of alcohol is between 0.05 and 0.10 per cent, the individual, if a gentleman, is apt to be *dashing and debonair,* while if a lady, she may well be *delightful and desirable.* On the other hand, if the concentration of alcohol rises in a person to a level between 0.1 and 0.2 per cent, the person is often *daring and devilish.* If the concentration reaches between 0.2 and 0.3 per cent, the person may become *dangerous and disheveled.* If the concentration is around 0.4 per cent, the individual is *delirious and disgusting.* If the concentration reaches 0.5 per cent, the person is clearly *drunk.* If the concentration reaches 0.6 per cent, the person is *dead drunk,* and if the concentration reaches 0.7 per cent, the individual is *dead.*

These generalizations suggest that a person may regulate his or her alcohol intake in order to hold the concentration giving the behavior characteristics that are most socially acceptable. Most gentlemen like to be dashing and debonair, and most ladies are pleased if they are considered delightful and desirable. Concentrations of alcohol that may give patterns of behavior described by these adjectives may be achieved in an average individual after the ingestion of a couple of cocktails or a couple of glasses of wine or as many steins of beer. It is important to remember that if this desired behavior is to be maintained, one should not drink more than one-fifth to one-half again per hour of what has been drunk so far; the exact amount depends largely on body weight. Under these circumstances, it is highly probable that the person may remain, at least for the social period involved, either dashing and debonair or delightful and desirable. Here can be an instance of the important civilizing function of alcohol, but as is so often the case in civilizing factors, the matter is clearly up to individual responsibility.

Alcoholism The disturbances in overall mood, nervous function, and behavior, which occur with increasing concentrations of alcohol in the body, indicate the progressive dissociation of nervous pathways as the alcohol concentration increases. Fortunately, the concentration is reversible as the alcohol is metabolized, disappearing slowly from the body. However, there are always the dangers that the metabolic process of destruction of alcohol may be faulty, with resulting serious hangovers or psychological conditioning in the development of alcohol addiction. There is, however, no reversibility of the lethal effects of a high enough concentration of alcohol.

Alcoholism is a disease. The civilized approach to alcoholism is to handle it on a medical basis. There may be metabolic problems involved, but usually the condition is psychiatric. Often an alcoholic is a person who consciously or unconsciously is seeking to get some rest and peace from an irritating, annoying, and generally unbearable environment. This may involve family, business and working associates, or other more intolerable social situations.

Sometimes an alcoholic can be cured if taken from the unfavorable environment. On returning to that unbearable environment, memory suggests that prompt escape can be obtained again by enough alcoholic drink. For people suffering from metabolic disorders which cause difficulty when alcohol is drunk, or for persons who have become psychologically conditioned to the use of alcohol as an escape mechanism, total abstinence from alcoholic beverages is perhaps best. Alcoholics Anonymous does a great social service and certainly has been lifesaving for many individuals. Here is a civilizing aspect of alcohol working in reverse, as a result of the pooling of individual experience in the common group endeavor for the benefit of each person in the group. It is a remarkable instance of psychological group insurance.

Social and medicinal use   Alcohol generally causes a reduction in anxiety, tension, irritability, and mental stress. Under the hectic conditions of our status-cursed urban-suburban treadmill, the use of alcoholic drinks at the end of an emotionally grueling day may have a real civilizing effect on the overtense, overwrought, overanxious, and overirritable husband who comes seeking rest and peace in his own home. Here, the civilizing effects of a couple of cocktails or a couple of glasses of wine or steins of beer will really perform wonders in helping husbands and wives to feel tolerant and understanding of each other. These amenities help adults generally to adjust themselves in a socially acceptable way to the stresses of our complex social situations.

Alcohol has many effects on the various organ systems of the body. In general it tends to dilate peripheral blood vessels, and thus may take something of the work load away from the heart. Again, this may be helpful in adults who are overanxious, overtense, overirritable, and overtaut. It may help greatly in reducing the tendency to cardiovascular stress. Ordinarily, alcohol acts as a mild diuretic, and there are indications for the medicinal use of alcoholic beverages.

In a clear medicinal manner, alcoholic drinks may be used to advantage in many chronic ailments. They may be helpful in promoting appetite in anorexia, and they may aid in convalescence from debilitating diseases or surgical operations. They may be comforting in old age when there are so many physical infirmities and so few satisfactions. They may be pleasantly and civilizingly relaxing in chronic anxiety and stress patterns, and they may help in preventing or alleviating cardiovascular accidents or overloads. In many ways alcoholic drinks may be used, as anciently, for worthy medical purposes, both for physical and mental health.

Alcohol has a substantial caloric value and may give energy in emergency situations. Nevertheless, it is not an appropriate food as such. If there is real alcoholism, the excessive drinking may provoke various nutritional and vitamin deficiencies as a result of loss of appetite and neglect of good diet.

It is amusing that the effects of alcohol on germ plasm have been studied. Indeed some scientists have thought that alcohol may be a potent factor in the elimination of unfit human genes. This may be stretching things a bit far, but Raymond Pearl felt that he could support this contention statistically.

The interactions of alcohol and living material have been well studied, well analyzed, and deserve fully to be well understood by everyone. Alcohol is probably the most widely used drug in the world, and certainly it is the drug with which humanity has had the longest experience. As is the case with any drug, it has its toxic and lethal dangers, and these must be clearly recognized if it is to be used wisely for individual and social benefit. The long experience of humanity with alcohol testifies abundantly to its overall civilizing influence, if used wisely. Alcohol may indeed be, as has been often suggested, a good servant to humanity.

IN PROSPECT

Alcoholic drinks can be used for their civilizing influence if people understand the basic pharmacological facts about the actions of alcohol and how to apply these facts individually and socially for human benefit. Alcohol, like any source of energy, nuclear or otherwise, has determinable properties which are scientifically confirmable. This verifiable knowledge constitutes the best approximation we have about the "truth" of the matter. To what purposes this truth is applied is an ethical problem, to which many solutions, individual and social, have been attempted. The attempted social solutions have always had the basic purpose of promoting human welfare, even though the methods employed have sometimes been esthetically, and thus practically, inappropriate. Alcohol, if used appropriately, with understanding of its individual effects, and with conformity to social standards, may long remain a major factor in the process of civilizing human beings everywhere, contributing to their tolerance for and sympathy with each other, and thus to the lowering of individual and social tensions and to the establishment of the peace we all want for our self-actualization.

It remains, as often is the case, for individual responsibility to determine whether alcohol shall be used for human weal or woe. If the determinable facts about alcohol can be individually understood, we may have faith that it may have increasing civilizing effects in our ever-evolving social endeavor.

REFERENCES

Billings, J. S. (ed.), *Physiological Aspects of the Liquor Problem*, 2 vols., Boston, Houghton Mifflin, 1903.

Bogen, E., Tolerance to Alcohol. Its Mechanism and Significance, *Calif. West. Med.* 44:262–271, 1936.

Connor, C. L., Cirrhosis of the Liver, *Quart. J. Studies Alc.*, 1:95–103, 1940.

Emerson, H. (ed.), *Alcohol and Man*, New York, Macmillan, 1932.

Haggard, H. W., and Greenberg, L. A., Studies in the Absorption, Distribution, and Elimination of Ethyl Alcohol, *J. Pharmacol.*, 52:137–149, 150–166, 167–178, 1934.

Hirsh, J., *The Problem Drinker*, New York, Duell, Sloan & Pearce, 1949.

Lucia, S. P., *Wine as Food and Medicine*, New York, Blakiston, 1954.

Miles, W. R., *Alcohol and Human Efficiency*, Washington, D.C., Carnegie Institution, 1924.

Newman, H. W., *Acute Alcoholic Intoxication, a Critical Review*, Stanford, Stanford University Press, 1941.

Pearl, R., *Alcohol and Longevity*, New York, Knopf, 1926.

Smith, W. H., and Helwig, F. C., *Liquor, the Servant of Man*, Boston, Little, Brown, 1939.

Waddell, J. A., and Haag, H. B., *Alcohol in Moderation and Excess*, Richmond, Va., William Byrd Press, 1940.

Williams, R. J., *Nutrition and Alcoholism*, Norman, Okla., University of Oklahoma Press, 1951.

Leonard Goldberg, M.D.

Professor and Chairman, Department of Alcohol Research
Karolinska Institutet, Stockholm, Sweden

THE METABOLISM
OF ALCOHOL

Editor's Note   *In the following presentation Dr. Goldberg takes us step by step through the processes by which the body disposes of alcohol. What exactly happens to the alcohol after it is swallowed? He shows how it is absorbed into the circulating blood, partly from the stomach directly, mostly from the small intestine; how it is then distributed through the blood stream into all the fluids of the body; and how it is gradually and steadily metabolized (broken down, oxidized, burned, changed) until the carbon, hydrogen, and oxygen atoms which constituted the original molecule of alcohol are converted to carbon dioxide and water. In the course of these internal bodily events, mediated by various enzyme systems, energy becomes available —about 7 calories from each gram of alcohol (about 100 calories from an ounce of 100-proof whiskey), and this enters into the economy of the organism like the calories from ordinary foods. Through the above process nearly all the alcohol finally leaves the body. Only a very small part is excreted, as alcohol, in the urine, sweat, and breath. Dr. Goldberg describes also the many different conditions which can modify the pace at which these metabolic events take place. Finally, he discusses the problem of tolerance and habituation to alcohol; the significance of different possible patterns of drinking in determining what effects the drinking of various amounts of alcohol will have; and some physiological signs of the aftereffects of alcohol—the hangover phenomenon. In the course of his discussion Dr. Goldberg frequently takes us into his laboratory, describing the experiments on which much of his presentation is based.*

In this, as in all the following texts, "alcohol" (without further specification) means ethyl alcohol, that is, ethanol (CH_3CH_2OH).

The amount of ethyl alcohol found in the human body after drinking various alcoholic beverages is primarily the result of interplay between three processes: (1) the *absorption* of the alcohol from the gastrointestinal tract; (2) the *distribution* of the alcohol by the circulating blood to various organs and body fluids; (3) the *rate of disappearance* of alcohol from the body through two processes: (*a*) the *excretion* of a small part, 2 to 5 per cent, mainly by the kidneys and (*b*) the *metabolic breakdown* of the larger part, 95 to 98 per cent.

FATE OF ALCOHOL IN THE BODY

Absorption The absorption of alcohol from the stomach into the blood stream begins immediately after drinking. Under normal conditions, about one-fifth of the total quantity is absorbed from the stomach; the rest passes down into the intestine and is absorbed from that organ. Absorption gives rise to the blood alcohol concentration, that is, the alcohol content in the blood. Between individuals, or in the same person at different times, the rate of alcohol absorption is not always uniform. A high rate of absorption induces a rapid, early-occurring peak of blood alcohol concentration; the maximum blood alcohol level may be high; there may be a temporary "overshooting" of the general course of the blood alcohol curve, indicating that distribution equilibrium has not yet been attained. A slow rate of absorption is followed by a slower rise in blood alcohol and a lower maximum, the curve in some instances following a horizontal course, lasting for a few hours.

The *rate* at which alcohol is absorbed into the blood stream depends on a number of factors:

(*a*) *The alcohol content of the beverage.* Beverages with a high alcohol content are more rapidly absorbed than diluted ones. Thus, drinking distilled spirits is usually followed by a high blood alcohol maximum, especially when taken on an empty stomach, whereas if the liquor is diluted, the resulting maximal blood alcohol concentration may be lower by 20 to 30 per cent. Wines, after absorption, produce a lower blood alcohol maximum than distilled spirits; table wines, lower than fortified wines; beer and cider, the lowest.

(*b*) *The presence or absence of other substances in the gastrointestinal tract.* Alcohol taken on an empty stomach is absorbed rapidly. The maximum appears, on the average, after forty to sixty minutes, ranging from twenty minutes to two and one-half hours. Intake of food together with alcohol delays absorption; the blood alcohol maximum will be lower and appear later, at about sixty to one hundred minutes, ranging from thirty minutes to three hours, and the curve often appears horizontal for one to two hours.

The influence of food is most obvious on the maximum of the curve. If distilled spirits are taken with food, the resulting blood alcohol maximum will be lowered by 30 to 50 per cent. Some lowering will also be seen with diluted spirits, but not of the same magnitude. In the case of wines taken with food, a lowering of the blood alcohol peak by 15 to 30 per cent is observed. With various kinds of beers the conditions vary. With some beers, especially those with a low alcohol content in relation to the solids, the taking of food does not further lower the curve.

Various foodstuffs may act in different ways. The simultaneous intake of protein and fat causes a longer delay in the absorption of alcohol than does the ingestion of carbohydrates. Further knowledge is needed, however, as to the exact mechanism of this delaying action of various food constituents; for example, whether it is mediated through a possible effect on the emptying time of the stomach.

(c) *The kind of beverage.* Besides the effect of the concentration of the beverage, other factors, too, play a role. Wine and beer have a slower absorption rate and produce a lower maximum blood alcohol than pure alcohol diluted to the same concentration. Differences do exist between various beverages of the same concentration, for example, between various kinds of wines or beers.

Systematic studies have so far been carried out only on beer. The experiments show that the ratio between the alcohol concentration and the concentration of solids is one important factor. The higher the relative content of solids, the lower the absorption rate and, hence, the maximum blood alcohol.

(d) *Buffer capacity.* Another factor of importance is the buffer capacity of the beverage. The higher the buffer capacity, the lower the absorption rate and the lower the blood alcohol curve.

(e) *The emptying time of the stomach.* When the emptying of the stomach is delayed, as by the presence of foodstuffs, the passage of alcohol into the intestines may be delayed. The absorption rate will then be slower because the passage of alcohol into the blood stream is more rapid from the intestines than from the stomach.[1]

Nausea may also cause a delay in the emptying of the stomach,

[1] The reader may find useful, also, the summarized statement about the role of absorption on the effects of alcohol in the discussion by Dr. Greenberg on pp. 259–260.

and hence in absorption, resulting in a horizontal blood alcohol curve. Nausea and vomiting are most probably elicited by the action of the ingested alcohol on the vestibular system.

When the emptying time of the stomach is increased, as in various gastric disturbances, the passage of alcohol into the intestine is accelerated, and all the alcohol may be absorbed in one-half to one hour. This process may account for the finding that alcoholics show an earlier occurring and higher absorption peak than moderate drinkers.

(f) *The blood flow through the mucous membranes of the gastrointestinal canal.* Theoretically, the blood flow in the gastro-intestinal tract may play a role in the absorption of alcohol. More experimental and clinical studies, however, are needed in order to evaluate the importance of this factor under normal and pathological conditions.

Distribution After alcohol is absorbed into the blood stream, it is distributed by a diffusion process into various tissues, following the body water. A number of factors determine the final concentration of alcohol at any locus, two main ones being the rate of blood flow in an organ, and the water content of the various tissues or body fluids. After diffusion equilibrium is reached, the alcohol concentration is high in body fluids and in organs rich in blood vessels (brain, liver, kidney, muscle) and low in tissues that are low in water content and sparsely vascularized (body fat, bone).

Equilibrium will be reached very fast, within minutes, in some tissues or body fluids, as in the ventricular fluid in the cerebrum, or in the urine freshly formed in the kidney. It may take a considerably longer time, sometimes hours, for equilibrium to be reached in fat or in the cerebrospinal fluid.

For a *quantitative* analysis of the distribution of alcohol, Widmark introduced the factor r, defined as the ratio between the relative content of alcohol in the body and the alcohol level in the blood. The ratio r may be looked upon as an expression of the general "level" of the blood alcohol curve after absorption. A low value of r, about 0.6 to 0.7, is found after ingestion of distilled spirits, corresponding to a high blood alcohol level. Wines, beer, and cider have an r of 0.8 to 0.9, indicating a lower blood alcohol level.

Disappearance The disappearance of alcohol from the body is due mainly to two processes: (1) its elimination by excretion, and (2) its metabolic breakdown and conversion to other constituents.

1. Excretion. After moderate amounts of alcohol are drunk, the part of alcohol eliminated in the urine, breath, saliva, and sweat comes to between 2 and 5 per cent of the total. When large quantities of alcohol (2 g of alcohol per kg of body weight,[2] or more) are consumed within a short period of time, 7 to 10 per cent of the alcohol may be excreted by these routes. That leaves, on an average, 90 to 93 per cent of the alcohol to be converted by the body through metabolic processes.

2. Metabolic processes. Alcohol is metabolized (oxidized, burned) mainly in the liver. This has been shown by in vitro experiments with incubated liver brei and with liver slices using the Warburg technique, and by in vivo experiments with perfused livers and eviscerated animals. A small, quantitatively negligible, amount of alcohol is probably metabolized in the kidney, whereas no alcohol, or only an insignificant trace, is metabolized by the muscles. Alcohol also enters into metabolic exchange with other tissues—for example, brain tissues, as shown by its different behavior in various substrates when added to brain slices [Sutherland, Hine, and Burbridge].

The metabolism of alcohol can schematically be said to proceed in three main steps: The first step is from alcohol to acetaldehyde; the second is from acetaldehyde to acetyl-coenzyme A; and the third is from acetyl CoA or acetate to carbon dioxide and water. If the alcohol undergoes an incomplete oxidation, the acetyl CoA or the acetate formed as an intermediate product after entering the general metabolic pool of the body, may enter into other reactions.

Judging from both "test tube" experiments and those in live organisms, chiefly studies on liver slices and perfused livers, the metabolism in the liver is primarily limited to the first two steps—the oxidation of alcohol to acetaldehyde and from acetaldehyde to acetyl CoA or acetate. The third step most probably proceeds at all sites where energy from acetyl CoA is needed.

The presence of acetaldehyde as a metabolic product of alcohol has been demonstrated by several workers. Likewise, a number of other intermediate products have been demonstrated either by direct isolation or by the use of alcohol tagged with radioactive carbon at one or both of its carbon atoms.

With regard to the systems involved in the metabolism of alcohol, Batelli and Stern in 1909 indicated that there existed an enzyme system in the tissues capable of metabolizing alcohol. Lehmann, and

[2] Equal to about 10 oz of whiskey for a man weighing 160 lb.

also Lutwak-Mann, studied animal alcohol dehydrogenase. The enzyme alcohol dehydrogenase (ADH) was isolated and crystallized from horse liver in Theorell's laboratory by Bonnichsen and Wassén in 1948, and its properties were thoroughly studied by Theorell and his coworkers. It was found that ethanol, reacting with diphosphopyridine nucleotide (DPN), is converted to acetaldehyde in the presence of alcohol dehydrogenase, reduced diphosphopyridine nucleotide (DPNH) being formed from DPN. Kinetic studies showed the Michaelis constant to be low, which implies a constant rate of metabolism down to concentrations of about 0.01 per cent alcohol in the blood, independent of the amount of alcohol present. Moreover, 1 mmole (73 g) of the enzyme[3] is able to oxidize 6.9 g of alcohol per minute, the yield being about 1 g of enzyme per kg of liver. Assuming the same relation to hold for man, and the liver to weigh 1.5 kg, the human would contain approximately 1.5 g of enzyme, or enough to metabolize 8.3 g of alcohol per hour in an individual weighing 70 kg. The average disposal rate found in man under normal conditions is 7 g per hour, which would imply a good agreement between theoretical considerations from in vitro studies and experimental findings in vivo.

A catalase enzyme system, involving the oxidation of ethanol by hydrogen peroxide in the presence of catalase, has also been studied. The kinetics were investigated by Chance, his results indicating that this is a second-order reaction, the rate of which is dependent upon the dose. L. Dontcheff[4] has suggested that the hydrogen peroxide necessary for this reaction might be formed, for example, during the oxidation of amino acids. Such a reaction would account for a dependence of the metabolic rate upon dose. It still remains to be investigated whether such a mechanism actually comes into operation in man under special conditions—for example, in heavy drinkers imbibing large amounts.

By using radioactive alcohol, tagged with C^{14}, Dontcheff and also Casier were able to show that after the major part of the C^{14} in the alcohol had disappeared, a portion was still left, indicating a delay in the conversion of the radioactive carbon dioxide, and its very slow elimination, lasting for many hours after all the alcohol as

[3] Mol. wt 73,000; turnover, 150 mole of alcohol by 1 mole of enzyme per minute.
[4] Personal communication.

such had disappeared. That portion of the alcohol atoms (C^{14}) which showed a delayed elimination amounted to 15 per cent of the total amount administered to mice [Casier]. According to Dontcheff, a part of this portion is probably converted to fat or other liquids.

Thus the possibility must be taken into account that the acetyl CoA or acetate formed as an intermediate product in the oxidation of alcohol, and added to the general metabolic pool in the body, may either undergo complete oxidation to carbon dioxide and water, or may in part enter into other secondary reactions and undergo partial oxidation to other intermediates—leading, for example, to the formation of fat. Dontcheff has suggested that in the case of alcohol the energy liberated by the oxidation of its intermediary products, such as acetyl CoA or acetate, might not be available to the body.

3. *Quantitative aspects.* A number of investigators have determined the rate of disappearance of alcohol from the blood in man by giving various doses of alcohol to subjects and following the course of the blood alcohol curve at certain intervals for a long period of time.

The declining portion of the blood alcohol curve, after all alcohol is absorbed and diffusion equilibrium is reached, is rectilinear, suggesting that the disappearance of alcohol proceeds at a constant rate.

(*a*) *Rate of disappearance of alcohol from the blood.* Widmark assumed the *slope* of the curve to be the best expression for the rate of disappearance of alcohol from the blood stream; he denoted the slope by the symbol β. The factor β is calculated according to the method of least squares from the actual values found, assuming a rectilinear curve. The rate of disappearance of alcohol from the blood in man (β) is, on an average, 0.0025 mg of alcohol per g of blood per minute, corresponding to 0.015 per cent per hour. There is considerable *individual* variation in the rate of disappearance of alcohol from the blood; the rate of decline ranges from 0.0008 to 0.0030 mg per g per minute, or 0.0048 to 0.018 per cent per hour.

(*b*) *Relation between dose and rate of decline.* A classical important problem within this field is whether the rate of disappearance of alcohol from the body is constant and independent of the dose administered, or whether it is related to the dose. Earlier studies suggested that the metabolic rate is constant and independent of the dose. This seemed to be confirmed by the in vitro studies on the kinetics of alcohol dehydrogenase in the liver, which implied a constant rate and a rectilinear curve, assuming that the ADH enzyme would be the bottleneck of the metabolic process.

Experiments in dogs and in cats suggest, however, that under certain conditions a relationship may exist between dose and rate of metabolism. This problem was touched upon by Hjelt and has been taken up for systematic study in man in our laboratory [Goldberg, 1949]. By varying the dose and the kind of beverage within wide limits, and by closely following the resulting blood alcohol curves in some 450 subjects, it was conclusively shown that a relationship does exist between the rate of disappearance of alcohol from the blood stream (β) and the dose ingested. The rate increases with an increase in dose. The relation, however, varies with various kinds of beverages. Statistically, the correlation was highly significant $(P < .001)$ for various kinds of wines—fortified wine, red and white wines—and for beer (the correlation coefficient varying between .8 and .9). For distilled spirits, the correlation was found to be of a lower order, with a correlation coefficient of .5, which was barely significant $(P < .05)$. A doubling of the dose, from 0.5 to 1.0 g of alcohol per kilogram of body weight, increases the rate (β) by 15 to 20 per cent for distilled spirits, by 20 to 30 per cent for wines, and 20 to 40 per cent for beer.

(c) *Amount of alcohol disappearing.* Based on the foregoing, it is possible to compute the amount of alcohol disappearing from the body. The amount is on an average 105 mg of alcohol per kilogram of body weight per hour, assuming the rate of decline to be 0.0025 mg per g per minute and r to be 0.7. Actual experiments have shown the amount of alcohol disappearing to be 92 mg of alcohol per kilogram per hour on an average, ranging from 65 to 128 mg per kg and varying from individual to individual and from beverage to beverage.

As with the rate of disappearance, the amount, too, varies with the dose ingested. There is a clear correlation for wines and beer (correlation coefficient, .8 to .9; $P < .001$) and a significant or probable correlation for distilled spirits and cider (correlation coefficient .5 to .6; $P < .05$).

(d) *Total amount of alcohol disappearing from the body.* The total amount of alcohol which disappears from the body, per unit time, whether metabolized or excreted, can be calculated in several ways: It can be done by dividing the total quantity ingested by the time elapsed until the blood alcohol becomes zero; or it can be done by multiplying the amount of alcohol which disappears from the blood by the body weight. Assuming an average body weight of 70 kg (154 lb), the total amount of alcohol disappearing is 7 g of alcohol per hour, or 0.3 fl oz of alcohol. The average found in our laboratory with various beverages, in a moderate drinker imbibing moderate amounts, was ⅔ oz of whiskey, 1½ oz of fortified wine (vermouth, sherry, port, madeira), 3 to 4 oz of red or white table wine, 5 to 7 oz of strong beer or 8 to 10 oz of light beer.

There is a correlation between the amount of alcohol that disappears from the body in a given time and the dose ingested; the amount of alcohol increases with larger doses. A correlation is also found with body weight; a lighter body weight leads to an increase in the total amount of alcohol that disappears from the body in a given time.

The relations found mean that a larger intake of distilled spirits —for example, 7 oz of whiskey rather than 3½ oz—increases the rate of disappearance from 6 g of alcohol per hour to 7 g. With wines, the rate of disappearance increases from 7 to 9 g of alcohol per hour if the intake is raised from 14 to 28 oz. The same is also true with regard to differences in body weight.

(e) *Individual variations.* The preceding facts indicate that large variations exist between individuals with regard to the disposal rate of alcohol. These variations are due to (1) inherent individual variability in the rate of metabolism of alcohol; (2) differences in body weight; (3) differences in amounts of alcohol ingested; and (4) differences related to the kinds of alcoholic beverages.

As an example, a moderate drinker weighing 50 kg (110 lb) who drinks one-half bottle of wine containing 35 g of alcohol may metabolize as little as 3.5 g of alcohol per hour, which means that it would take ten hours for all the alcohol to disappear from his body. Another man weighing 90 kg (200 lb) who drinks two bottles of wine containing 140 g of alcohol, thus four times as much, could metabolize 14 g of alcohol per hour and hence get rid of four times as much alcohol in the same time.

EFFECTS OF DIFFERENT BEVERAGES

One way of studying if the effect of various alcoholic beverages in man is due solely to the alcohol content, or whether other factors enter the picture, is to administer different beverages to the same subjects under fixed conditions and follow the blood alcohol curve to see whether any systematic differences occur in the absorption, distribution, or metabolism of the ingested alcohol.

A series of studies of this kind has been carried out in our laboratory, comprising a total of about 450 experiments in 150 subjects with some twenty different beverages ranging from distilled spirits, fortified wines and table wines to beer and cider. When various beverages are given to the same subjects on different occasions, but always measured so as to contain the same quantity of alcohol each time, the resulting blood alcohol curves are not identical. As an example, 35 g of alcohol (1.5 fl oz of absolute alcohol) was given in the form of 3.7 fl oz of whiskey, 7.5 fl oz of sherry, 15 fl oz of red wine, or 37 fl oz of beer. The blood alcohol curve after whiskey showed the highest peak; the fortified wine produced a lower curve, and the lowest came following the table wine and beer [Goldberg, 1943, 1947, 1949].

The results of the systematic experiments carried out so far clearly indicate that the main differences observed were caused by differences in the rate of absorption of the different beverages, as reported above. The distribution ratios (r) show the same trend (see above). Differences in rate of metabolism were also found, but of a lower order of magnitude.

As to the mechanism of action, a number of factors are recognized to be of importance and are under study. The diffusion rate has already been discussed. The *relative* content of solids is so far elucidated only with regard to beer. The *buffer capacity* of the beverages has been referred to earlier and the same is true about the *emptying time* of the stomach. A thorough study will be undertaken to look for the presence of specific factors, primarily those delaying the absorption; preliminary experiments have been started.

SINGLE AND REPEATED ADMINISTRATION

The quantitative considerations so far have been concerned mainly with the case when a single dose of an alcoholic beverage is imbibed within a limited length of time. *Repeated* administration during a prolonged period of time, however, makes it possible to study the interplay of these processes under other conditions, by varying the amount of alcohol given per time unit and the spacing of the different doses.

Alcohol administered in doses less than the metabolic rate, that is, on an average less than 7 g of alcohol per hour, will not lead to any noticeable increase in blood alcohol. With the intake distributed evenly over one hour this limit corresponds, on an average, to ⅔ oz of whiskey, 1⅓ oz of fortified wine, 2 to 3 oz of table wine, or 6 to 7 oz of beer.

In the individual case, however, these amounts may be as little as half or as much as twice the indicated average. Alcohol administered in a dose higher than the individual metabolic rate will bring about an increase in the blood alcohol level. If, as an example, after the larger "priming" dose, a dose equal to the metabolic rate is given, a horizontal level is maintained as long as absorption, distribution, and metabolic processes balance each other. Other factors may, however, enter into the equation, as already indicated. The presence or absence of food and the occurrence of nausea are some examples. If a variety of beverages are taken on the same occasion, their different actions with regard to absorption, distribution, and metabolic rates will also add to the complexity of the picture.

MAXIMAL DAILY INTAKE OF ALCOHOL

Based on the preceding values, it is possible to calculate the maximal amount of alcohol that under certain circumstances could be ingested during twenty-four hours without alcohol accumulating in the blood.

The "maximal daily intake" that can be disposed of in twenty-four hours by an "average" person weighing 70 kg amounts to approximately ½ liter of distilled spirits (about 1 pt of whiskey), or 2 liters of light wine (4 pt), or 4½ liters of beer (9 pt).

A person weighing less will, as a rule, dispose of lesser amounts, while a person weighing more, as a rule, will be able to dispose of larger quantities per twenty-four hours. With a larger intake, as may occur in heavy drinkers, the disposal rate is increased, and larger amounts of alcoholic beverages might be disposed of in twenty-four hours. It is evident from the foregoing that the "maximal daily intake," as well as the disposal rate, differs considerably between different individuals, that is, from a low of ¼ liter of whiskey, 1 liter of wine, or 2 liters of beer per twenty-four hours to a high of 2 pt of whiskey, 4 liters of wine, or 10 liters of beer. These latter amounts are of an order of magnitude actually encountered in heavy drinkers and alcohol addicts.

It is important to point out that the range of variation between individuals, in the amount of alcohol that can be disposed of in a given time, increases from a factor of 0.5 for the rate of decline (β) —from 0.012 to 0.018 per cent per hour—to a factor of 4 when discussing the metabolized amount in grams per individual (3.5 to 11.7 g per hour), combining the variability due to variation in dose, in beverage, and in body weight.

NUTRITIONAL ASPECTS

When completely metabolized to carbon dioxide and water, alcohol yields 7.1 calories per g. Based on our present knowledge of the amount of alcohol metabolized per kilogram and per hour, the total amount of calories available from alcohol metabolized in the body may be computed. On an average, 50 calories would be available per hour when distilled spirits or wine is taken, or 75 calories per hour from beer. The values may vary from 30 up to 85 calories per hour, depending upon individual variability in metabolic rate and in body weight and in kind of beverage. Under extreme conditions, when large amounts are imbibed, as might be the case with alcoholics, theroretically larger amounts might be available.

Computing the "maximal daily intake" and the calories derived from these maximal amounts of alcohol indicates that 1200 calories will be available from alcohol metabolized in the body per twenty-four hours when taken as distilled spirits or wine, and about 1800 calories, when taken as beer. Depending on individual variations in metabolic rate and body weight, this amount may vary from 650 to 20,000 calories per twenty-four hours. For heavy drinkers and alcohol addicts with a larger intake, even higher values might be possible.

A number of studies have attempted to elucidate whether the whole of these 7.1 calories per g of alcohol is available to the body, or only a part.

Our present knowledge implies that under normal conditions, during the first two steps of the metabolism of alcohol—to acetaldehyde and to acetyl CoA and acetate—approximately 2.6 calories are liberated, being available to the body. Acetyl CoA or acetate enters into the general metabolic pool in the body and, provided that these substances are oxidized completely, the remaining 4.5 calories should be available to the body—thus a total of 7.1 calories per g of alcohol.

If, under certain conditions, a small part of the alcohol enters into secondary reactions—for example, coupled to catalase and hydrogen peroxide, or being converted to fat—the energy liberated by that part of the alcohol would not be available to the body [Dontcheff]. This part may, under normal conditions, i.e., after ingestion of moderate amounts, play only an insignificant role, but might theoretically, under extreme conditions, account for a decrease of the total calories available—for example, in heavy drinkers with an excessive consumption of alcohol. Studies are needed to show whether such a mechanism actually exists in man.

Considering the limited rate of alcohol metabolism, it is clear that only 50 calories on an average are available per hour, or 1200 calories per twenty-four hours, thus somewhat less than the basal metabolism in an individual weighing 70 kg. Hence, these calories from alcohol may cover as much as one-third to one-half of the energy requirements of a man per twenty-four hours, but only one-fifth to one tenth of the energy requirement per hour for heavy work.

Even if the total calories derived from alcohol may not be available for muscular work, a number of studies [Dontcheff] indicate that the calories from alcohol are available for other energy purposes and thus may spare carbohydrates and fat.

The prolonged daily intake of alcohol, becoming part of the daily diet, may lead to an increase in body weight, if the intake of food is kept at the same level as without alcohol, since the calories from alcohol are added to the calories derived from carbohydrates, fat, and protein. Or, the prolonged intake may lead to a decrease in food intake, one reason being that the calories from alcohol provide energy for basal requirements and substitute for the energy usually derived from carbohydrates, fat, and, possibly, protein. Under certain circumstances, persistent heavy drinking may lead to deficiency diseases caused by a low intake of protective foodstuffs [World Health Organization].

BLOOD ALCOHOL LEVEL AND ALCOHOL EFFECTS

In order to study the possible relation between the effects of alcohol and the blood alcohol concentration, a series of experiments have been carried out in our laboratory. Alcohol was given under fixed conditions, and the blood alcohol level was followed by analyzing samples taken repeatedly at short intervals. Effects were studied by assessing changes in a number of functions: flicker fusion frequency of the eye, sensitivity of the cornea to a graded jet of air, standing steadiness, finger coordination, striking out letters, and subtracting backwards [Goldberg, 1943].

In our sample of moderate drinkers, the results showed that a minimal blood alcohol content, a "critical" level, had to be surpassed before a significant departure from normal could be measured. This level varied somewhat among the subjects on any one test, and in the same subject on different tests. It was lower for more complicated tests and higher for simpler ones. The term "tolerance to alcohol" can thus be defined in quantitative terms. One way is to define tolerance as the critical level at which performance deteriorates on a specified test or set of tests; a change in tolerance would mean a change in the critical level.

When plotting departure from normal against blood alcohol, a logarithmic curve was obtained, the slope increasing gradually with increase in dose.[5]

In order to obtain an expression of the overall effect of an alcoholic beverage, a formula has been worked out as a first approximation to a quantitative approach. The area of the blood alcohol curve that is over the critical level is used as an expression of the effect. The maximum of the blood alcohol curve, the time when the maximum appears, the rate of disappearance of alcohol from the blood, and the critical level enter into the formula, as well as the logarithmic relationship between effect and blood alcohol.

This method not only allows the study of the relation between dose and effect (the dose-response curve) but also the possible differences in effect between different beverages, if their blood alcohol curves are known.

TOLERANCE AND HABITUATION

One of the ways of testing whether there is any difference in the effects and disposal of alcohol between moderate and heavy drinkers

[5] Tolerance can hence also be defined as the abscissa in origo plus the slope of the curve.

has been to administer alcohol to subjects with different drinking habits and to follow one or more functions before and after alcohol ingestion. The results are then compared with the blood alcohol concentration. Analysis of these data reveals any changes in absorption, distribution or metabolism, or in the relation between the degree of impairment of a function and the blood alcohol concentration.

A series of experiments of this nature was performed in our laboratory under identical conditions in abstainers, moderate drinkers, and heavy drinkers [Goldberg, 1943].

The same dose of alcohol seemed to give the same blood alcohol curve in all three classes of subjects. No gross changes in absorption, distribution, or overall metabolism could be demonstrated. The heavy drinkers were, however, able to drink considerably larger quantities than the other two groups. This means that under those circumstances the metabolic rate would be considerably higher.

With regard to the effects of alcohol, the heavy drinkers showed the lowest degree of impairment in relation to the blood alcohol level, and abstainers the highest; the moderate consumers were intermediate.

Plotting of the actual data against blood alcohol showed that the critical level was lowest in abstainers and rose with increased habituation to alcohol, being highest in heavy drinkers.

The dose-response curve was shifted to the right, and for a number of tests showed a change in slope.

These differences in critical level were not limited to the averages among the groups studied; they exist even among moderate drinkers and are related to variations in drinking habits within a group, thus being part of a physiological variation.

When the experimental setup was changed and the subjects were allowed to drink at will during a fixed period of time, two things were noted. The amount of alcohol imbibed during the time given was related to the degree of alcohol habituation of the subject; it increased from abstainers to moderate drinkers to heavy drinkers. These differences between the groups in the amount imbibed were, however, larger than the differences between their critical levels. This led to the paradoxical situation that those with a low critical level, the abstainers, imbibed such a small amount as barely to reach their limit, and they showed almost no impairment. The heavy drinkers, on the other hand, drank such an amount of alcohol in the time assigned that they surpassed their limit and showed the highest impairment in function; the moderates, as before, reached an intermediate position.

It is, therefore, tempting to form a hypothesis that intake of a moderate quantity of alcohol during a prolonged period of time brings about an increased tolerance which, in turn, brings about a further increase in the amount of alcohol taken. In the majority of drinkers these changes stay within physiological limits, and drinking remains under control. Under some circumstances, however, the intake increases at a higher rate and the critical level increases more rapidly. The large amounts of alcohol taken then lead to a higher blood alcohol level; the critical level is surpassed, impairment of various functions is induced, and blood alcohol rises to levels which involve an increasing risk of chronic damage.

The metabolic changes governing this development are not known but most probably must be looked for within the central nervous system at the cellular receptor sites rather than in the overall absorption, distribution, or metabolism of the alcohol imbibed.

DRINKING PATTERNS

It is of great interest to study actual drinking patterns in relation to the known facts about the fate and action of alcohol in the human body. Various drinking patterns must be considered—the cocktail hour, the dinner starting with highballs, the taking of wine with a meal, the formal dinner involving a number of different drinks, as well as the spacing of drinks. The drinking of two or three glasses of table wine with a meal gives a blood alcohol level of anywhere from 0.015 to 0.04 per cent, depending on the spacing. A formal dinner party starting with 1⅔ fl oz of some distilled spirits or some beer (5 or 6 fl oz) and including two glasses of table wine (7 to 9 fl oz), one glass of port or madeira (1½ to 2 fl oz) with the dessert, and 1½ to 2 fl oz of cognac with the coffee after dinner, means a total of 55 to 70 g of alcohol, spread over a total of 4 to 5 hours. The resulting blood alcohol curve shows no definite peak but reaches a horizontal level of between 0.04 and 0.06 per cent after about 1 or 1½ hours and stays thus for 3 or 4 hours, then declines at a constant rate, all alcohol having left the body 8 hours after the start of drinking.

The same amount taken within 1 hour as distilled spirits only

(6 to 7 fl oz) would cause a peak of blood alcohol of 0.14 per cent and would leave the body over roughly the same time as in the first case, but would produce completely different effects.

Drinking patterns vary not only between drinkers but also in one and the same person at different times, depending upon a large number of factors, endogenous and environmental, inherent or acquired. The general pattern varies between moderate and heavy drinkers. It varies from country to country and between different parts of the same country.

Studies have been started on ordinary patterns in general and on the actual amounts of alcohol imbibed by a representative sample of the general population in a number of countries [e.g., Luzzatto-Fegiz and Lolli] initiated by, among others, the California Wine Advisory Board.

In order to be able to understand the meaning of the information concerning average intake of alcoholic beverages by a population, the actual drinking patterns of the population must be known. Extensive studies of drinking patterns, supplemented by actual blood alcohol analyses, are needed in different cultural groups under various circumstances, in order to understand the importance of the kinds and amounts of various beverages imbibed and their differential effect on the human body.

AFTEREFFECTS

The experiments discussed thus far have been based on the blood alcohol curve and the processes connected with the presence of alcohol in the blood.

A number of aftereffects of alcohol, however, are also important. They appear late in the sequence of alcohol symptoms. One such syndrome consists of dizziness, vertigo, nausea, and possibly vomiting.

A series of studies on the possible connection between nystagmus (i.e., rhythmic eye movements with one rapid and one slow component) and alcohol intake have incidentally shed some light on the nature of these aftereffects [Aschan et al., Goldberg, 1961; Walter].

The technique consisted in electronic recording of spontaneous or induced eye movements by applying electrodes to the outer corners of the eyes, the instrument recording the variations in the standing cornea-retina potential, the eye bulbs acting as dipoles. The method was developed by G. Aschan at the University of Uppsala.

A healthy subject closing his eyes displays, under normal conditions, no spontaneous nystagmus. After drinking alcohol, a positional alcohol nystagmus is evoked, mainly behind closed eyes with the head in the right or left side position. The positional alcohol nystagmus appears in two distinct phases.

The first phase, after a single dose of alcohol, starts within thirty minutes and lasts for three to four hours. It has a characteristic direction, the rapid component beating to the same side as the head is turned, and changing with the position.

The second phase, reversing the direction of its beat compared to phase I, starts five to six hours after alcohol intake and, in every single case, lasts for several hours *after* the alcohol has disappeared from the blood. Recording of the presence of a positional alcohol nystagmus is an objective way of demonstrating an objective after-effect of drinking.

The labyrinths are involved in this mechanism. Damage of one labyrinth changes the pattern in a characteristic way. Loss of function of both labyrinths abolishes the positional alcohol nystagmus completely.

Administration of repeated doses gives a clue as to another part of the mechanism. A mixed pattern of phase I and phase II occurs. Analysis of the pattern in relation to the blood alcohol level shows a number of features. A rising blood alcohol level induces phase I, and a declining blood alcohol level induces phase II, the actual nystagmus recorded being the algebraic sum of the induced and the possibly existing nystagmus.

The effect of a new dose of alcohol ("the hair of the dog that bit you") can also be demonstrated, its effect depending upon where in the sequence of various nystagmus patterns the new dose is added. If taken during phase II, the new dose induces phase I, which will diminish, completely abolish, or reverse the existing phase II, depending on the difference in beating direction and the intensity of the nystagmus existing and induced.

It is challenging to speculate what metabolic changes might induce these patterns. A direct effect of alcohol is not unlikely during phase I, whereas a trigger mechanism, the effect of secondary metabolites, or a rebound phenomenon, are some suggestions of the mechanism of action underlying phase II.

Under various conditions, spontaneous as well as drug-induced (e.g., by tranquilizers), another type of eye movement occurs, so-called *roving movements*, blocking the positional alcohol nystagmus. The roving ocular movements are accompanied by drowsiness and tiredness. They can also in many cases be recorded as objective after-effects. They have a different mechanism of action, most probably being elicited in the reticular system.

The demonstration of a nystagmus as one example of an objective aftereffect of alcohol makes it possible to use this phenomenon as a model for understanding tolerance and withdrawal phenomena as well as long-term effects of prolonged intake of alcohol.

Even if the metabolic rate of alcohol seems to be large enough to dispose of considerable amounts in a twenty-four hour period, as noted previously, the presence of an aftereffect as an indication of some continued process in the central nervous system makes it likely that an "actual metabolic rate," allowing *no* aftereffect after twenty-four hours, is considerably less.

A close study of this criterion as a limiting condition seems indicated as one approach to a study of the underlying mechanism of moderate drinking with controlled intake versus loss of control in some individuals. It seems not unlikely that such an approach might shed light on the borderline cases and help to get some clues as to the limits between moderate drinking and the danger zone.

Knowledge of the difference in metabolism between various beverages will prove to be indispensable in order to attack this problem, if various beverages should show differences not only in acute but also in long-term effects.

REFERENCES

Aschan, G., Bergstedt, M., Goldberg, L., and Laurell, L., Positional Nystagmus in Man during and after Alcohol Intoxication, *Quart. J. Studies Alc.*, 17:381–405, 1956.

Battelli, F., and Stern, L., L'Alcoolase dans les tissus animaux (Alcoholase in Animal Tissue), *Compt. Rend. Soc. Biol.*, 67:419–421, 1909.

Bonnichsen, R. K., and Wassén, A. M., Crystalline Alcohol Dehydrogenase from Horse Liver, *Arch. Biochem.*, 18:361–363, 1948.

Casier, H., Etude du métabolisme de l'alcool éthylique au moyen d'alcool éthylique radioactif (CH_3-$C^{14}H_2OH$) chez la souris (Study of the Metabolism of Ethyl Alcohol by means of Radioactive Ethyl Alcohol in the Mouse), *Arch. intern. Pharmacodynamie*, 100:175–214, 1954.

Chance, B., An Intermediate Compound in the Catalasehydrogen Peroxide Reaction, *Acta Chem. Scand.*, 1:236–267, 1947.

Dontcheff, L., Etude de l'oxydation de l'alcool chez le rat au moyen d'éthanol marqué au C[14] (A Study of the Oxidation of Alcohol in the Rat by means of C[14]-labeled Ethanol), *Compt. Rend.*, 231:177–178, 1950.

Goldberg, L., Quantitative Studies on Alcohol Tolerance in Man. The Influence of Ethyl Alcohol on Sensory, Motor and Psychological Functions Referred to Blood Alcohol in Normal and Habituated Individuals. *Acta Physiol. Scand.*, 5 (Suppl. 16): 1–128, 1943.

Goldberg, L., Några nyare undersökningar över alkoholens fysiologiska verkningar (Some New Investigations on the Physiological Effects of Alcohol), *Tirfing*, 41:150–166, 1947.

Goldberg, L., Alcohol Research in Sweden, 1939–1948, *Quart. J. Studies Alc.*, 10:279–288, 1949.

Goldberg, L., Alcohol, Tranquilizers and Hangover, *Quart. J. Studies Alc.*, Suppl. 1, pp. 37–56, 1961.

Hjelt, E., Vissa undersökningar angående det widmarkskablodprovet på finskt folkmaterial (Some Investigation with Widmark's Blood Test among Finns), *Tirfing*, 43:150–154, 1949.

Lehmann, J., Aktivierung von Alkoholdehydrogenase in Muskel, Leber und Tumorgeweben durch Coenzym (Activation of Alcohol Dehydrogenase in Muscle, Liver and Tumor Tissues by Co-enzyme), *Biochem. Z.*, 272:144–152, 1934.

Lutwak-Mann, C., Alcoholdehydrogenase of Animal Tissues, *Biochem. J.*, 32:1364–1374, 1938.

Luzzatto-Fegiz, P., and Lolli, G., The Use of Milk and Wine in Italy, *Quart. J. Studies Alc.*, 18:355–381, 1957.

Sutherland, V. C., Hine, C. H., and Burbridge, T. N., The Effect of Ethanol on Cerebral Cortex Metabolism *in vitro*, *J. Pharmacol.*, 116:469–479, 1956.

Theorell, H., and Bonnichsen, R., Studies on Liver Alcohol Dehydrogenase. I. Equilibria and Initial Reaction Velocities, *Acta Chem. Scand.*, 5:1105–1126, 1951.

Theorell, H., and Chance, B., Studies on Liver Alcohol Dehydrogenase. II. The Kinetics of the Compound of Horse Liver Alcohol Dehydrogenase and Reduced Diphosphopyridine Nucleotide. *Acta Chem. Scand.*, 5:1127–1144, 1951.

Walter, H. W., Alkoholmissbrauch und Alkohollagenystagmus (Abuse of Alcohol and Positional Alcohol Nystagmus), *Deut. Z. ges. gerichtl. Med.*, 43:232–241, 1954.

Widmark, E., *Die theoretischen Grundlagen und die praktische Verwendbarkeit der gerichtlich-medizinischen Alkoholbestimmung* (The Theoretical Foundations and the Practical Applicability of the Medico-Legal Determination of Alcohol), Berlin, Urban & Schwarzenberger, 1932.

World Health Organization, Expert Committee on Alcohol, First Report, WHO Technical Report Series, no. 84, Geneva, March, 1954.

Olof A. Forsander

Research Laboratories of the State Alcohol Monopoly (Alko), Helsinki, Finland

INFLUENCE OF ALCOHOL
ON THE GENERAL METABOLISM
OF THE BODY

Editor's Note   *The metabolism of alcohol having been described in the foregoing presentation by Dr. Leonard Goldberg, the next major question is, What effect does this process have on the general metabolism of the body? Dr. Olof A. Forsander answers this question chiefly by showing the important nutritional role of alcohol in the energy economy of the body. He makes an interesting distinction between the two separate functions of alcohol—the pharmacological, which influences behavior, and the nutritional, which can influence physical health in more than one way. Some of the ground covered by Dr. Goldberg in dealing with the metabolism of alcohol is of necessity repeated here. The reader, especially the nontechnical reader, will find the different style in which this material is treated by Dr. Forsander helpful in grasping the total picture of alcohol metabolism. Dr. Forsander's knowledge is derived both from laboratory experiments and from study of populations in life—such as his study of the blood sugar of persons arrested for drunkenness.*

Alcohol influences the human body in two ways, which differ fundamentally from each other. First, the alcohol (ethanol) molecule has a pharmacological effect on the central nervous system which may be reflected by intoxication. Second, alcohol has a high nutrient value, and the human body is quite capable of utilizing the energy which alcohol provides. Since fairly large amounts of alcohol are used, in comparison to other substances such as coffee, its role in the energy economy of the organism may be considerable.

The human senses are capable of registering only the first of these effects of alcohol, intoxication. We can observe, feel, that our nervous system does not function in the usual way when enough alcohol is consumed; but we cannot feel that alcohol is being oxidized in the body, or that we are making use of the energy from it. When alcohol is being broken down (metabolized), considerable changes take place in the normal bodily metabolism, as will be shown, but we have no special senses by which these changes can be registered. We are aware of these changes in metabolism only as an undefinable exhilaration, if these changes are of a positive nature, or as a depression, if they are of a negative character.

It is principally the effect of alcohol on the central nervous system, and the changes in behavior this effect brings about, that psychiatrists, psychologists, and sociologists deal with. It is probably quite correct to say that alcohol is consumed chiefly because of this effect; but we cannot avoid the fact that alcohol, after having been consumed, is oxidized in the body and that this process brings about changes in the normal metabolism of the body. These changes will be the subjects of the present discussion.

NUTRITIONAL ROLE OF ALCOHOL

Hippocrates, the "father of medicine," said that "unthinned, wine appeases hunger." But this observation was purely subjective, and modern science does not acknowledge observations that are only subjective. By the end of the last century, objective methods in the field of nutritional physiology had been elaborated, and these methods were also used in experiments for determining the nutrient value of alcohol. Poul Bjerre [1899] in Sweden was one of the first to use the new methods; he learned that alcohol has a considerable nutrient value, and that when alcohol is oxidized, the breakdown of fats and carbohydrates diminishes. It is thus said that alcohol spares fats and carbohydrates; it has no effect on protein metabolism.

A few years later [1902], Atwater and Benedict made their well-known experiments on the nutrient value of alcohol. They found that during rest, a part of the total energy utilized was taken from the alcohol, while during work, a smaller part of the energy requirement of the body was taken from the alcohol. They also showed clearly that the potential energy of alcohol could be converted in the body into kinetic energy in the same way as the potential energy of food.

Just before World War I, Krieger tried to find out how alcohol could be utilized for muscular work. His experiments seemed to show that alcohol could be directly used as an energy source for work; later investigations, however, have shown that he was only partly correct in his assumption. Alcohol, as such, is not used in the muscles, but rather the acetate formed in the partial breakdown of alcohol.

QUANTITATIVE SHARE OF ALCOHOL IN FOOD

Until recently, in most calculations of the nutrient supply of individuals, no attention was given to the amount of alcohol consumed. Actually, in many wine- and beer-consuming countries the people obtain considerable portions of their calories from these beverages. It would be of special interest to know how much alcohol the alcoholic consumes and the type of food he eats. Unfortunately, only very limited information exists on this question.

In 1936 Jolliffe, Colbert, and Joffe reported their calculations of the caloric intake of a large number of alcoholics. The patients were interviewed concerning their eating and drinking habits during the time they had misused alcohol; only cases in which the answers were considered reliable were taken into consideration. The individuals were divided into groups according to symptoms of vitamin deficiency. Table 1 shows the total caloric intake of two of the groups and the proportions derived from alcohol and from foodstuffs. The first group, composed of individuals who showed no symptoms of vitamin deficiency, derived 73 per cent of its calories from food. The second group, also composed of excessive drinkers, derived 75 per cent of its calories from alcohol and only 25 per cent from food. This group showed many signs and symptoms of vitamin-deficiency disease. Several individuals in the first group had lived up to forty years on a diet wherein some 40 per cent of the calories came from alcohol. In the second group, ten years was the longest period during which an alcoholic had lived on a diet deriving up to 60 per cent of its calories from alcohol.

Table 1   Caloric intake by two groups of alcoholics (calculated from Jolliffe, Colbert, and Joffe)

Group	Average daily intake in calories				
	Total	Alcohol	%	Food	%
I. 8 persons	4216	1325	27	2936	73
II. 26 persons	4017	3188	75	829	25

It is definitely difficult for a person to remember exactly how much he has eaten or drunk some time before he is interviewed. In one investigation in Finland, Dr. K. Bruun[1] asked a number of people how much they drank on the last day of their last drinking period. This day was not too remote, and it is assumed that the persons interviewed could recall correctly how much they had drunk. Their eating habits were not considered. If the investigation is extensive enough, the last day of the drinking period can be taken as an average for the whole drinking period. If, in Finland, the average energy consumption of persons between forty and fifty years of age is estimated to be 3225 calories, it follows that the persons consuming the smallest amount of alcohol get only 3 per cent of their calories from alcohol, while the group of excessive drinkers gets a little over 50 per cent.

How do these findings correspond with theoretical calculations? The basal metabolism of a human subject has been estimated to use 1500 calories per twenty-four hours. An individual can, on an average, oxidize 7 g of alcohol per hour, which gives 1200 calories if alcohol is oxidized over twenty-four hours. Thus, 80 per cent of the energy requirements for the basal metabolism can be covered by the oxidation of alcohol. But an estimation of the actual energy consumption, which is much higher than the basal requirement, shows that alcohol can furnish only some 30 to 40 per cent of the total energy need. This difference between the calculated possible average and the high value obtained in the study by Jolliffe and his associates and also the values of Bruun may depend on an unusually rapid oxidation of alcohol. Widmark found that the oxidation rate varied considerably among different individuals, the decline in blood alcohol ranging between 10 mg and 24 mg per 100 ml per hour.

When alcohol is oxidized in the human body at a constant rate, independent of environmental changes or of the amount of alcohol consumed, about one-third of the energy need of a normal individual doing normal work is taken from alcohol during the time that it is being oxidized. The oxidation of other materials diminishes correspondingly, by about one-third. This is valid if the alcohol is completely oxidized to carbon dioxide. In reality the process does not take place exactly in this way; the alcohol metabolites, the products

[1] Personal communication.

of the first step in the breakdown of alcohol in the liver, are oxidized outside the liver only after some time [Casier and Polet].

The metabolism of some body organs is influenced by alcohol to a greater degree than is reflected in the overall metabolism of the organism. In order to explain how different organs are affected by the oxidation of alcohol, I shall summarize briefly the intermediary metabolism of alcohol.

STEPS IN THE METABOLISM OF ALCOHOL

There are two different steps in the breakdown of alcohol in the human body. First, the alcohol is oxidized in the liver to acetaldehyde and then to acetate, which is carried away from the liver by the blood and is ultimately broken down into carbon dioxide and water. Not all the acetate, however, is carried away as such; some of it can form acetoacetic acid, which is partly reduced further to β-hydroxybutyric acid [Forsander and Räihä]. Some of the acetate may go into the formation of fat or cholesterol; it can also be incorporated into amino acids via other intermediate steps. Further, a small part can be completely oxidized to carbon dioxide in the liver. Figure 1

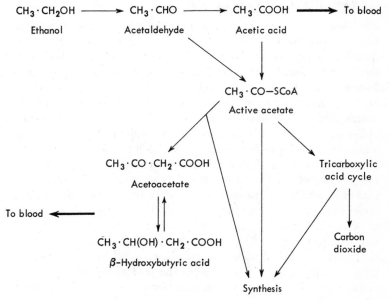

Fig. 1   Scheme for the metabolism of ethanol in the liver.

shows schematically how alcohol is broken down and how it is incorporated into new compounds in the liver. In a normal liver almost
all the alcohol oxidized is carried away as acetate, but depending
on the functional state of the liver, the acetate may, in large or
small quantities, be incorporated into ketone bodies or into fat, and
will be carried away in these forms [Forsander, Räihä and
Suomalainen; Forsander]. However, about 90 per cent of the total
amount of alcohol broken down in the body under normal conditions
undergoes a partial oxidation to acetate in the liver. The remaining
10 per cent is broken down directly into carbon dioxide in different
organs.

When alcohol is oxidized to acetate, one-third of its energy
content (calories) is liberated, and during the continued breakdown
into carbon dioxide the remaining two-thirds is liberated. In this way
the liver obtains a considerable part of the nutrient value of alcohol.
Let us now consider how the oxidation of alcohol and its metabolites
influences the normal metabolism of the liver and of organs outside
the liver.

METABOLISM IN THE LIVER

The liver has an intensive metabolism with a high oxygen consumption. Although the weight of the liver is only 2 to 3 per cent of the
total body weight, it uses between 25 and 30 per cent of the body's
total oxygen supply. When alcohol is oxidized, the oxygen consumption is not changed very much, but a marked decrease occurs
in the carbon dioxide output. In liver perfusion experiments
Lundsgaard in 1938 found respiratory quotients as low as 0.37, thus
indicating that alcohol is oxidized only partially in the liver. In the
same year Leloir and Muñoz, using liver homogenate, showed that
the main part of the alcohol oxidized was found again as acetate. As
the oxygen consumption of the liver does not increase during alcohol
oxidation, and since the production of carbon dioxide diminishes,
it must be concluded that alcohol is oxidized preferentially and that
other substances are broken down to a lesser extent during the oxidation of alcohol. Since 75 per cent of the oxygen consumption was
used in the partial alcohol oxidation, Leloir and Muñoz presumed
that, correspondingly, 75 per cent of the normal oxidation had not
taken place. How does this value correspond to the values obtained

in experiments on human subjects, and what can be expected theoretically?

Lundqvist [1961] has recently performed some experiments with human subjects in which he measured the content of acetic acid in arterial and venous blood. He found values of the same order as Leloir and Muñoz had obtained in their model experiments. Lundqvist is of the opinion that, at a low estimate, 75 per cent of the energy consumption of the liver can be covered by the partial alcohol oxidation.

According to theoretical calculations the following results have been obtained: Of the 7 g of alcohol that an average human individual is able to break down per hour, about 90 per cent is oxidized to acetate in the liver. As previously stated, the liver is estimated to use between 25 and 30 per cent of the basal oxygen consumption of the whole organism. If the oxygen consumption is considered to be as high as the energy production, the result will be that the partial alcohol oxidation, producing 375 to 450 calories per twenty-four hours, covers as much as 70 to 90 per cent of the energy needed by the liver. These values correspond well to the experimental results. As the energy consumption of the liver is relatively independent of the energy needs of the rest of the body, the part played by alcohol in energy production in the liver is always of this order.

These calculations are valid during the time that alcohol is being oxidized. If a cocktail is taken and the duration of alcohol oxidation is only one hour, the share of alcohol in the energy production of the liver during this hour is about 75 per cent. This is not dependent on the alcohol concentration in the blood, since the oxidation rate of alcohol is independent of the concentration. The rate of alcohol oxidation is not altered if physical work is performed at the same time because the intensity of liver metabolism is influenced very little by work.

When alcohol is oxidized, the energy production in the liver takes place through some very simple enzyme systems. In the oxidation of alcohol to acetaldehyde, which reaction is catalyzed chiefly by the alcohol dehydrogenase enzyme, one molecule of DPN (diphosphopyridine nucleotide) is reduced to DPNH. In the further oxidation of the formed acetaldehyde to acetate, which is catalyzed mainly by the acetaldehyde dehydrogenase, another molecule of the DPN is reduced. In the oxidation of the DPNH (reduced diphosphopyridine nucleotide) molecules, which takes place via the respiratory system, the energy liberated forms energy-rich phosphate bonds. In the oxidation of alcohol, only two dehydrogenase enzymes are necessary, and here also the ordinary respiratory system is needed. The liver is well supplied with these dehydrogenase enzymes, and the oxygen transfer system is always needed for normal metabolism. In a normal liver the DPNH content increases when alcohol is oxidized [Räihä], which may indicate that the reoxidation of DPNH is strained; but the explanation might also be that the energy state of the liver is so good that energy-rich phosphate bonds need not be formed and, because of this, the DPNH is not oxidized. In the liver of a fasted animal, too, a rise in the DPNH content occurs during alcohol oxidation. Table 2 shows these relations as reported by Räihä.

Table 2   Levels of di- and triphosphopyridine nucleotides in fed and fasting livers of control animals and animals metabolizing alcohol. (From Räihä)

	No. of rats	DPN, mμmole/g	DPNH, mμmole/g	DPN+DPNH, mμmole/g	DPN:DPNH
Fed	6	542	138	680	3.95
Fed metabolizing alcohol	6	403	285	688	1.44
Fasted	10	476	149	625	3.25
Fasted metabolizing alcohol	16	453	288	741	1.57

All the enzymatic reactions which take place in the human body have a special task. The oxidation reactions serve the purpose of supplying the body with energy in a form which can be utilized easily. The intensity of the oxidation processes is regulated by the energy need, and it is presumed that the oxidation rate of alcohol is regulated by the energy need of the liver. The energy need of the liver is constant and, correspondingly, the oxidation rate of alcohol is constant. As shown by Widmark, it is not possible to raise this oxidation rate above a certain maximum value.

Fritz has recently shown how the liver covers its energy need under normal conditions. The total oxygen consumption of the liver is 75 ml per minute. Approximately 6 ml of this is needed per minute to convert 0.04 mmole of free fatty acids to 0.16 mmole of ketone bodies; and 52 ml per minute is needed to oxidize completely 0.10 mmole of free fatty acids to carbon dioxide, whereas 17 ml of oxygen per minute is needed for oxidative deamination of amino acids, oxidation of glycerides, and oxidation of glucose.

As far as is known, alcohol does not influence the formation of ketone bodies, nor does it affect the conversion of amino acids. Consequently, the most important effect of alcohol must be that on the total oxidation of the free fatty acids and on the oxidation of glucose. Quastel has shown that the latter is correct. The oxidation of glucose, however, plays only a small part in the total metabolism of the liver. If a tissue has many substrates which are oxidizable, they are usually broken down at different rates. The tissues have a preference for some substrates, and it can be said that some substrates are more oxidizable than others. This is primarily due to the fact that when the same enzyme system converts different substrates, the first to be oxidized is the one with the highest affinity for that enzyme system. The competition for DPN concerns mainly the affinity for the common enzyme system in the oxygen transfer system. The dehydrogenase which has the highest affinity for DPN catalyzes the oxidation of its substrate. The alcohol dehydrogenase and the acetaldehyde dehydrogenase must have a high affinity for DPN because they are preferentially oxidized. It is to be expected that those substrates which are oxidized at a slower rate when alcohol is present are the ones that need DPN for their breakdown. All the substrates which are oxidized in the tricarbonic acid cycle belong to this group.

This change in liver metabolism is not, however, injurious; if it were, noticeable disturbances would appear. It may, on the contrary, be assumed that alcohol is a good substrate for producing the energy the liver needs, since it is the most easily oxidizable substrate known. Only two steps are needed for the oxidation of alcohol in the liver, and in these two steps usable energy is produced. Almost no other substrate exists with similar favorable characteristics. Many enzymes are needed to convert both carbohydrates and fats into such a form that the energy is lost.

The human body adapts itself quickly to the use of new food

substances. An individual who has lived for some time on a diet poor in fat becomes ill if he must suddenly change to a diet rich in fat. But if this individual can increase his fat intake gradually, he can ultimately tolerate a considerable amount. Although alcohol usually is not included in the diet, at least not in the northern European countries, it is not necessary to adapt oneself to it in order to utilize alcohol as a source of energy. Man is born with a very effective system which is able to break down alcohol and utilize the energy formed thereby. Many experiments have been performed on the effect of adaptation to alcohol on the rate of oxidation. Newman, Wilson, and Newman investigated the oxidation of alcohol in moderate and excessive drinkers and found that prolonged use of alcohol in no way influenced the rate at which alcohol disappeared from the body. Eggleton, and later also Knox, Auerbach, and Lin, fed alcohol to rats over a long period, and they found that the effect of this adaptation to alcohol was that it was oxidized more slowly. Some investigators studied the oxidation rate of alcohol by using, as a measure, the amount of radioactive carbon dioxide produced from labeled alcohol. Thus, Von Wartburg and Roethlisberger found that the oxidation rate accelerated if the laboratory animals were adapted to alcohol. In these experiments, however, the sum of two oxidation processes is measured, the oxidation of alcohol to acetate in the liver and the further oxidation of acetate to carbon dioxide outside the liver. The first process cannot be accelerated once it has reached its maximum. The latter is, as will be shown, dependent on energy need and is influenced by many factors. Furthermore, a diluting effect is added, which depends on the nutritional state. If the acetate pool is large, which is the case during high fat consumption, the acetate formed from alcohol will disappear more slowly in the form of carbon dioxide than if the pool is small. It can be postulated that adaptation to alcohol involves only the extrahepatic oxidation of the alcohol metabolites.

A small amount of alcohol is also oxidized in the kidneys. Here it is possible to establish a marked increase in the rate of oxidation by adaptation to alcohol. By giving rats only alcohol to drink for one month, the oxidation rate in kidney slices was increased tenfold [Leloir and Muñoz]. The alcohol oxidation in this organ must have been so low originally that only a part of its energy support was covered by alcohol, and therefore the rate could be increased.

OXIDATION OUTSIDE THE LIVER

Under normal conditions alcohol is oxidized in the liver chiefly to acetate. Thus the extrahepatic oxidation of the alcohol metabolites is mainly a breakdown of acetate. The acetate concentration in the blood of a normal person on a normal diet is very low, 0.3 to 0.7 mg per 100 ml [Lundqvist, 1960]. In ruminants the concentration of acetate, and also of other short-chain fatty acids, is very much higher, and it is estimated that these animals cover the main part of their energy need by the oxidation of acetate. The short-chain fatty acids are formed in the rumen by fermentation of the cellulose in grass. Acetate is, consequently, a first-rate nutrient.

In the liver of an average man weighing 70 kg, about 100 mg of alcohol is oxidized per minute and this process gives 125 mg of acetic acid. The circulating blood volume in the liver is 1,175 to 2,110 ml per minute, with an average of 1,500 ml per minute [Horning et al.]. The blood emerging from the vena hepatica has a concentration of 8.3 mg of acetic acid per 100 ml. This amount, however, is diluted immediately by blood with a low acetate concentration, and therefore lower analytical values are obtained. Lundqvist [1960] found values between 2.1 and 5.2 mg per 100 ml in individuals who had drunk alcohol. The acetate concentration was, as expected, independent of the amount of alcohol consumed and independent of the alcohol concentration in the blood.

Probably because free acetate has little quantitative importance in normal human metabolism, acetate metabolism has been neglected in physiological research. However, it is known that acetate is oxidized in most types of tissues. It is oxidized in the tricarbonic acid cycle in which the main part of the aerobic oxidation of the carbohydrates takes place and in which the fatty acids and the amino acids finally are oxidized. The acetate must be converted into the active form in order to be oxidized, and the enzyme systems necessary for this process seem to be present in most tissues. The rate at which acetate is broken down in the muscular tissue is dependent on the acetate concentration and on the functional state of the muscle [Fritz et al.]. The higher the concentration and the more work the muscle performs, the more intensive the acetate oxidation. Even at low concentrations the oxidation rate is high, as indicated by the fact that the concentration in the blood never increases.

The influence of carbohydrates on the breakdown of alcohol has been investigated quite extensively, whereas studies of the effect of alcohol and its metabolites on the metabolism of carbohydrate are relatively few. The effect on fat metabolism also requires a close examination. Glucose does not affect the oxidation of acetate, whereas it strongly increases the oxidation of long-chain fatty acids [Lossow and Chaikoff]. Acetate is much more easily oxidizable than higher fatty acids. If the nutritional state is good, acetate is oxidized nineteen times faster than tripalmitate, which may be used as an example of normal fat. As far as I know, the question of how acetate oxidation quantitatively influences fat oxidation has not yet been investigated. It is known that acetate markedly decreases the oxidation of glucose [Drury and Wick].

Two-thirds of the energy obtained from alcohol is contained in acetate but the amount of acetate formed from alcohol cannot cover the energy need of man even under basal conditions. Another substrate must be oxidized simultaneously with acetate. The amount of energy taken from this other substrate is primarily dependent on the amount of work performed. Under certain conditions acetate is converted into ketone bodies in the liver [Forsander, Räihä, and Suomalainen]. These form an excellent substrate, and they are always present in human blood in varying quantities.

INDIRECT INFLUENCE ON METABOLISM

So far only the competitive influence of alcohol and alcohol metabolites on normal metabolism in the tissues has been discussed. Alcohol, however, has another metabolic effect which can be released via the nervous systems and is, thus, dependent on the pharmacological effect of alcohol. This influences, in the first place, the transportation of substrates, and this in turn affects the general metabolism of the body.

It has been known for a long time that alcohol influences the glycogen content of the liver and the blood sugar level. If alcohol is consumed, the blood sugar will first rise for a short time, but soon it drops again below the normal value. Experiments in human subjects [Forsander, Vartia, and Krusius] and with rats [Lange] have given equal results. Figure 2 shows the changes in the blood sugar level after the consumption of 150 ml of whiskey. The curve is based on an average of ten individuals. The first rise is independent of the

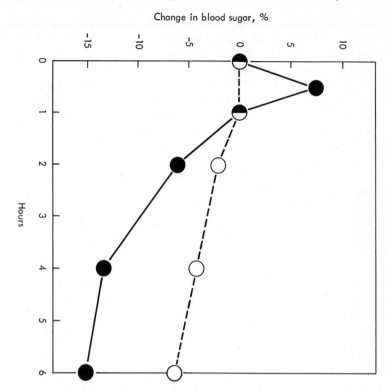

Fig. 2   The changes in the blood sugar level after alcohol
consumption (●) and in controls without alcohol consumption (0).
(From Forsander, Vartia, and Krusius.)

amount of alcohol consumed, but the drop in the later phase of the
curve is proportional to the amount of alcohol consumed [Lange;
Vartia, Forsander, and Krusius]. In an investigation performed with
fifty-three persons who had been arrested for drunkenness, it was
found that on the morning after the alcohol intake, the blood sugar
value was below normal in almost each case; and further, that the
values decreased in inverse proportion to the amount of alcohol that
had been consumed. In the group that had drunk the largest amounts
of alcohol the average blood sugar was 28.7 per cent under the
normal value, and in the whole group it was 19.5 per cent below
normal. Many of the symptoms which appear during a hangover
may derive directly from the low blood sugar concentration. Sub-

sequently, if an individual suffering from a hangover with an accompanying low blood sugar value takes a "recovery drink," the blood sugar level rises. The fact that he immediately feels better may be related partly to this rise.

The first rise in blood sugar after drinking is due to a release of the glycogen from the liver depots into the blood. This mobilization of the glycogen is not caused by a direct action of alcohol on the liver cells, but takes place via the sympathetic nervous system, and the extent depends, naturally, on the condition of the liver, that is, whether it is rich or poor in glycogen [Matunaga].

The mechanism involved in the decrease of blood sugar is unknown, but it is assumed that it might be a consequence of the changed metabolism in the whole body. It is hardly due to a total emptying of the glycogen depots of the liver. It is possible to produce a similar drop in animals by giving them exclusively fat-rich food, and in experiments with rats it has been shown that the drop was proportional to the fat content in the food [Mayes]. The glycogen depots of the animals were not emptied at all, and that they were larger in animals with a low blood sugar value [Tintera and Lovell] is related to a similar alteration in metabolism.

The fat content of the liver is changed after alcohol consumption, depending on a variety of factors. In the first place, the fat is not broken down in the liver as it was before; secondly, a transport of fat from the fat depots to the liver takes place [Horning et al.]; and finally, a considerable synthesis of fat from alcohol occurs [Schulman, Zurek, and Westerfeld]. The first factor can be expected to be relatively constant whereas the other two may vary considerably. The synthesis of fat is dependent on many factors; and although a substrate for the synthesis, acetate, is present during the partial alcohol oxidation, and although the DPNH concentration rises in the normal liver, a fat synthesis of the expected order does not take place. A parallel breakdown of the carbohydrates is necessary for fat synthesis, and the failure of the expected order of fat formation may be related to the fact that the liver preferentially oxidizes alcohol rather than glucose.

DISCUSSION

This discussion of the effect of alcohol on the utilization of substrates in the human body may raise a question regarding the expected consequences of this alteration in metabolism. The effect on the drinker is not noticeable because he is not aware that an alteration is occurring. If the alteration would cause an immediate injury —as, for example, in cases of excessive ingestion of fat—it would certainly be noticed. The intake of large quantities of fat produces a ketosis which results in a subjective feeling of discomfort.

The most remarkable change in metabolism effected by alcohol takes place in the liver. It is not necessary for the body to build up new enzyme systems in order to break down alcohol, because the liver is well equipped for this purpose from birth. As long as alcohol is being oxidized, only a small part of the activity of the liver is needed for the oxidation of the normal substrate and the production of energy. Alcohol is an elegant substrate, and it is oxidized in a very simple enzyme system. If alcohol is oxidized in large amounts for a relatively long period, the normal enzyme equipment is not used and may well degenerate in the same way as other tissues, for instance, an unused muscle. Everything is in order and no disturbances occur as long as alcohol continues to be present as a substrate; but when the excessive drinker attempts to return to a normal diet, difficulties may appear. The alcoholic is poorly equipped with the enzyme systems needed to utilize the food in a normal diet, and at this point medical aid is advisable. Fortunately, the human body is usually able to adapt itself to new conditions, and it can often resume normal functions even without medicines. However, if the changes are irreversible, as in cirrhosis of the liver, a return to normal is no longer possible.

In the muscles, in which the main part of the oxidation of the alcohol metabolites occurs, the influence on normal metabolism is relatively slight. Here other metabolism always goes on parallel to the metabolism of the alcohol metabolites, i.e., chiefly acetate. The acetate from alcohol alone cannot cover the energy need, and the more work done, the smaller its part in the total metabolism.

It is relatively common to relate the effect of alcohol on the human body only to its pharmacological action in the central nervous system, and it is certainly here that the most striking effect is seen. However, alcohol metabolism strongly influences the normal metabolism of the body, and the resulting consequences should not be overlooked in the treatment of alcoholics, especially during the first part of the treatment. Furthermore, a thorough knowledge of the metabolic effects of alcohol is requisite if a more effective drug is to be

developed against hangover—one of the most important factors
leading to alcoholism.

Finally, I wish to say that I do not find it out of the question to
assume that there may exist a biological element in an individual's
attitude toward alcohol and that this element may be found in the
metabolic influence of alcohol on normal metabolism [Forsander,
Kohonen, and Suomalainen].

REFERENCES

Atwater, W. O., and Benedict, F. G., An Experimental Inquiry Regarding the
   Nutritive Value of Alcohol, *Mem. Nat. Acad. Sci.*, 8:255–397, 1902.
Bjerre, P., Ueber den Nährwert des Alkohols (Food Value of Alcohol), *Skand.
   Arch. Physiol.*, 9:323–335, 1899.
Blixenkrone-Møller, N., "Ketonstofferens stilling og betydning i det intermediäre
   stofskifte" (The Position and Significance of Ketone Bodies in Intermediary
   Metabolism), Copenhagen dissertation, 1938.
Carpenter, T. M., and Lee, R. C., The Effect of Glucose on the Metabolism
   of Ethyl Alcohol in Man, *J. Pharmacol.*, 60:264–285, 1937.
Casier, H., Polet, H., and Bruyneel, N., The Metabolism of Ethyl Alcohol and
   Acetaldehyde Labeled with C14, *Arch. intern. Pharmacodynamie*, 120:498–
   501, 1959.
Drury, D. R., and Wick, A. N., Effect of Insulin on Metabolism of Acetate
   by Extrahepatic Tissues, *J. Biol. Chem.*, 203:411–417, 1953.
Eggleton, M. G., Some Factors Affecting the Metabolic Rate of Alcohol,
   J. Physiol., 98:239–254, 1940.
Forsander, O. A., "Influence of Insulin on the Intermediary Metabolism of
   Ethanol," 5th Intern. Congr. Biochem., Moscow, 1961, *Abst. of Communs.*,
   p. 270.
Forsander, O. A., Kohonen, J., and Suomalainen, H., Physiological Alcohol
   Consumption, *Quart. J. Studies Alc.*, 19:379–387, 1958.
Forsander, O. A., and Räihä, N. C. R., Metabolites Produced in the Liver
   during Alcohol Oxidation, *J. Biol. Chem.*, 235:34–36, 1960.
Forsander, O. A., Räihä, N. C. R., and Suomalainen, H., Alkoholoxydation und
   Bildung von Acetoacetat in normaler und glykogenarmer intakter Ratten-
   leber (Alcohol Oxidation and Acetoacetate Formation in Normal and
   Glycogen-deficient Intact Rat Liver), *Hoppe-Seyler's Z. physiol. Chem.*,
   312:243–248, 1958.
Forsander, O., Vartia, K. O., and Krusius, F.-E., Experimentelle Studien über
   die biologische Wirkung von Alkohol. 1. Alkohol und Blutzucker (Experi-
   mental Studies on the Biological Effects of Alcohol. 1. Alcohol and Blood
   Sugar), *Ann. Med. Exp. et Biol. Fenniae*, 36:416–423, 1958.
Fritz, I. B., Davis, D. G., Holtrop, R. H., and Dundee, H., Fatty Acid Oxidation
   and Synthesis in Mammalian Systems, *Physiol. Revs.*, 41:52–129, 1961.
Fritz, I. B., Davis, D. G., Holtrop, R. H., and Dundee, H., Fatty Acid Oxidation

by Skeletal Muscle during Rest and Activity, *Am. J. Physiol.*, 194:379–386, 1958.

Horning, M. G., Williams, E. A., Maling, H. M., Brodie, B. B., and Butler, W. M., Depot Fat as Source of Increased Liver Triglycerides after Ethanol, *Biochem. Biophys. Res. Commun.*, 3:635–640, 1960.

Jolliffe, N., Colbert, C. N., and Joffe, P. M., Observations on the Etiologic Relationship of Vitamin B (B_1) to Polyneuritis in the Alcohol Addict, *Am. J. Med. Sci.*, 191:515–527, 1936.

Karvonen, M. J., Väestöryhmien kalorintarpeen arviointi (Assessment of Caloric Requirements for Different Populations), *Duodecim* 73:369–375, 1957.

Knox, W. E., Auerbach, V. H., and Lin, E. C. C., Enzymatic and Metabolic Adaptations in Animals, *Physiol. Revs.*, 36:164–254, 1956.

Krieger, K., Die Verwertung der Energie des Alcohols für die Muskelarbeit (Utilization of Energy from Alcohol for Muscular Work), *Pflüger's Arch. ges. Physiol.*, 151:479–522, 1913.

Lange, K., Blutzucker- und Blutalkoholspiegel bei weissen Ratten nach Alkoholbelastung und toxischer Leberschädigung (Blood Sugar and Blood Alcohol Levels in White Rats after Administration of Alcohol and after Toxic Liver Damage), *Hoppe-Seyler's Z. physiol. Chem.*, 321:49–56, 1960.

Leloir, L. F., and Muñoz, J. M., Ethyl Alcohol Metabolism in Animal Tissues, *Biochem. J.*, 32:299–307, 1938.

Lossow, W. J., and Chaikoff, J. L., Carbohydrate Sparing Fatty Acid Oxidation. I. The Relation of Fatty Acid Chain Length to the Degree of Sparing, *Arch. Biochem. Biophys.*, 57:23–40, 1955.

Lundsgaard, E., Alcohol Oxidation As a Function of the Liver. *C. R. Lab. Carlsberg* (Chem. Ser.), 22:333–337, 1938.

Lundqvist, F., The Concentration of Acetate in Blood during Alcohol Metabolism in Man, *Acta Physiol. Scand.* 50 (Suppl. 175):97, 1960.

Lundqvist, F., "The Regulation of Liver Metabolism during Alcohol Oxidation," 5th Intern. Congr. Biochem., Moscow, 1961, *Abst. of Communs.*, p. 466.

Matunaga, H., Über die Wirkung des Alkohols auf den Blutzuckerspiegel und den Glykogenhalt der Leber mit besonderer Berücksichtigung seines Wirkungsmechanismus (On the Effect of Alcohol on Blood Sugar Level and Glycogen Content of the Liver with Special Consideration of the Mechanism of Its Action.), *Tôhoku J. Exp. Med.*, 44:130–157, 1942.

Mayes, P. A., An Inverse Relation between the Liver Glycogen and the Blood Glucose in the Rat Adapted to a Fat Diet, *Nature*, 187:325–326, 1960.

Newman, H. W., Wilson, R. H. L., and Newman, E. J., Direct Determination of Maximal Daily Metabolism of Alcohol, *Science*, 116:328–329, 1952.

Quastel, J. H., Effects of Aliphatic Alcohols on the Metabolism of Brain and Liver, *Quart. J. Studies Alc.*, 20:428–431, 1959.

Räihä, N. C. R., "Effect of Alcohol Oxidation on Levels of Pyridine Nucleotides in Rat Liver, presented at 1st International Pharmacological Meeting, Stockholm, 1961.

Schulman, M. P., Zurek, R., and Westerfeld, W. W., The Pathway of Alcohol Metabolism, in Himwich, H. E. (ed.), *Alcoholism*. Washington, D.C., American Association for the Advancement of Science, 1957, pp. 29–37.

Tintera, J. W., and Lovell, H. W., Endocrine Treatment of Alcoholism, *Geriatrics,* 4:274–280, 1949.

Vartia, O. K., Forsander, O. A., and Krusius, F.-E., Blood Sugar Values in Hangover, *Quart. J. Studies Alc.,* 21:597–604, 1960.

von Wartburg, J. P., and Roethlisberger, M., Enzymatische Veränderungen in der Leber nach langdauernder Belastung mit Aethanol und Methanol bei der Ratte (Enzymatic Changes in the Liver after Prolonged Administration of Ethanol and Methanol in Rats), *Helv. Physiol. et Pharmacol. Acta,* 19:30–41, 1961.

Widmark, E. M. P., Hormonale Einflüsse auf den Alkoholumsatz (Effect of Hormones on Alcohol Metabolism.), *Biochem. Z.,* 282:79–84, 1935.

Claudia Balboni, M.D.

International Center for Psychodietetics,
Rome, Italy

ALCOHOL IN RELATION
TO DIETARY PATTERNS

Editor's Note   *In their presentations, Drs. Goldberg and Forsander both found it necessary to allude to patterns of drinking. By this they meant to inform that the metabolism of alcohol, and its effects, as studied in the laboratory, represents only what happens under the ideal conditions for controlled observation. But what happens when people drink under social conditions? Actually, there is no such thing as the effect of alcohol alone. Not only are there always differences according to the amount of alcohol, the kind of beverage, the speed of drinking, the accompanying food, and the condition of the drinker, but there can be great differences according to the frequency of drinking and the whole context of the drinking behavior. Dr. Claudia Balboni reviews a number of studies in which she has participated, which reveal the role of alcohol, and its varied effects, particularly in relation to the dietary habits of a number of populations. These include such different groups as patients with diabetes, obesity, and coronary disease—people with health problems as well as several normal populations studied in Italy and in the United States, including special groups of women and elderly men. In each of these studies the important feature is the relation of a drinking pattern to the total dietary pattern of the group.*

The contemporary pattern, the cocktail hour, is the theme of a major presentation elsewhere in this symposium. (See The Cocktail Hour: Physiological, Psychological, and Social Aspects, by Dr. Giorgio Lolli.) The importance of drinking patterns is also touched upon in several other discussions, including that of Dr. Kettil Bruun (pp. 217–228).

Psychodietetics is a word which, as far as I know, was coined by an American psychologist, Martin Fritz, of Iowa State College, almost thirty years ago. It was devised to link diet and nutrition with the mental processes of men and women. At first, the word went almost unnoticed. It seldom appeared in the literature until it was resurrected recently with the organization of the International Center for Psychodietetics in Rome and New York.

This Center was developed as a medium for international cooperation between workers in the United States and Europe in research projects on eating and drinking habits, with the ultimate goal of helping to prevent or correct undesirable deviations. The approach which the Center fosters, both in research and in prevention and treatment, is a combination of medical, psychological, and social techniques. Individually, these techniques are not new. They are well known to modern clinicians, psychologists, and sociologists. Their combination, however, appears to represent a new and, we hope, a valuable approach.

Such a new attack has long been necessary. Although the impact of nutrition on the prevention and correction of disease has been outstanding in recent years, it has not been commensurate with the wealth of available knowledge relative to the nutritive processes.

The reasons for the gap between this knowledge and its practical application seem to be linked to the fact that the biochemical and physiological processes of nutrition have been explored more thoroughly in the past than have the psychological and social facets of eating and drinking habits. We face here a situation almost opposite to the one observed in the area of sex. In the latter, knowledge of the psychological and social aspects of sexual activities far outweighs that of the physiological and biochemical aspects of the sexual life of the individual.

In the case of nutrition, and especially in the case of drinking, it has taken all the explosiveness and the tragic consequences of a distorted drinking habit—namely, addiction to alcohol—to make scientists aware that a study of the physiological aspects would be almost meaningless unless complemented by a study of the psychological and sociological aspects. Furthermore, we recognize that a study of the various aspects of distorted drinking habits would be almost meaningless unless complemented by a similar study of normal drinking patterns.

Finally, it seems evident that drinking habits, whether normal or deviant, represent only one part of an individual's general nutrition, and his drinking pattern must thus be examined as part of his total dietary pattern, all studied medically, psychologically, and sociologically. It is this approach which represents what we term psycho-dietetics.

From the purely physiological or biochemical point of view, it has long been evident that the study of alcoholic beverages is part and parcel of the study of nutrition. Ethyl alcohol, the key component of every alcoholic beverage, is an energy-yielding food item which in its own right has a place in the field of nutrition. It has been shown by research workers both in the United States and in Europe that the calories in alcohol can be utilized by the human body and that, in all likelihood, the metabolism of alcohol has a sparing action on other foods.

Fermented beverages—notably beer and wine—may contain significant amounts of vitamins, mainly those of the vitamin B complex [Perlman and Morgan; Randoin and Billand]. At this symposium, it is particularly appropriate to note the outstanding contributions to research in this field made by Agnes Fay Morgan and her associates at the University of California. Similarly, we recognize the important contributions made by other scientists here in California to our knowledge of the essential minerals which are present in wine and other beverages, and which likewise serve as nutritional aids [e.g., Amerine]. It should be noted here that there are still many other constituents of wines, beers, and distilled spirits which deserve further investigation as they may well prove to be useful in human nutritional processes.

From these preliminary findings it appears that alcoholic beverages can serve as foodstuffs. These laboratory results have now been tested in the field, by ourselves and by others, partly to study the role of alcoholic beverages in the development of normal, healthy drinking patterns and partly to investigate the use of these beverages in the control of actual disease [Lolli et al., 1958].

WINE IN THE DIABETIC DIET[1]

Many physicians in the United States do not include alcoholic beverages in the diets prescribed for patients suffering from diabetes.

[1] This and the following series of research projects were carried out by the International Center for Psychodietetics in the United States and Italy, under the direction of Dr. Giorgio Lolli, and with the collaboration of Dr. Carlo Ballatore, Dr. Claudia Balboni, and others in Rome, and Renee Wile and her associates in New York.

Many European specialists, on the contrary, specify moderate amounts of alcohol in diabetic diets. In Italy, where wine is the national beverage, the reasons for including this beverage in the diet of diabetics were initially empirical. Italians do not like to be deprived of wine, which always has been an integral part of their meals. Some years ago, Serianni showed that moderate amounts of wine cause a moderate but consistent lowering of the blood sugar curve in diabetes. Accordingly, it appeared desirable to Dr. G. Lolli and myself to investigate this use of alcohol in a substantial number of patients. At the same time, because of the recent and successful introduction of new and effective oral hypoglycemic agents, we were interested to learn whether these compounds and alcoholic beverages could safely be administered simultaneously to the same patient.

The patients chosen for this study were all male diabetics, free from complications and other disease. Thirty patients were studied: three aged between thirty and thirty-nine, twenty-five aged between forty and sixty-nine, and two aged seventy or more. The weight of each of these patients was close to accepted normal according to their height. All the subjects were studied at the Rome Diabetic Center, a branch of the National Italian Diabetic Association.

The effects of wine on blood sugar levels were studied in one-third of the subjects under dietary control alone, one-third under insulin treatment, and one-third under treatment with tolbutamide, one of the new oral hypoglycemic agents. With each patient, blood sugar measurements were made before the administration of wine, and 30, 60, 120, and 180 minutes after such administration. The beverage, a red table wine containing 12 per cent alcohol, was given in amounts of 0.4 to 1 liter per day, divided almost evenly between lunch and dinner.

Group I   In the first group of subjects, whose diabetes had been kept under adequate control by dietary measures alone, wine in these amounts did not alter the blood sugar levels but in all likelihood contributed to the maintenance of satisfactorily low levels. Blood sugar concentrations determined three hours after the consumption of a mixed meal—including sizable quantities of carbohydrates and wine—were consistently low. It appeared that the addition of wine to such a mixed meal helped to maintain the metabolism of carbohydrates within normal ranges. In this group the occurrence of lowered blood pressure, hot flashes, or a feeling of warmth over the skin after drinking wine was minimal or insignificant in every case.

Group II   In the second group, the patients had been taking a slow-acting insulin in amounts ranging between 15 and 42 units daily, given early in the morning before breakfast. On the day of the experiment, breakfast was omitted and wine was given 1½ to 2 hours after the insulin injection. Under these conditions, wine in the amount given caused no untoward hyperglycemia but apparently contributed to the maintenance of satisfactorily low blood sugar levels. In this group the wine produced only minor drops of blood pressure, or none at all. Very mild and almost unnoticeable feelings of warmth over the skin were experienced by three of the ten patients. Finally, when blood sugar values were determined after a mixed meal including quantities of carbohydrates and wine, no untoward hyperglycemic reactions were found. Again, in this second group, wine apparently contributed to the maintenance of reasonably low blood sugar levels.

Group III   In the third group, wine was administered to patients who had been taking tolbutamide orally for weeks or months. With the exception of one patient who needed only 0.5 g of tolbutamide after lunch, all the subjects took the drug both after lunch and after dinner, in doses ranging between 1 and 2 g daily. Because the typical main meal of Italians is consumed at noon, the larger dose of tolbutamide was usually taken after lunch. It should be noted that most of these subjects had already been drinking wine as part of their normal diet. When they first began taking tolbutamide, four of these ten patients had experienced mild but transient discomfort soon after drinking wine. As a result, two of these patients had moderately decreased their wine intake, but none felt that the discomfort was marked enough to justify total abstinence. When these subjects were tested in the laboratory, with wine plus tolbutamide on an empty stomach, a slight drop of 5 to 25 mm Hg systolic pressure was constantly observed. A similar but less marked drop, from 5 to 10 mm, was noted in diastolic pressure. Mild hot flashes, dizziness, and a feeling of warmth over the skin were also experienced by nine of these patients. Such symptoms, which are somewhat reminiscent of the alcohol-disulfiram reaction, have been reported by other observers when alcohol in any form is administered to patients undergoing treatment with sulfonamide or sulfonyl derivatives [e.g., Lisboa et al.]. When the wine was administered to the tolbutamide-treated patients, not on an empty stomach but with meals, the side effects were less noticeable. In this group, as in the two others, when wine was administered with the standard test meal, including carbohydrates, no untoward rises in the blood sugar levels were observed.

Conclusions   From this investigation it appears that wine can be safely and usefully included in the diet of very large segments of the diabetic population, not only because this regimen seems to be harmless but also because it may contribute significantly to adequate control of the carbohydrate metabolism. Because of the pleasurable and relaxing effects of wine, this and perhaps other dilute forms of alcohol may aid markedly in making rigid diets more tolerable psychologically.

WINE IN THE REDUCING DIET

Increasing evidence from laboratory and clinical research has shown that alcohol in moderate quantities can produce a relaxing or tranquilizing response in many individuals, and for this reason we decided to explore the use of alcohol in the treatment of weight problems. It seemed possible that small amounts of wine might alleviate the underlying anxieties and the hunger of obese patients under treatment, and thus make their reducing diets more tolerable.

In a preliminary experiment, thirty-five obese patients in New York were observed for a total of 918 weeks during which time, periods of diet including dry table wine were alternated with periods of diet without wine. The wine was given in amounts of 3 to 4 oz daily. In many of the patients, drinking wine with or after dinner was accompanied by a lowered daily caloric intake, as reported by the subjects themselves in daily dietary records, and by a gradual but consistent loss of body weight as indicated by actual measurement.

In part, at least, the wine seemed to act through an alleviation of those anxieties over hunger which are so frequently observed in obese patients trying to reduce. Whether or not the alcoholic beverage had any direct action in taming the hunger itself remains to be determined. It is obvious, of course, that neither wine nor any other alcoholic beverage represents, or ever will represent, the "cure" for obesity. This preliminary investigation, however, suggests that wine may have a useful place in many reducing diets.

DRINKING PATTERNS

Although investigations on the use of alcohol as a nutritional aid may be of some interest to substantial groups of patients, larger groups may eventually benefit from long-range studies on the development of normal, healthy drinking patterns.

One of the contributions in this area has been the carefully detailed study by Lolli and his associates [Lolli et al., 1952, 1953, 1958; Lisansky et al.] on the eating and drinking habits of Italians living in Italy and Americans of Italian extraction living in the United States. From this research has come the discovery that Italians in their native country not only use alcohol—in this case wine, taken almost exclusively with meals—as a normal part of their daily diets, but in quantities large enough in some cases to represent 25 per cent of their total caloric intake, and yet without either physiological or psychological problems.

More recently we have begun studies on the eating and drinking habits of special groups in a further attempt to clarify the role of alcoholic beverages in nutrition. In all cases, the combined medical, psychological, and social approach was used, as indicated by the personnel participating in the research—teams of physicians, psychiatric social workers, and psychiatric nurses, all conversant with the emotional and social implications of drinking habits.

Nonalcoholic women The first project deals with the drinking habits of nonalcoholic women—women who use alcoholic beverages but without drinking to excess.

Scientific data on the drinking habits of women in general are scanty. What research there is has usually been centered on the extreme excesses of drinking, together with detailed if not always accurate descriptions of the similarities and differences between alcoholic and nonalcoholic women. The evidence on whether or not alcoholism is increasing in women is confusing and controversial. In the United States, there is some indication that the ratio of five or six alcoholic men to one alcoholic woman has kept almost constant for many years [Keller and Efron]. But we suspect that the statistics, in the United States and even more in other countries where a statistical conscience is not so well developed, may be misleading when one deals with an elusive entity like alcoholism. Even the scanty available statistics are vitiated by the virtual impossibility of defining an alcoholic with precision [Keller and Seeley]. Unquestionably, data on feminine drinking excesses are further invalidated by the fact that society judges obtrusive drinking by women with greater suspicion, hostility, and severity than it does in the case of men. Drinking excesses which would not be classified as "alcoholism" in men are labeled as such when observed in women.

In America, there is evidence that more women use alcoholic beverages now than in the past [Public Opinion News Service]. Participation in activities which were once considered exclusively masculine; the stress and strain involved in these activities; and the uncertainties about the nature of feminine roles in our society seem —among other causes—to account for this keener contemporary interest in alcohol as exhibited by women. But very little is known about how, when, and why American women, and women of other countries of the world, use alcoholic beverages. Until there is clear understanding of such factors—especially why nonalcoholic women drink—similar information on alcoholic women will be of relatively little value. Accordingly, in this pilot study, major emphasis was placed on the attitudes and reasons for drinking rather than on exact quantities of alcohol consumed. The subjects were not random-selected, and obviously no statistical conclusions will be presented.

One group of women was selected in Italy, all of whom drank wine in accordance with Italian custom. The other group was selected in the United States. All the American subjects were of Italian descent and were users of wine, either regularly or irregularly, along with other beverages, and were selected on this basis. In both groups, all the women were reasonably adequate, "functioning" persons; they were drinking women only in the sense that they used alcoholic beverages more or less regularly and without any feelings of guilt or shame. All of them were in what might be termed the middle-income bracket.

Some of the subjects in both groups had drunk a little too much a few times in their lives, but none was an excessive drinker in the sense that alcohol interfered consistently and decisively with the efficiency of her personal or occupational life. In other words, all of them knew how to drink and also how to stop drinking. Never did they drink excessively when excess might be detrimental, and the few excesses reported by them were mild and of brief duration.

All the American women participating in this study used not only wine but also beer and distilled spirits in moderate amounts. The reasons given for their use of all three types of alcoholic beverage were mostly relaxation, pleasure, and social habit. A number of them stated that they used wine because it was less expensive.

In studying both users and nonusers of alcoholic beverages, one must not overlook economic or financial factors. For example, it has already been shown by Lolli and his collaborators that alcoholics generally are accustomed to turn eventually to the beverage which provides the least expensive source of alcohol in their particular area —generally fortified wines in the United States [Lolli et al., 1960], distilled spirits in Brazil [Parreiras et al.], and beer in some parts of Switzerland [Devrient and Lolli]. It must be stressed, however, that there is a major difference between the selection of inexpensive wines by alcoholics to obtain the morbid effects they seek, and the selection of such inexpensive beverages by women to obtain a mild degree of relaxation which apparently never gets out of control. Again, it should be noted that episodes of inebriety and intoxication were highly infrequent among all these women. The few instances of inebriety which did occur during the ten years preceding the inquiry were all of brief duration and in most cases were associated with the drinking of distilled spirits.

By and large, these American women felt that wine is less intoxicating than whiskey because of its lower alcohol content. Interestingly, these women never used wine or beer or distilled spirits for the relief of pain, menstrual or otherwise. While most of them felt that alcoholic beverages should be used by normal individuals as a source of mild relaxation and pleasure, none of them used any such beverage regularly at the dinner table. All of them, however, felt that the occasional use of wine at meals adds to the appeal and to the esthetic value of a sophisticated gathering.

In the Italian group, which was broadly comparable socially to the American group, selection of beverages was markedly different. Much larger quantities of wine were used by these Italian women and, conversely, much smaller quantities of beer and distilled spirits. The total amounts of all alcoholic beverages consumed were larger in Italy, and yet these Italian women, like their American counterparts, had evidently learned to drink safely and reported a very low incidence of episodes of inebriety. While all the Italian women used wine regularly at mealtime, it is noteworthy that they did not emphasize the alimentary value of the beverage but, like the Americans, viewed it as a source of pleasure or relaxation. The Italians often stated that they used wine as a tonic or digestive but did not use any alcoholic beverages to relieve menstrual or other pain or to aid sleep.

These findings seemingly represent the beginning of a change in the Italian pattern, which for centuries was marked by a universal use of wine, and wine only, both for its nutritional and medicinal values. Now it appears that the pattern among Italian women is tending to become more like that among American women. New beverages—beer and distilled spirits—are beginning to gain acceptance, and all alcoholic beverages are prized less for their nutritional importance than as a source of relaxation. Also, there is a beginning of change in America, with a growing use of wine with meals along the general historical pattern of Italy. Larger groups of subjects must be studied before definitive conclusions can be drawn, but there is at least preliminary evidence that women in these two countries, and perhaps in others, are moving toward a common drinking pattern.

Elderly men The principles and techniques involved in the foregoing study are likewise being applied in an investigation of the drinking patterns of elderly men who presumably have been exposed to alcohol in one form or another for periods of forty-five to fifty years or more, often in considerable quantities, but without suffering any demonstrable deleterious effects.

It is somewhat remarkable that very little information and a good deal of misinformation has been available for many years on the drinking by elderly alcoholics who, on their way to physical, mental, and social ruin, use whatever beverage is available as the cheapest source of alcohol. In contrast, very little is known about the uses of alcoholic beverages by the many more elderly individuals who are neither alcoholics nor excessive drinkers. Accordingly, it appeared desirable to undertake preliminary investigation on the uses of alcohol, and particularly the attitudes toward alcohol, in such a group.

Our investigation involves two groups of subjects, one in the United States and one in Italy, all of them sixty-five years of age or older, reasonably adequate in the emotional and social spheres, not suffering from major incapacitating illnesses, and all known to be users of wine, either regularly or irregularly, as well as other beverages in some cases.

Among the American men, few indicated that they drank wine because of habit or tradition, or because it aids sleep. Some felt that wine "is good with food," and that all alcoholic beverages have value in dulling some minor aches and pains and in at least temporarily decreasing fatigue. In general, it is our impression that these elderly men used alcohol mostly for relaxation, pleasure, and social reasons, rather than for clear-cut nutritional or medicinal reasons. Some episodes of inebriety or intoxication were reported, but these were not numerous. Because of the age of these subjects, however, it is possible that failing memory had allowed recall of only the most recent or the most obvious episodes of excessive drinking. Interestingly, nearly all of them indicated some familiarity with the fact that alcoholic beverages, notably wine, were less intoxicating when consumed with meals, giving a lower concentration of alcohol in the body. Similarly, these Americans expressed the belief that distilled spirits are more useful than either wine or beer in controlling anxiety.

In contrast, the elderly subjects in the Italian group used large amounts of wine daily, but only limited quantities of beer, distilled spirits, aperitifs, or liqueurs. More than any other beverage, wine was described as giving pleasure and having value as a tonic or digestive. This latter quality does not necessarily imply a medicinal use of wine but rather appears to be linked to the fact that a meal without wine is almost unthinkable for Italians who have been accustomed to this use since their youth. Episodes of intoxication appear to be somewhat more frequent among these elderly Italian men than among their elderly American counterparts. These were of brief duration, however, lasting in most instances from a few minutes to a maximum of two or three hours, and only in a few cases more than four or five hours. Because of availability and custom, wine was the beverage most frequently involved in such episodes.

Like the Americans, the Italian subjects did not emphasize the nourishing value of wine or spontaneously mention the anxiety-taming value of wine or other alcoholic beverages. When this tranquilizing action was suggested to them, however, most of the subjects recalled its occurrence and described this as a highly valuable characteristic of the beverage.

As with the preliminary study conducted on women, this pilot study on elderly men has thus far reached essentially the same tentative conclusion: the nutritional and medicinal qualities of alcoholic beverages are generally unrecognized, and these beverages are used mainly for pleasure and relaxation.

Patients with coronary artery disease In the last project, a beginning has been made toward a long-overdue analysis of the drinking patterns of patients with coronary disease or myocardial infarction. It is needless to note that many investigations have been conducted on the rates of coronary disease reported, with more or less accuracy, in various countries, and that a multitude of studies have been carried out on the dietary factors which may be involved [e.g., Jolliffe; Jolliffe and Archer]. From these investigations have come reports that heart disease is less frequent in Italy than in the United States, but more frequent than in Mexico. Similarly, the literature now contains many important but still controversial statements on the possible significance of total calories, total fats, the ratio of unsaturated to saturated fats, and total cholesterol. There has even been sporadic interest in the possible significance of the intake of such elements as potassium.

The concern over the eating habits of cardiac patients has not been matched by an equal concern over their drinking habits. Data on the drinking histories of patients with myocardial infarction are scanty, and most of the emphasis has been placed on the dangers of excessive and uncontrolled drinking. For these and related reasons, it was felt advisable to investigate as thoroughly as possible the eating and drinking habits of a group of Italian patients during the years, months, and days immediately prior to their coronary episode.

Eighty patients were included in these studies. All of them had experienced one or more episodes of myocardial infarction as confirmed by clear-cut clinical data and electrocardiographic records. Of the 80 subjects, 34 were still hospitalized at the time of the inquiry, most of them convalescing from the cardiac attack, while the others were regularly attending an outpatient clinic. As might be expected, the overwhelming majority, 72 of the 80, were men. Half of the subjects were moderately overweight at the time of the cardiac episode, but only three men were significantly obese. Data on cholesterol levels at the time of the infarction were available on 31 patients and showed levels of 150 to 200 mg per 100 ml in 9, 200 to 300 mg per 100 ml in 18, and more than 300 mg per 100 ml in 4.

An investigation of their drinking histories showed that 13 of the 80 patients were abstainers, a fairly high percentage in a country in which the use of wine is widespread. Among the others, the daily intake of wine was less than 0.5 liter in 32 patients, 0.5 to 1 liter in 27, and more than 1 liter in 8. These quantities are not strikingly different from those reported by the general Italian population.

Of some interest was the observation that 25 patients, 37 per cent of the wine users, had significantly decreased their wine intake a relatively short time before the myocardial infarction. The decrease occurred six months before the cardiac episode in 18 patients, and seven days before this episode in seven patients. Only 1 subject who had been an abstainer in the past started drinking wine six months before the attack.

As an additional part of the study, information was obtained on alterations in the intake of potassium. It was found that the intake of this element had been increased by only 3 patients during the period immediately preceding the cardiac episode but had been reduced by 33. This reduction in potassium intake was paralleled in some but by no means in all these patients by a reduction in the drinking of wine.

The possible significance of these two observations is not clear. A more thorough analysis of a large amount of dietary information is still under way, and the data will be reported as rapidly as possible. Even at this point, however, although it would be presumptuous to suggest correlations, it appears that an intensive study of the drinking habits in coronary disease is urgently required.

The study of drinking habits, the correlation of drinking habits to eating habits, and the study of the psychological and social aspects of nutrition are all in an embryonic stage at this point. This is evident to us, and to all who are engaged in this phase of research. The projects conducted so far are few in number and limited in scope. Yet I believe it is also evident that some have already yielded significant results.

It is to be hoped that ways and means will be found to continue this work on an ever broader scale in this country, in Italy, and in every other country in the world in which nutritional problems remain to be solved.

REFERENCES

Amerine, M. A., The Composition of Wines. I. Organic Constituents, *Advances in Food Research*, 5:353–510, 1954.

Devrient, P., and Lolli, G., Choice of Alcoholic Beverage among 240 Alcoholics in Switzerland, *Quart. J. Studies Alc.*, 23:459–467, 1962.

Jolliffe, N., Fats, Cholesterol and Coronary Heart Disease, *Circulation*, 20:109–127, 1959.

Jolliffe, N., and Archer, M., Statistical Associations between International Coronary Heart Disease Death Rates and Certain Environmental Factors, *Chronic Diseases*, 9:636–652, 1959.

Keller, M., and Efron, V., The Prevalence of Alcoholism, *Quart. J. Studies Alc.*, 16:619–644, 1955.

Keller, M., and Seeley, J. R., *The Alcohol Language. With a Selected Vocabulary*, Brookside Monograph 2, Toronto, University of Toronto Press, 1958.

Lisansky, E. S., Golder, G., and Lolli, G., Relationship of Personality Adjustment to Eating and Drinking Patterns in a Group of Italian Americans, *Quart. J. Studies Alc.*, 15:545–561, 1954.

Lisboa, P. E., Castel-Branco, N., and Sá Marques, M. M., Anorexia para bebidas alcoólicas, um efeito ainda não descrito da administração de fenformina (Anorexia for Alcoholic Beverages, an Effect of Phenformin Administration Not Previously Described), *J. Méd., Port.* 44:113–116, 1961.

Lolli, G., Schesler, E., and Golder, G. M., Choice of Alcoholic Beverage among 105 Alcoholics in New York, *Quart. J. Studies Alc.*, 21:475–482, 1960.

Lolli, G., Serianni, E., Banissoni, F., Golder, G., Mariani, A., McCarthy, R. G., and Toner, M., The Use of Wine and Other Alcoholic Beverages by a Group of Italians and Americans of Italian Extraction, *Quart. J. Studies Alc.*, 13:27–48, 1952.

Lolli, G., Serianni, E., Golder, G., Balboni, C., and Mariani, A., Further Observations on the Use of Wine and Other Alcoholic Beverages by Italians and Americans of Italian Extraction, *Quart. J. Studies Alc.*, 14:395–405, 1953.

Lolli, G., Serianni, E., Golder, G. M., and Luzzatto-Fegiz, P., *Alcohol in Italian Culture. Food and Wine in Relation to Sobriety among Italians and Italian Americans*, Glencoe, Ill., Free Press, and New Brunswick, N.J., Rutgers Center of Alcohol Studies, 1958.

Lolli, G., Serianni, E., Golder, G., Mariani, A., and Toner, M., Relationship between Intake of Carbohydrate-rich Foods and Intake of Wine and Other Alcoholic Beverages. A Study among Italians and Americans of Italian Extraction, *Quart. J. Studies Alc.*, 13:401–420, 1952.

Morgan, A. F., Nobles, H. L., Wiens, A., Marsh, G. L., and Winkler, A. J., The B Vitamins of California Grape Juices and Wines, *Food Research*, 4:217–219, 1939.

Parreiras, D., Lolli, G., and Golder, G. M., Choice of Alcoholic Beverage among 500 Alcoholics in Brazil, *Quart. J. Studies Alc.*, 17:629–632, 1956.

Perlman, L., and Morgan, A. F., Stability of B Vitamins in Grape Juices and Wines, *Food Research*, 10:334–341, 1945.

Public Opinion News Service, May 11, 1960.

Randoin, L., and Billand, S., La bière (Beer), *Bull. soc. sci. hyg. aliment.*, 44:3–28, 1956.

Serianni, E., L'azione dell'alcool e del vino sulla glicemia di malati di diabete mellito, *Boll. ed atti accad. med. Roma*, 60:385–395, 1934.

William Dock, M.D.

Professor of Medicine, State University of New York
Downstate Medical Center, Brooklyn, New York

THE CLINICAL VALUE
OF ALCOHOL

Editor's Note   *The medicinal use of alcoholic beverages from the most ancient times is noted in a number of presentations. (Cf. Preface, pp. vii–ix , Dr. Balboni, pp. 63–66; Dr. Leake, pp. 6–8, 20–21; Dr. Lucia, pp. 151 ff.) In spite of this history, physicians in the United States seem to have abandoned the prescription of alcohol in all but a few particular situations. How did this come about, and is it justified? Dr. William Dock here takes issue with the attitudes and the teaching in American medical schools concerning alcohol as a medicine. He suggests that American physicians are too dependent on drug salesmen for their education in some aspects of therapeutics, and that the lack of patent rights and advertising value in medicinal alcohol may be largely responsible for its neglect. Another reason may be the ill repute that the prescription of whiskey gained in the prohibition era. On the positive side he emphasizes that alcoholic beverages provide a body fuel and a mild sedative, highly useful in certain acute and chronic illnesses, and that, unlike many tranquilizers, alcohol has almost no undesirable side effects in prescriptive amounts.*

The clinical value of any medicament is not based solely on its properties in affecting the growth of some invading microbe or altering the functions of human tissues in a favorable way. It is based chiefly on the skill with which doctors employ it. Many fine drugs are scarcely used at all; many futile drugs are sold by the millions of pills daily. I wish to devote this talk to relating the true value of alcohol to its extremely modest place in American medicine.

The history of therapeutics shows that when the botanists or the chemists provide a new substance which alters specific symptoms or functions, there is a lag in its acceptance by the profession. This lag can be greatly shortened by shrewd and well-financed advertising. Then there is a peak of use, which may last months or years, followed by a decline, either to zero or to a steady level lasting for decades. What happens if the advertisement is lacking?

The widespread and often fatal disease pellagra is due to lack of a certain substance in the diet. This substance was isolated from liver by laborious fractionation and biological testing. It should have brought great wealth to any drug firm which invested in it, held patent rights, and pushed the advertising, for every newly isolated vitamin cures all incurable diseases. But alas, this agent, chemically, proved to be an old item on the chemist's shelf—it had been prepared in 1867. Because not patentable, nicotinic acid, the antipellagra vitamin, is neither advertised nor pushed by the detail men who haunt doctors' offices. Several leading clinics have reported that in large but comfortably tolerated doses, nicotinic acid is far more effective in lowering the blood fats believed to cause coronary disease than are the widely advertised, patented but less potent competitive drugs. But doctors are not urged to try it, and few drugstores even stock the half-gram pills. So much for an illustration of why we do not use many useful drugs—it does not pay anyone to educate us to use them.

IMAGINARY NEW MIRACLE DRUG

Let us suppose that methyl methanol, a substance recently synthesized, was found to be completely free of any ill effects, allergic reactions, blood cell damage, and the other hazards associated with nearly all our antibiotics and sedatives. But methyl methanol, in small doses, proved to be a superb tranquilizer; in larger doses, a good sedative; and in even larger doses, an effective anesthetic agent. Small doses even improved ability to solve certain kinds of difficult problems in the calculus [Carpenter et al.]. In addition, it dilated blood vessels, caused a decrease in the production of the pituitary antidiuretic hormone, and could be used as a readily absorbed body fuel, up to one-third the daily need for calories. It also increased the absorption of fats in patients with intestinal malabsorption and gave better appetites to many sick people.

We all know what would happen. The sales of all other sedatives and tranquilizers would slump, four-page spreads in medical journals and neat stories in the papers and news weeklies would make M-M a household word, like aspirin and Miltown. The stock of the patent licensees would go through the ceiling on Wall Street. The lucky discoverer would get every possible honor, as did the men who gave us insulin and hay-fever pills. The medical school where the studies were made would found an institute, supported by millions in royalties. Humanity would be benefited for untold thousands of years, and the Russians would announce that they had discovered M-M back in Czar Nicholas's day.

As you know, methyl methanol, ethanol, or alcohol, was first introduced to the West by the Arabs over a thousand years ago. They may have gotten it from India or China. It was produced by the alchemists and monasteries and entered pharmaceutical use as aqua vitae, the water of life. This was a drug of infinite value, capable of solubilizing active principles of many other drugs. It was used for extracting opium to produce laudanum, the great pain-killer of the sixteenth to nineteenth centuries. But no one holds patents on ethanol, and aqua vitae isn't advertised in the medical journals. Two familiar forms of aqua vitae, brandy and whiskey, had honored places in the United States Pharmacopeia from its earliest editions. But they were dropped in the last decade, and even in the National Formulary, where they remain, ethanol is considered along with less heavily taxed undrinkable alcohols, of which seven, such as isopropyl alcohol, are listed for external use only.

IGNORING THE FACTS

During the past century, in Anglo-Saxon lands, there has developed a great gap between the pharmacological effect or the therapeutic usefulness of alcohol and the use of alcohol by physicians in the management of disease. As a result, most of the clinical value of alcohol has been lost to our patients. American and British textbooks on medicine, or on the specialties such as cardiology, gastroenterology, neurology, and psychiatry, have much to say about the disabilities resulting from a too high daily intake of alcohol and a too low daily intake of protein and vitamins, but nothing about alcohol in therapy. Even therapeutic encyclopedias have only casual mention of alcohol —one recommending ten drops of brandy in water for infants with diarrhea, and several conceding that alcohol has some value as a tonic for the stomach and a relaxant for the mind and the blood vessels. We seem to have a nihilistic attitude toward a chemical which is a proved diuretic [Haggard et al.], a stimulant of gastric secretion [Ogden], a dilator of blood vessels [Brooks; Cook and

Brown], and, which, above all, has an action on the mind, which, by varying the dose and the rate of ingestion, can bring either cheerful bustle or profound anesthesia. This neglect is most remarkable when contrasted with the respect for wine shown by Hippocrates. The father of medicine not only gave details on how to choose, dilute, and drink wine for acute and chronic disease, but he told us, in "A Regimen for Health," how we should alter our wine not only with the seasons and with age, but with body build and complexion.

Physicians in Europe and in San Francisco still have good things to say for wine and brandy. They point out that alcohol can safely replace fat as a source of calories, to the extent of several hundred calories per day, the amount available in nearly a quart of wine with 10 per cent alcohol content. In France, the recommended prescription for sick or convalescent patients, Peter's potion, contains 40 per cent cognac, 4 per cent Peruvian bark (quinquina), in syrup of gum arabic and orange flowers. The patients get a tablespoonful every two hours—about 8 ml of alcohol—and about eight or ten doses per day. This provides nearly one-third the calories the body will require, restores the appetite, and cheers the invalid greatly.

When I was ill, as a boy, my good Texan mother used a similar remedy—essencia Calisaya—which kept her busy, relieved both her fears and mine, and made my ears ring. My father, a professor of medicine, regarded such treatment, and his patients' patent medicines, as "mild and cheering tipple." In many countries, if not in North America, the natural alcoholic beverages have a respected place in treating those with decreased desire or ability to handle nourishment by mouth. They provide the only tonic for the appetite which actually supplies an easily metabolized fuel. In Teutonic lands, as readers of Mann's *The Magic Mountain* remember, wine, beer, stout, port, or madeira, rather than alcoholic tonics, are used to augment appetite, improve morale, and supply extra calories for invalids.

Although, as our speakers will continue to emphasize, the chief action of alcohol is to change men's minds, this is almost never mentioned in textbooks of medicine. It is recognized that those who are accustomed to a high daily intake of alcohol, even though they function very effectively decade after decade, as have some distinguished generals, statesmen, and artists, may become acutely manic, delirious, or convulsive if alcohol suddenly is withdrawn. The same occurs with daily users of barbiturates and other sedatives, and with all these, as with alcohol, the illness is controlled when a steady intake at the usual level is provided. Many physicians and some textbooks advise the use of alcohol to relieve such symptoms of withdrawal of alcohol, while others consider this wrong, and use only sedative drugs.

Every one realizes that something must be done for the patient with severe symptoms due to cessation of a high daily intake of liquor. But most physicians forget that the normal apprehension and restlessness of people sent to hospitals is exaggerated in many patients who are accustomed to a few drinks in the evening, or at lunch and supper, when they enter a hospital where little or no potable alcohol is provided. Prescribing the continued intake of the usual beverage does relieve the mild but undesirable disturbance in the ordinary citizen when drinking is cut off by hospital custom.

THE HISTORICAL BACKGROUND

If one seeks the cause for the neglect of these facts and the ignorance of other medicinal uses of alcohol in North America, two historical tragedies come to mind. One was the enormous popularity of patent medicines in which alcohol was the only effective component, and the long struggle of the American Medical Association and the Federal government to expose and eliminate these nostrums and sources of untaxed alcohol.

When I was a boy there was a popular song, with this chorus:

So we sing, we sing, we sing to Lydia Pinkham
And her love for the human race.
She makes her Vegetable Compound
And the papers publish her face.

The verses gave case histories, all with happy endings. Lydia Pinkham's Vegetable Compound, before the law had drawn its kick, was 20 per cent alcohol, and its sales, especially in states or counties legally dry, were consistently high.

The discovery by charlatans of the value of foxglove did not prevent Withering's testing its effects and providing us with an invaluable drug, digitalis. The exploitation of alcohol by the patent medicine trade should not have blinded us to the fact that patients, especially those of strong temperance persuasion, benefited greatly from the regular use of the equivalent of a fortified wine. A modern

Withering would have made a careful study of this component of the patent medicines, noted its superiority to bromide or barbiturate as a sedative, and described how to use it to benefit the patients who consulted physicians.

An even greater tragedy was our fifteen years in the wilderness of national prohibition. This well-intentioned experiment, providing a windfall for gangsters, led even prosperous and high-minded physicians to prescribe whiskey or port for friends who never had been in better health, and the venal fringe to write prescriptions for patients they never saw. This created a sense of shame or guilt in the profession, which made many physicians banish all thought of alcohol as a valuable clinical weapon.

When Henry Newman at Stanford University was studying the metabolism of alcohol a quarter of a century ago, he gave weak solutions intravenously to patients without letting them know when the infusion changed from glucose to alcohol. It was common to observe that patients seemed more at ease and talkative at low dosage levels. When the higher dosages were given, they revealed, sometimes tearfully, rather personal facts previously concealed from skilled psychiatric probing. If full awareness of shocking or shameful episodes and their communication to an apparently sympathetic friend is a useful therapeutic experience, alcohol is equal and perhaps superior to many of the barbiturates given for a similar purpose.

It is the mollifying effect of alcohol which led the Oxford don[1] to write:

Malt does more than Milton can
To justify God's ways to Man.

It led the Psalmist to praise Him who brought forth "food out of the earth, And wine that maketh glad the heart of man" [Pss. 104:15]. The Proverbs of Solomon stressed the dangers of wine and "strong drink," and Lemuel, in the last proverb, repeats his mother's warning that wine and strong drink are not for princes and kings. But he relents when it comes to the sad and the sick. "Give strong drink unto him that is ready to perish, and wine unto those that be of heavy hearts. Let him drink and forget his poverty and remember his misery no more" [Prov. 31:6–7]. Lemuel, in first warning "Give not your strength to women, Your heart to those who are the ruin

---

[1] A. E. Housman, A *Shropshire Lad*, LXII.

of kings" [Prov. 31:3], seems to be at one with Yeats, who said, "I have certainly known more men destroyed by the desire to have a wife and child and keep them in comfort than I have seen destroyed by drink."[2] It is well to be reminded of such hazards as uxorious living so that the risk of excessive dependence on alcohol can be brought into proper perspective in an age and land where the therapeutic and civilizing functions of alcohol are concealed by its abuse among those crippled in the urban rat race.

PROPER MEDICINAL USE

Modern enthusiasts for proper use of alcohol can repeat the advice which shrewd St. Paul gave to Timothy in Ephesus: "I charge thee before God and the Lord Jesus Christ . . . Drink no longer only water, but use a little wine for thy stomach's sake and thine often infirmities" [I Tim. 5:21–25]. The infirmities for which alcohol, taken in this agreeable nonmedicinal form, seems to me the most effective treatment are the annoying or alarming chronic disorders for which the patient knows there is no dependable cure. This includes the neoplastic diseases in all their forms (except Hodgkin's disease), uremia, heart failure, and, above all others, the aging process. Even in the liver injury of malnourished alcoholics, a modest daily ration of alcohol with proper meals may aid recovery during the first few weeks in the hospital, although complete abstinence from alcohol is necessary to prevent relapse into alcoholism and malnutrition.

Alcohol, as the human race discovered thousands of years ago, makes one's troubles, whether organic or emotional, seem much less alarming and allows one to consider them with the detached sympathy which we have for the troubles of others. This carefree attitude, so dangerous for the automobile driver, is most helpful for the aging parents of normally ungrateful children as well as for the man or woman with failing sense organs or failing vital organs, with dying contemporaries and a narrowing circle of friends, or with income eroded by that "clipping of the coins" which rulers from the Pharaohs to Kennedy have found to be the surest way to make the aging generation pay for its errors. After all, only when the ruler is eighty-five are we likely to see the gold value of the coin increased. All these inscrutable "ways of God to man" seem justified when one has the proper blood alcohol level. Our neighbors seem more inter-

[2] Quoted by Lyle Stuart in *The Great Quotations*, p. 760.

esting, and more interested in us. And if the drug is not taken before noon, or after supper, it can be continued for years at reasonable and effective levels with none of the unpleasant or dangerous effects exhibited by nearly all agents with similar actions on the mind.

In my own family the beneficent action of alcohol in geriatrics was strikingly demonstrated. Three maiden aunts, who had led active and useful lives up to age seventy, lived on with all the difficulties noted above until they were past ninety. Miss Lavinia, who reached the age of ninety-nine, had been assistant superintendent of nurses when Johns Hopkins Hospital opened and recalled William Osler as "that ribald young man." She discovered by intuition, at about eighty, that her metabolism required port before lunch and dinner and passed on this wisdom to her youngest sister. The rural general practitioner who looked after the third lady, who had some serious disabilities, used a prescription whose splendid effects were ascribed to valerian. Possibly the alcohol it provided twice a day contributed, for the prescription gave her as much as port gave the other two ladies. At any rate, conversation was livelier, and Miss Lavinia no longer upbraided me because we doctors were keeping everyone alive too long. The lady on valerian took pride in *not* needing port, like her wayward sisters, who in turn took pride in *not* taking drugs or patronizing doctors.

Ever since seeing this change in the household, I have felt that what is needed in our city hospitals, nursing homes, and other retreats for ailing or aged people is a regular alcohol ration, such as is normal everywhere in Europe. Ziba, in going out to succor David, did not neglect "wine that such as may be faint in the wilderness may drink" [II Sam. 16:2]. But we, who should be bringing help to many in the wilderness of old age, wasting disease, or an "unlovely struggle against unfair odds" from which, unlike David, they have no hope of emerging in triumph, seem to forget how much Ziba's "bottle of wine" did to raise morale and give new strength for the struggle.

In a country which spends some 10 billion dollars a year on legal liquor and perhaps a billion more for bootleg alcohol, it may seem queer to suggest that more people should be using alcohol under medical supervision. But the fact is that too many people are now using "strong drink"; too few, proper daily dosage of drinks such as Hippocrates and St. Paul prescribed.

"Strong drink," as used in the Bible, does not refer to distilled spirits, which were not known, at least in the West, before the

Crusades, and which, before the sixteenth century, were regarded only as powerful drugs which the apothecary might have or the local monastery provide. "Strong drink" is the translators' sixteenth century equivalent for the Hebrew word "inebriator"—a drink good only to get drunk on, as distinguished from wine, the delicious component of any good meal. Inebriator was made from honey, palm juice, barley, or anything which would ferment and tasted as queer as Peruvian chicha or Mexican pulque. One drinks all these only when determined to get alcohol and bravely accepts repellent flavor.

The Roman soldier's "posca," a cheap dry wine taken for the same purpose, was offered to men going to execution or torture. It was this drink (translated as "vinegar" for King James, but as "sour wine" by modern scholars) which Christ was offered at Calvary, thus carrying out the Proverbial sanction, "Give strong drink unto him that is ready to perish." Luke, the physician, said that the soldiers' offer was a mockery [Luke 23:36]. Mark reported that the sour wine was made bitter with myrrh [Mark 15:23]; Matthew, that gall was added [Matt. 27:34]; both agree that it was refused. John tells us that after the Savior said "I thirst," he was offered and drank sour wine and hyssop [John 19:28–30], the ancient equivalent of the Victorian drink, sherry and bitters. I find John's version credible, for thirst is severe in anyone dying of injuries and is better assuaged by bitter or sour drinks than by sweet or insipid ones. Here is august precedent for the use of wine in relieving suffering.

It is my practice to follow the Biblical injunction and recommend our "strong drink" only to those approaching a painful and inevitable death. Wine is prescribed for the "stomach's sake," for those with poor appetites, or for "those that be with heavy hearts." This includes those who are irritable or weary because of the "often infirmities" of advancing age, and those who are not cheered toward evening by feeling they have done a good day's work, but need something to help them "forget their poverty" of purse, of occupation, or of interest in the world.

I have rarely had occasion to advise the use of alcohol except in acute fevers or uremia to anyone under the age of forty. Young people with hopeless and disabling diseases are often euphoric without alcohol, but ethanol can help relieve suffering and maintain nutrition in those who falter under such a menace. In the older group, who have used alcohol moderately or little in earlier decades, I have never seen harm done by the regular use of wine before or during meals, and it is most unusual for such people, even with cancer, to become unpleasantly drunk or to develop any of the tissue damage seen in alcoholics.

This is one valuable form of therapy in which harmful sequelae, or what are called "unwanted side effects" or "drug idiosyncrasies" are almost unknown. But there is a small group of patients, those with vascular disease and hyperlipemia, for whom even 20 ml of alcohol per day may be harmful [Amatuzio]. Alcohol, which stimulates the liver to convert carbohydrate to fat, acts like the saturated fats and causes a rise in blood cholesterol and triglyceride [Feigl]. In most people even 80 ml of alcohol per day is harmless, as one can see from the low coronary death rates in the Latin countries. However, in some overfed Americans with vascular disease, half that intake may raise plasma lipid levels significantly, and in the rare cases of familial hyperlipemia, even smaller doses cause a disturbing effect. Since nearly all the other damage ascribed to alcohol is dependent on the patient's poor nutrition, it is well to be aware of this metabolic effect of alcohol in well-nourished people, which may be harmful to a small minority of our patients. In the chronic diseases, such as high blood pressure and heart failure, where a diet low in salt is important, the low-salt drinks such as wine and whiskey help to make such diets acceptable.

Society in general, and we physicians in particular, must do all we can to create an enlightened, energetic population with few injured minds who seek inebriation from strong drink rather than mollification and cheer from appetizing natural beverages. We should try to rescue and reeducate those, rich or poor, who have drifted into the abuse of alcohol, combined with contempt for good food and physical activity. But the difficulties resulting in chronic malnutrition and alcoholism are almost never due to beverages prescribed by physicians. It is noteworthy that alcoholism is most serious among Negro, Celtic, and Scandinavian populations, the last to be reached by the products of the vine. These people do not use wine at meals. Abuse of alcohol is rare in those who come from the lands of the "olive and the vine," where children see and participate in moderate wine drinking at mealtime now as they have for many centuries.

Thus we conclude that alcohol in what one may describe as its natural form has a real, if neglected, place in the management of disease. During febrile illnesses, alcohol may be invaluable in lessening apprehension and improving nutrition. In larger and more frequent doses, alcohol, without causing stupor or confusion, may relax the nerves of those with acute and threatening disorders and reduce the need for more dangerous sedation or narcosis. In order to obtain full benefit from the medicinal use of alcohol, physicians must shed the prejudices arising from the era of alcoholic nostrums and prohibition, and from the widespread evils of alcohol addiction in many parts of the world.

Many years ago, when digitalis was prescribed in drops and usually in wholly inadequate doses, my father expressed his admiration for a colleague by telling me, "Why, he knows how to use digitalis!" Perhaps today one could express one's admiration for a physician by saying, "Why, he knows when *not* to use antibiotics!" But another good index to the wisdom of the physician is his skill in guiding patients, as Hippocrates did, to the most health-giving regimen of food and drink. Only those with profound prejudices or inherited risk of addiction will need to have alcohol prescribed in combination with gentian, quinine, or valerian. For most patients, during hospitalization or at home, the proper quantities of the most acceptable beverages, including those containing caffeine or alcohol, should be discussed and prescribed along with the diet. Only in this way can we realize the clinical value of alcohol. While the young doctor can get much information on prescribing drugs, he will find little dependable advice on how to teach patients to accept a good diet, and he will find practically nothing on the therapeutic uses of alcohol, in textbooks, reviews, or journals for physicians. His mastery of this important phase of practice is therefore a real proof of native intelligence and of wisdom acquired from experience. Without such skill, how can any physician be considered a disciple of Hippocrates?

REFERENCES

Althausen, T. L., Uyeyama, K., and Loran, M. R., Effects of Alcohol on Absorption of Vitamin A in Normal and in Gastrectomized Subjects, *Gastroenterology*, 38:942–945, 1960.

Amatuzio, D. S., Dietary Control of Essential Hyperlipemia: Effect of Dairy Foods, Phospholipid, Coconut Oil, and Alcohol, *A.M.A. Arch. Internal Med.*, 102:173–178, 1958.

Brooks, H., The Use of Alcohol in the Circulatory Defects of Old Age, *Med. J. and Rec.*, 127:199–206, 1928.

Carpenter, J. A., Moore, O. K., Snyder, C. R., and Lisansky, E. S., Alcohol and Higher-order Problem Solving, *Quart. J. Studies Alc.*, 22:183–222, 1961.

Cook, E. N., and Brown, G. E., The Vasodilating Effects of Ethyl Alcohol on the Peripheral Arteries, *Proc. Mayo Clin.*, 7:449–452, 1932.

Feigl, J., Neue Untersuchungen zur Chemie des Blutes bei akuter Alkoholintoxikation und bei chronischem Alkoholismus mit besonderer Berücksichtigung der Fette und Lipoide; chemische Untersuchungen zur Kenntnis der Entwicklung und des Aufbaues von Lipämien (New Studies on the Chemistry of Blood in Acute Alcohol Intoxication and in Chronic Alcoholism, with Special Consideration of Fats and Lipids; Chemical Studies on the Development and Increase of Lipemias), *Biochem. Z.*, 92:282–317, 1918.

Haggard, H. W., Greenberg, L. A., and Carroll, R. P., Studies in the Absorption, Distribution and Elimination of Alcohol. VIII. The Diuresis from Alcohol and Its Influence on the Elimination of Alcohol in the Urine, *J. Pharmacol.* 71:349–357, 1941.

Leary, T., The Therapeutic Value of Alcohol; with Special Consideration of the Relations of Alcohol to Cholesterol, and Thus to Diabetes, to Arteriosclerosis and to Gallstones, *New Engl. J. Med.*, 205:231–242, 1931.

Newman, H. W., Alcohol Injected Intravenously. Some Psychological and Psychopathological Effects in Man, *Amer. J. Psychiat.*, 91:1343–1352, 1935.

Ogden, E., The Influence of Wine on Gastric Acidity, *Federation Proc.*, Pt. II, 5:77, 1946.

PANEL DISCUSSION

PRESENT KNOWLEDGE
OF THE PHYSIOLOGY
OF ALCOHOL

Moderator   Dr. Nello Pace
Participants   Dr. Claudia Balboni, Dr. Olof A. Forsander, Dr. Leonard Goldberg, and Dr. William Dock

Dr. Pace   As I listened to the session this afternoon, the thought came to me that we ought to change our views on the patron god of drinkers, from Bacchus to Janus. I think we are dealing with a two-faced problem. We see indications here of the dilemma that is involved, where alcohol can rightly be said to have both beneficial effects and deleterious effects.

To get on with some discussion by our experts, Dr. Goldberg, I would like to ask you a question. You pointed out that when alcohol is given in a very large dose, a single drink, the blood alcohol concentration reaches a very high level and then comes down relatively rapidly. But if the alcohol is given in a more spaced-out fashion, or with food, the absorption is delayed; the blood alcohol level does not rise as high, but the area under the two curves is essentially equal. Then a little later you compared the effects of drinking equal amounts of alcohol in the form of distilled spirits, such as whiskey, with sherry, with table wine, and with beer, and in those curves you not only found a reduced peak concentration of alcohol, but here the area under the curve was substantially lower, in the order that I mentioned. This raises a very natural question: What happened to the rest of the alcohol?

Dr. Goldberg   To establish the facts first, if you give two different beverages and you give the same amount of alcohol in these two beverages, you will find a definite difference in absorption: it takes the same time for the total amount of alcohol to leave the body, whether you give it in divided doses or not. But we have seen that the peak of the curve can occur earlier or later, varying with the beverage. This could be due to various events. For example, part of the alcohol may not be absorbed. Or the alcohol taken in one type of beverage may be metabolized at a faster rate. You can also see this when you give any beverage with food.

Dr. Pace It is evident that considerable more research is needed in this particular area.

Dr. Goldberg Very much so, yes.

Dr. Pace Dr. Balboni, I was quite interested in a figure that you cited concerning the Italians. You mentioned that it is not uncommon for something on the order of 25 per cent of their caloric intake to be accounted for in the form of red wine. Yet Dr. Forsander told us of two groups of alcoholics, one of which had received 27 per cent of its calories in the form of alcohol. In the other group, the caloric contribution of alcohol came to 75 per cent. I am sure the 27 per cent figure cited by Dr. Forsander and your 25 per cent figure do not mean that the major population of Italy are to be characterized as alcoholics. But I was a little disturbed by this coincidence, and I wonder if you might have some comments about it?

Dr. Balboni We studied large groups of Italians from all the regions of Italy, north, central, and south, in a survey we made in 1952 and 1953. We studied their dietary total intake and the alcohol intake, and we saw that the contribution of calories from alcohol to the diet was around 10 per cent as an average value.[1] The figure of 25 per cent was present in only a few, a low percentage, of these subjects, and not in the average group, so it is an exceptional figure. The only thing I want to stress is that these subjects did not present any particular clinical or physiological disturbance, although there was this high percentage of calories from alcohol in the diet.

Dr. Pace Thank you. Would you like to amplify that, Dr. Goldberg?

Dr. Goldberg There are two points here: One is the difference in the spacing of the alcohol during the day. The Italians drink

---

[1] G. Lolli, E. Serianni, F. Banissoni, G. Golder, A. Mariani, R. G. McCarthy, and M. Toner, The Use of Wine and Other Alcoholic Beverages by a Group of Italians and Americans of Italian Extraction, *Quart. J. Studies Alc.*, 13:27–48, 1952.

G. Lolli, E. Serianni, G. Golder, C. Balboni, and A. Mariani, Further Observations on the Use of Wine and Other Alcoholic Beverages by Italians and Americans of Italian Extraction, *Quart. J. Studies Alc.*, 14:395–405, 1953.

G. Lolli, E. Serianni, G. Golder, A. Mariani, and M. Toner, Relationship between Intake of Carbohydrate-rich Foods and Intake of Wine and Other Alcoholic Beverages. A Study among Italians and Americans of Italian Extraction, *Quart. J. Studies Alc.*, 13:401–420, 1952.

wines of low alcohol content; they take it with their meals, so the blood alcohol concentration is low, and therefore I would guess that the damage they might get would be very little. This is one point. The other point actually concerns the caloric intake. I guess some of the doctors know of patients who take something like a quart or more of whiskey per day. We have people in Sweden who drink 15 to 20 liters of beer per day, which is something like 4 or 5 gal. That large an intake, according to theoretical calculations, would add up to something like 4000 calories per day. This raises the immediate question whether or not the calories from alcohol are really available under these conditions. Somebody has suggested that maybe, in the alcoholic, not all of them are available because part of the alcohol may follow other pathways.

Dr. Forsander The kind of food they consume with their alcohol is very important.

Dr. Balboni That is what I was going to say. The Italians take wine almost exclusively with their meals. Their midday meal, which is the biggest, is very high in calories, and high in carbohydrates, especially the slowly absorbable carbohydrates in the form of pasta, rice, etc. Thus the absorption of alcohol is slowed down. This is an effective mechanism for avoiding harm from the alcohol.

Dr. Pace Thank you. Dr. Dock, you made a very compelling story for the legitimate use of alcohol as an adjunct at the disposal of the physician in a great many situations. However, we still have with us a very real problem in what is termed "alcoholism." Certainly, from the medical point of view, it has always been my understanding that there is a very substantial fraction of the population that develops cirrhosis of the liver as, shall we say, an occupational hazard of the drinking. How do you balance this?

Dr. Dock These two are unrelated things. There are people who die from digitalis prescribed by doctors. I never heard of anybody dying from alcohol prescribed by a doctor. The fact that you can buy alcohol without a prescription obviously puts it in a different class, and things like tobacco and wine, which entered our civilization in various ways, can be abused. The amount of smoking we do would make the poor Indians a little upset. We use this agent all day long, whereas they passed a pipe around on occasion to get one acute feeling of dizziness and rapport with the gods.

We can abuse anything—tobacco, alcohol, eggs, olive oil—anything you want can be abused. The fact is, of course, that alcohol is abused by a relatively small percentage of the population. In the last three decades it happens to have been spread around in the population in an interesting fashion, but this is entirely unrelated to the medicinal use of alcohol. It is like getting the use of an antihistamine agent, say amphetamine, mixed up with taking pep pills. They are entirely unrelated. If people want to take amphetamine as a drug, that has nothing to do with the doctor's prescribing amphetamine for somebody to whom it is a useful medicinal agent, and alcohol is a very useful medicinal agent. I maintain that the analogy I gave is correct: if we didn't already have alcohol and it was invented this year, then it would be the most valuable drug in the Pharmacopeia.

Dr. Pace I hope, Dr. Dock, that you're not recommending that alcohol and alcohol products be sold only by prescription.

Dr. Dock We had that once.

Dr. Pace Along these lines, one thing that I have not heard discussed here is one of the questions usually raised when the physiological effects of alcohol are considered, and that is the role of the so-called congeners in alcoholic beverages. Now among the small fraction of the population that abuses this drug that we have at our disposal, there is a disease which is said to be found only among people who drink excessive quantities of red wine. How would you explain this kind of a fairly specific sort of difficulty being associated with a particular form of alcoholic beverage?

Dr. Balboni I can't give you an exact answer; I would like to know myself. The study of congeners seems to be a very promising field.

Dr. Pace Dr. Goldberg, do you have any comments on this?

Dr. Goldberg Yes. I think that with moderate use the congeners play an honored role in our society, but with continual use in large amounts, an alcoholic may take one hundred to two hundred times as much as a moderate drinker, over a year or more. Then you have the problem of chronic intoxication. You can very well imagine that the addition of congeners, some of which may accumulate in the body, not being as readily metabolized as ethyl alcohol, might become important over a period of months or years.

Dr. Forsander Some industrial alcohols which alcoholics consume contain other alcohols than ethyl—often methyl—alcohol. There is a very big difference in the metabolism and the physiology of methyl alcohol. Ethyl alcohol is metabolized very much like carbohydrates, while methyl alcohol is metabolized like fat.

Dr. Goldberg The point is that ethyl alcohol is quite a bit more toxic. I think it interesting that in studying the alcohol-induced nystagmus, we found that phase II does not exist in animals. This is a human characteristic. We have not been able to produce phase II in rabbits, dogs, cats, or guinea pigs, but it does seem to exist in the monkey. This immediately brings up the problem of the organization of the central nervous system, which enables man to get to phase II.

Now let's go one step down to methanol, or wood alcohol. Methanol and ethanol are both metabolized by the same enzyme system. If the two are taken at the same time, there is a competition for the enzyme, and ethanol gets the preference, so ethanol is oxidized and methanol is not. This means that the cure for wood alcohol intoxication is to give ordinary alcohol, because then you inhibit part of the metabolism of methanol, the wood alcohol. This illustrates the very large difference in the metabolism of the different alcohols.

Dr. Dock I would like to ask, Dr. Goldberg, what is the level for a moderate steady drinker at which this nystagmus phenomenon appears?

Dr. Goldberg We have produced it in people, in females, with as little as 0.02 or 0.03 per cent alcohol in the blood. In most moderate drinkers it appears roughly at about 0.05 or 0.06 per cent alcohol in the blood, something like that.

Dr. Pace Dr. Dock, and perhaps Dr. Balboni, you may have some information on this: What is the incidence of coronary heart disease among alcoholics, or at least, shall we say, chronic heavy drinkers?

Dr. Dock Among the patients who take alcohol in doses which have overstimulated the liver, vascular disease not only is rare, but the lesions they have undergo regression, just like they do in starvation. The concentration-camp victims are often cirrhotic. The sclerosis actually vanishes, so at that stage cholesterol is very low; triglyceride is very low. But in well-nourished people there is pretty good evidence now that being an alcoholic does not protect you.

In the studies made in San Francisco by Dr. Meyer Friedman among patients with coronary diseases, it was shown that the intake of alcohol is higher in this group. These are well-fed men, busy, active people, functioning well in society, who developed coronary disease, and they had higher alcohol intakes than the control population in the same jobs and in the same area.

Dr. Pace This ought to take care of the idea that alcohol dissolves the cholesterol.

Dr. Dock Unless you take enough of it, enough to paralyze your liver and get histological changes—then you may prevent arteriosclerosis.

Dr. Pace You can take your choice between cirrhosis and coronary disease.

Another aspect that we ought to consider somewhere along the line is the question of the effect of alcohol on the endocrine system. As I understand it, isn't there a fairly specific stimulation of the adrenal medulla by alcohol?

Dr. Goldberg We have some work going on in this area. It appears that moderate amounts of alcohol induce a rise in adrenalin. But I don't think that this is a direct effect on the adrenals—rather, that it is mediated through the hypothalamus.

Dr. Pace We have been interested in this question ourselves, and it is, I think, fairly evident that the explanation lies in the depressing action of alcohol on the central nervous system; at least it makes a good theory. Clearly the hypothalamus is inhibited with respect to its role in the production of the antidiuretic hormone, which results in the diuretic action of the alcohol. We have fairly good indirect evidence that large single doses of alcohol very markedly alter the sodium-potassium ratio, which is in the direction, again, of the inhibition of the hypothalamus. However, there are a couple of things about this that bother me: We have fairly good evidence that following a large dose of alcohol there is increased adrenal-cortex activity, as judged by the production of 17-hydroxycortical steroids, but this increased production of adrenalin by the adrenal medulla doesn't seem to fit in.

I have read some of the speculation that has been going on in this respect, and it is of considerable interest, and fairly well established, that there are inhibitory fibers coming from the hypothalamus both to the adrenal cortex and the adrenal medulla. So perhaps the explanation is simply that with the low-grade depression of function, by alcohol, perhaps what we are depressing here are the inhibitory fibers. I wonder what your feeling about this approach would be?

Dr. Goldberg I can see your point very clearly. It is very good, and this brings me back to the fact that the dose must be one of the points we have to consider. You affect the inhibitory fibers with low doses, and you block the stimulant fibers with higher doses. This is still a hypothesis, but it should be very fruitful for further research.

Dr. Pace I have a question here that has been submitted from the audience. This is directed to Dr. Dock and is a very interesting question: "To what extent should efforts to exclude alcoholism be made before prescribing alcohol in connection with its medical use?"

Dr. Dock In this country, by the time a patient is thirty years old, if he is going to become an alcoholic, he is usually pretty well started on his way. It may be different in other countries.

In older people it is part of knowing your patients, knowing what the intake of alcohol has been, what the family history has been, and whether other members of the family have become alcoholics. Obviously, if the patient comes from a family with a history of alcoholism, it is a good thing to stay away from it and give some other form of therapy.

I think these are two things you can find out in taking the family history and the history of the patient's own experience with alcohol. This is all you can do to find out whether you should give the patient alcohol along with something that makes it impossible for him to take large doses per day, which means putting quinine or something else in the prescription.

Dr. Pace Perhaps it would be helpful to try to project ahead a little bit and visualize what form you feel the research that you are engaged in will be taking in the next interval of time, or perhaps, you have some things in mind that you feel are most in need of further work at the present time.

Would you like to start with that, Dr. Goldberg?

Dr. Goldberg I think this problem about giving alcohol or not is part of a very general problem. This is a dichotomy: you have moderate use of alcohol for a long period of time by a great percentage of the drinking population who never show any damage; then you have 5 to 10 per cent who are in the risk zone, who can either become alcoholics or turn back to moderate drinking.

You have a substantial number of people in every single country who are alcoholics. Of course, in research, this problem of alcoholism is a very challenging and exciting one, because you have the similarity with addiction on the one side and you have the similarity with amphetamine abuse on the other.

What we are engaged in is to try to find out how and why some people become alcoholics. For example, there is the problem of how much does a person who is on his way to being an alcoholic have to increase his consumption? What levels are dangerous? How long a time, out of twenty-four hours, must he be alcohol-free to avoid the danger?

Then we have the problem that everybody starts his drinking as part of the environmental pattern, the pattern he has in his home, in military service, in his job, or whatever it may be. Drinking starts as a social custom, and your drinking is patterned after the society in which you live. If you come from some place, you bring that pattern with you; and when you come into the risk zone, you begin to deviate from the general pattern. You are more like a select number of people in this general pattern. When you are past the risk zone, something new comes in; you have an addiction then—you have to take this drug in order to overcome your symptoms. There are two phases. You have the physiological part—you have a border zone, physiological and psychological—and then you have the zone where the abnormal part comes in. This is what we would like to know: the general metabolic disorders; the general problems involving these two things; and how can we tell when one is passing from one to the other? Research of this kind requires a multidimensional, interdisciplinary approach.

Dr. Balboni I think it is essential to keep in mind, as Dr. Goldberg put it, that the approach to this complex question must involve many disciplines, such as physiology, psychology, sociology, the study of nutrition, etc., especially since it seems that drinking habits are so closely allied to eating habits. It is very interesting to study the normal eating and drinking habits and to study the deviant ones and to link them together for possible conclusions.

Dr. Forsander I am a biochemist by trade, and what I should like to know more about is the quantitative aspects. We know a good deal about the qualitative reactions of alcohol metabolism and what is produced from alcohol, but we know very little about the quantitative aspects, such as, how much alcohol the patient is actually drinking and using, and what kind of food and how much he is actually eating, and I think that would be very important for us to know.

2

ALCOHOL
AND THE MIND

Dr. Greenberg *In the United States some 75 million people are currently users of alcoholic beverages and the large majority—perhaps over 90 per cent—drink these beverages in small and what I would call moderate amounts.*

The occasional relief of anxiety and the temporary dissipation of tension by . . . the tranquilizing action of alcoholic beverages suggests a possible rationale for [their] very old and persistent use in society throughout the world.

Dr. Masserman *Wine was the first anesthetic—a nepenthic administered to cloud the imminence and mitigate the horrors of primitive surgery, and some of us are still inclined to take a "bracer" before asking for a raise, proposing marriage, or undertaking some other presumably dangerous experience.*

George C. Drew, M.A.

Professor of Psychology
University College, London, England

ALCOHOL
AND SKILLED BEHAVIOR

Editor's Note   *The "Mind," as used in the title of the present section, should not be thought of as a technical word. It is used here in the most general sense, to cover a realm of alcohol effects whose range is from seemingly simple skills involving the coordination of muscles to the profoundest involvements of personality, manifested sometimes in the extreme behavioral disturbances encountered in alcoholism.*

In the first presentation in this section, Prof. George C. Drew reviews the general knowledge about the effects of various amounts of alcohol on the performance of tasks requiring different orders of skill. The study of these effects has been the province of experimental psychology since the last century. Professor Drew criticizes many of the older research findings. He next describes some of the important and better-designed experiments of recent times, including alcohol effects on reflex responses, reaction time, and vision and hearing. Going on to more complex activities, he refers particularly to those which reflect on automobile-driving ability. Here he details the original experiments with simulated automobile driving in his own laboratory. The higher sophistication of modern experimental psychology next comes into view. Professor Drew and his colleagues were not satisfied that the inferior performance of their subjects, as scored under the influence of alcohol, was an effect solely of the drug. With the help of tests from another discipline—clinical psychology—they discovered that alcohol differentially affected the driving performance of various personality types—extroverts and introverts.

The literature on the effect of alcohol on skilled performance is very extensive; speculative essays on the subject have appeared almost since man began to write about his experiences. Even experimental work dates back some one hundred years [e.g., Exner, 1873]. In spite of this volume of work, however, we can still draw only the broadest

97

outline picture of the answer to this problem. The reason for this is that, on the whole, the level of methodological sophistication in experiments with alcohol is considerably lower than would be tolerated in almost any other field. It is now known that the absorption of alcohol from the stomach and intestine into the blood is affected by a large number of factors. The presence or absence of food, the form in which alcohol is taken, its dilution, the lean body weight of the individual, are just some of these factors, and they are capable of producing very large differences in the blood alcohol level resulting from the ingestion of a given amount of alcohol. In spite of this, it is not at all uncommon for the amounts of alcohol given to subjects in an experiment to be reported in terms of dose only, frequently with no mention of the factors which would enable one even to guess at the blood alcohol levels involved. Failure to control practice effects, and effects of the order in which different doses are administered, inadequate measurements of behavior, inadequate numbers of subjects, and so on, have all contributed to making the results of many experiments suggestive rather than definitive.

It is possible to describe the effects of alcohol on skilled performance. We will start first with its effects on the simpler, "component" parts of skills, and then deal with experimental studies of more complex situations. The effect of alcohol on reflex responses, on reaction times, and on all sensory processes seems to depend partly on the concentration of alcohol and partly on the complexity of the task.

REFLEX RESPONSES

The simpler, more vegetative, aspects of our adjustment to the environment seem to be made more rapid and more sensitive by small amounts of alcohol. Simple reflex responses like the patellar reflex, for example, seem to be made more rapid by low blood alcohol levels. Such an effect was reported by Dodge and Benedict [1915] and by Travis and Dorsay [1929]. Miles [1924], however, found that the eyelid responses were slowed. Though most of the work reported is old and needs confirmation, the bulk of the evidence seems to support the view that most reflex responses become quicker at low blood alcohol concentrations.

In a similar way, many experimenters reported that absolute

sensory thresholds are lower after comparably low doses of alcohol. Thus, increased sensitivity to light was found by Lange and Specht, and to sound by Specht; but Mullin and Luckhardt found no change in sensitivity to touch and a marked decrease in sensitivity to pain.

REACTION TIME

Simple reaction-time responses, in which the individual is "triggered" to make a given response to a defined stimulus, have also been reported as being speeded up with low doses, though it is in this field that experimental procedures have perhaps been least satis-factory. It seems clear, however, that where increased speed of re-sponse, whether reflex or simple reaction time, and increased sensi-tivity to light or sound have been reported, the blood alcohol levels involved have been about 0.05 per cent, if one can assume that the subjects weighed at least about 140 lb. There is a good measure of agreement that with doses producing larger blood alcohol values than this, all measures of performance show decreased efficiency [cf. Jellinek and McFarland; Carpenter, 1961]. Some authors [e.g., Kraepelin; Niemirowicz-Szczytt; Warren] using doses which must have produced peak blood alcohol levels well above 0.05 per cent, report a speeding up of simple reaction times in the first fifteen to twenty minutes after drinking, when the blood level must have been low, and a shifting at about that interval to a slower reaction time.

As soon, however, as slightly more complicated responses are considered, the picture changes. Behavior, now, begins to deteriorate at very low blood alcohol levels. Simple reaction times, and ab-solute sensory thresholds may, though the evidence is not conclusive, improve at blood alcohol levels below 0.05 per cent. Choice reaction times, and difference thresholds, however, begin to deteriorate at levels well below this. In reaction-time experiments where any element of choice or judgment is involved—that is, the subject must decide either to respond or not or which response to make or which stimulus should be responded to—the subjects seem to react more slowly at all blood alcohol levels. The ability to discriminate differences in sensory experience, whether it be in visual acuity, in brightness discriminations, in differentiating colors, in recognizing differences in intensity or pitch in sounds, or in differentiating be-tween one and two simultaneous touches, seems similarly to deteriorate at very low levels [cf. Jellinek and McFarland]. This apparent difference in the effect of low blood alcohol levels seems interesting and worthy of careful checking.

TUNNEL VISION

Newman and Fletcher, and others, have reported that at fairly high blood alcohol levels of the order of 0.15 per cent or more, the phenomenon known as "tunnel vision" is observable. This name is a graphic description of a reduction in the field of vision to which the individual responds, until ultimately he responds only to stimuli in a very limited field, as though he were looking through a tunnel or tube. It seems reasonable to suppose that any such reduction in the visual field will have marked effects on skilled performance, especially if the skill approximates the complexity of driving a car. A major characteristic of skill is the ability to anticipate, to be able to act on minimal cues; and many such cues arise, especially in driving, from the periphery. Any reduction in the capacity to perceive them is likely to be reflected in impaired performance.

It seems certain that this reduction in the visual field is by no means specific to alcohol. Instead, it has been demonstrated to occur in a number of conditions, unrelated to one another, except that they place the individual in a stress situation. It has been shown to occur in fatigue [Drew], in hot and humid conditions [Bursill], and in anoxia. In all these conditions it appears to be a progressive function of the degree of stress. With alcohol, only a fairly severe restriction at fairly high blood alcohol levels has been reported. It seems reasonable to assume, however, that here, too, it will be progressive. It seems likely, too, that, in this respect at least, there may be interaction between any two stress conditions. In England, it is common for drivers to pause and drink when tired from driving. It seems probable that this particular symptom, at least, may be exaggerated by this maneuver.

Tunnel vision appears not to be a sensory failure but a more "central" defect, a failure of attention, in fact. Experiments in America have shown that the normal restriction from the peripheral to the central visual field is really a product of the experimental situation. What appears in fact to happen is that it is possible only to attend to a more and more limited part of the visual field. Which part of the field is attended to—whether it is peripheral or central—

is a function of the expectancy built up from previous experience in the task.

COMPLEX SKILLS

In dealing with more complex skills, most modern investigators have used tasks which bear some resemblance to skills practiced in every-day life. Eggleton, for example, used typing; Newman and Abramson, target shooting; Aksnes, and Eyer and Ivers, the Link trainer, a device used in teaching instrument flying to aircraft pilots; and Vogel, the Toronto Complex Coordinator, an apparatus thought to be analogous to controlling an aircraft in bank and pitch. By far the greater number, however, have used skills based on those required in driving an automobile. Some experimenters have performed tests with simulators of automobile driving in laboratories, while others have made the task more realistic by requiring their subjects to carry out specified maneuvers in an actual automobile. The classic work in this latter field, as indeed in so much of the psychological experimental work with alcohol, has been carried out by Goldberg and his associates. For example, Bjerver and Goldberg compared the performance of two groups of experienced drivers on a test track involving driving around posts, reversing, and so on. They found that to perform accurately, experienced drivers with blood alcohol concentrations between 0.04 and 0.06 per cent needed about 30 per cent more time than did those without alcohol. Häkkinen used a similar kind of task and gave his experimental group of drivers four 10-ml drinks of whiskey, testing before and after each drink. He found that with blood alcohol levels of up to 0.04 per cent his subjects drove more quickly and made more mistakes. At 0.1 per cent and above, performance time grew longer and errors increased markedly. He concluded that in such a task, deterioration in driving skill is detectable at a blood alcohol concentration of 0.05 per cent. Borkenstein measured errors rather than time and found an increase of some 13 per cent in mistakes made (posts knocked over, etc.) with blood alcohol levels between 0.07 and 0.14 per cent and a 40 per cent increase in mistakes at blood alcohol levels above 0.15 per cent. Again, Coldwell et al., of the Royal Canadian Mounted Police, found deterioration in efficiency in all drivers at a blood alcohol level of 0.15 per cent, while five out of seven subjects were impaired at levels below 0.05 per cent. In almost all the other experiments quoted, too, signs of deterioration in efficiency were present at blood alcohol levels around 0.05 per cent.

In other experiments, Goldberg compared the appearance and disappearance thresholds (the blood alcohol level on the rising phase at which impairment appears, and on the falling phase at which behavior returns to normal) for perceptual, motor, and intellectual functions. All the measures showed impairment on the rising curve around 0.04 per cent of alcohol in the blood. Intellectual functions returned to normal on the falling blood alcohol curve at 0.07 per cent; motor functions, at 0.06 per cent; and perceptual ones, at 0.04 per cent.

Considerations such as these led Goldberg to postulate that there is a critical level, a threshold, for the effect of alcohol on skilled performance. He suggested that alcohol has no detectable effect below levels of 0.03 to 0.04 per cent in the blood, but that all forms of behavior deteriorate above that.

It seems clear that if alcohol has any effects on behavior at these very low blood alcohol levels, they will be small. It seems possible that the performances measured in the cited experiments are not sufficiently sensitive to measure changes below such blood alcohol levels. Time is a notoriously difficult measure, and errors measured as posts knocked over, etc., seem too all-or-none. Near misses escape record.

AUTOMOBILE DRIVING

Accordingly, an experiment was designed [Drew, Colquhoun, and Long] using a driving simulator, to allow continuous detailed recording of the subject's behavior during an extended period covering the rise and part of the fall of the blood alcohol curve. Forty subjects were used, all drivers, and each one was tested five times, for two hours on each occasion. To test for a threshold effect, four different doses of alcohol were used, and a placebo dose without alcohol. The doses were such that the mean peak blood alcohol levels reached between thirty and forty-five minutes after drinking were 0.02, 0.04, 0.06 and 0.08 per cent, approximately, on the four occasions when alcohol was given. Each subject was used as his own control, and a 5 by 5 reduplicated latin-square experimental design was used so as to partial out the effects of the order of doses on practice. Continuous graphic and counter records were kept of the position of the simulated car on the "road surface," of speed, of movement of the steering wheel, and of pressure on the clutch, brake, and accelerator pedal, and so on. Blood samples were taken before testing and at one-half-hour intervals throughout each test.

Change in the accuracy of performance was measured as a change in the amount of lateral deviation across the road surface made by each subject after alcohol, compared to his own performance without alcohol. It was a measure of the increased "wobble" or oscillation around a mean track. In this form, analysis of the measures showed that error increased with increasing blood alcohol concentration. In other words, there was a detectable error score as soon as there was any measurable quantity of alcohol in the blood, and this error score increased proportionately as the blood alcohol level increased.[1] If plotted against time, error scores showed a rapid rise to a peak occurring some ten minutes or so after the peak blood alcohol, and then began to fall off again. The curve of change in error, in fact, closely resembled the curve of the rise and fall of blood alcohol, but lagged slightly behind the blood alcohol in time. Changes associated with this increase in error appeared to be a progressive shift of mean driving position towards the crown of the road with increasing blood alcohol level, increased oscillation about this mean position, and a progressive breakdown in the timing of responses.

Movements of the controls, and especially of the steering wheel, proved especially sensitive to the presence of alcohol. Significant increases occurred within ten minutes of drinking and at very low blood alcohol levels.[2]

Mean speed showed no significant changes with changes in blood alcohol, but changes in speed were found to be closely related to individual differences.

In these experiments, measurable changes occurred in error scores and in control movements at very low blood alcohol levels, of the order of 0.01 to 0.02 per cent. These changes were not in themselves statistically significantly different from control performance, but they lie on the regression lines, which themselves pass through zero as a point of origin. The most reasonable interpretation of such

[1] A regression line through the mean error scores for each blood alcohol level was linear, and passed through zero as its point of origin.
[2] The regression of increases in steering-wheel movement on increasing blood alcohol also passes through zero. There is some evidence that this regression may be curvilinear.

data would appear to be that there is no threshold effect, at least for this type of skill. Rather, small but measurable changes occur as soon as there is a measurable quantity of alcohol in the blood. These changes become of sufficient magnitude to be statistically significantly different from control performance by the time the blood alcohol level reaches 0.04 to 0.05 per cent.

PERSONALITY DIFFERENCES

Though the average results were of the nature outlined, there were quite striking individual differences in performance after alcohol. For example, in error scores, while twenty of the forty subjects showed increased error of more than 20 per cent over their control performance, five showed a decreased error of more than 20 per cent and one, a decreased error as much as 50 per cent. That is, these people became significantly more accurate in their performance on this test after alcohol. Similarly, while seven slowed down, five speeded up by more than 20 per cent over their control speeds. An attempt was made to relate these individual differences, in response to alcohol, to some characteristics of the individual subjects. They were found not to be related to driving experience, initial level of skill, previous drinking experience, age or sex. As some previous investigators [Wierenga; Bartley and Chute; Cattell] had found some indication that personality variables were relevant, all the subjects had been given a battery of personality tests. It turned out that changes in performance after alcohol were related to personality differences, and especially to differences in the extrovert-introvert dimension. Typically, extroverts did not change their behavior pattern after alcohol: the amount of their control movements and the speed of their driving remained much the same; but the timing of their responses was seriously affected and, as a result, this group showed high error scores after alcohol. Introverts, on the other hand, showed a marked change both in steering wheel movement and in speed. From about the middle range to the extreme introverts, this group of subjects split into two subgroups, one of which drove faster and faster the more introverted they were, while the other drove more and more slowly. It was this latter subgroup which drove more accurately. The extreme subject who reduced her error score by more than 50 per cent was in this group. She drove, during her control run, at an average speed equivalent to 31 mph. After alcohol she slowed down so that she never exceeded 8 mph. On the surface, this subgroup appears to be a group who are made more "careful" and whose performance is improved by alcohol. This is the case only as long as they can themselves control the speed at which they are required to respond. In subsidiary experiments, in which speed was controlled for them, this subgroup showed panic reactions and their performance was worse than that of any of the others.

Using a rather different experimental technique, Cohen et al. have shown an interesting differential effect of low blood alcohol levels on subjective judgment and on actual performance. Experienced bus drivers, seated in their vehicles, were asked first to estimate the smallest gap through which they could drive their buses and then actually to drive through. At blood alcohol levels below 0.05 per cent some of the drivers were confident that they could drive through a gap smaller than the width of the vehicle. As blood alcohol levels rose, more and more were confident of getting through a smaller and smaller gap, whereas the gap actually required became larger and larger.

The effect of alcohol on traffic accidents has recently been admirably reviewed by Haddon and Bradess. This is not the place to repeat such a review, since it is not easy to draw conclusions about skill from such statistical information. The results of such surveys reveal close similarities to the experimental work discussed here. There appears, first, to be an increasing involvement in serious traffic accidents of drivers or pedestrians as their blood alcohol level rises from about 0.05 per cent up. In some studies, like the ones by Holcomb in Evanston and by Coldwell et al. in Toronto, and more recently that of Vámosi in Bratislava, increasing risk of involvement has been calculated by comparing the blood alcohol levels of those involved in accidents with those of controls not so involved.

In such studies, it has been shown that the increased risk is a curvilinear function of increasing blood alcohol concentration. The increase in risk is small, and probably not significant, up to about 0.05 per cent. Above that level it rises steeply.

There appears to be little doubt that as blood alcohol levels approach 0.1 per cent, significant impairment of skilled performance has been observed by almost all investigators. As might be expected, there is much less agreement on the effects of low blood alcohol levels. The area of disagreement largely resides around the question of whether or not there is a threshold effect. Part of the reason for this disagreement may well be methodological. Since personality variables produce different effects on component parts of a skilled response, it seems probable that sensitive and detailed scoring of a number of measures of behavior are needed. It may well be the case that skills of a given degree of complexity deteriorate before others. This may be a function of the complexity itself.

It is clear that a great deal more work is needed before author-itative answers can be given to these problems. It is fortunate that this problem is virtually unique in experimental psychology in that there is no shortage of willing subjects for the experiments.

REFERENCES

Aksnes, E. G., Effect of Small Dosages of Alcohol upon Performance in a Link Trainer, *J. Aviation Med.*, 25:680–688, 693, 1954.

Bartley, S. H., and Chute, E., *Fatigue and Impairment in Man*, New York, McGraw-Hill, 1947.

Bjerver, K., and Goldberg, L., Effect of Alcohol Ingestion in Driving Ability. Results of Practical Road Tests and Laboratory Experiments, *Quart. J. Studies Alc.*, 11:1–30, 1950.

Borkenstein, R. F., "Driving Tests to Determine Alcoholic Influence," *Indiana State Police Manual*, 1956.

Bursill, A. E., The Restriction of Peripheral Vision during Exposure to Hot and Humid Conditions, *Quart. J. Expl. Psychol.*, 114, 1958.

Carpenter, J. A., Effects of Alcohol on Some Psychological Processes. A Critical Review with Special Reference to Automobile Driving Skill, *Quart. J. Studies Alc.*, 22:183–222, 1961.

Cattell, R. B., The Effects of Alcohol and Caffeine on Intelligent and Associative Performance, *Brit. J. Med. Psychol.*, 10:20–33, 1930.

Cohen, J., Dearnaley, E. J., and Hansel, C. E. M., The Risk Taken in Driving under the Influence of Alcohol, *Brit. Med. J.*, 1:1438–1442, 1958.

Coldwell, B. B. (ed.), *Report on Improved Driving Tests*, Ottawa, Edmond Cloutier, Queen's Printer, 1957.

Coldwell, B. B., Penner, D. W., Smith, H. W., Lucas, G. H. W., Rodgers, R. F., and Darroch, F., Effect of Ingestion of Distilled Spirits on Automobile Driving Skill, *Quart. J. Studies Alc.*, 19:590–616, 1958.

Dodge, R., and Benedict, F. G., *Psychological Effects of Alcohol*, Washington, D.C., Carnegie Institution 232, 1915.

Drew, G. C., "Mental Fatigue." *Flying Personnel Res. Com. Rept.*, 227, 1942.

Drew, G. C., Colquhoun, W. P., and Long, H. A., "Effect of Small Doses of Alcohol on a Skill Resembling Driving," Privy Council, Medical Research Council Memorandum 38, London, H. M. Stationery Office, 1959. Abst. in *Brit. Med. J.*, 2:993–999, 1958.

Eggleton, M. G., The Effect of Alcohol on the Central Nervous System, *Brit. J. Psychol.*, 32:52–61, 1941.

Exner, S., Experimentelle Untersuchungen der einfachsten psychischen Prozesse (Experimental Studies of the Simplest Psychological Processes), *Pflüger's Arch. ges. Physiol.*, 7:601–660, 1873.

Eyer, S. W., and Ivers, J. B., "The Effect of Alcohol upon Link Trainer Performance," Naval Medical Research Institute, National Naval Medical Center, Bethesda, Md., Project NM 001 056.06.01, 1950, pp. 1–8 and tables.

Goldberg, L., Quantitative Studies on Alcohol Tolerance in Man. The Influence of Ethyl Alcohol on Sensory, Motor and Psychological Functions Referred to Blood Alcohol in Normal and Habituated Individuals, *Acta Psysiol. Scand.*, 5 (Suppl. 16): 1–128, 1943.

Haddon, W., and Bradess, V. A., Alcohol in the Single Vehicle Fatal Accident, *J. Am. Med. Assoc.*, 169:1587–1593, 1959.

Häkkinen, Sauli, "Traffic Accidents and Driver Characteristics, a Statistical and Psychological Study," *Scientific Researches* 13, Institute of Technology, Finland, 1958.

Holcomb, R. L., Alcohol in Relation to Driving Accidents, *J. Amer. Med. Assoc.*, 111:1076, 1938.

Jellinek, E. M., and McFarland, R. A., Analysis of Psychological Experiments on the Effects of Alcohol, *Quart. J. Studies Alc.*, 1:272–371, 1940.

Kraepelin, E., Ueber die Einwirkung einiger medicamentöser Stoffe auf die Dauer einfacher psychischer Vorgänge (On the Effect of Some Medicinal Substances on the Duration of Simple Psychological Processes), *Psychol. Stud.*, 1:573–603, 1883.

Lange, J., and Specht, W., Neue Untersuchungen über die Beeinflussung der Sinnesfunktionen durch geringe Alkoholmengen (New Studies on the Effect of Small Doses of Alcohol on Sensory Functions), *Z. Pathopsych.*, 3:155–256, 1914–19.

Miles, W. R., *Alcohol and Human Efficiency. Experiments with Moderate Quantities and Dilute Solutions of Ethyl Alcohol on Human Subjects,* Washington, D. C., Carnegie Institution 333, 1924.

Mullin, F. J., and Luckhardt, A. B., The Effect of Alcohol on Cutaneous, Tactile and Pain Sensitivity, *Am. J. Physiol.*, 109:77–78, 1934.

Newman, H., and Abramson, M., Relation of Alcohol Concentration to Intoxication, *Proc. Soc. Exptl. Biol.*, 48:509–512, 1941.

Newman, H., and Fletcher, E., The Effect of Alcohol on Vision, *Am. J. Med. Sci.*, 202:723–731, 1941.

Niemirowicz-Szczytt, C., Les modifications de la chronaxie vestibulaire déterminées par l'alcool chez les alcooliques. (Changes in Vestibular Chronaxy Caused by Alcohol in Alcoholics), *Encéphale*, 33^2:26–45, 1938.

Specht, W., Die Beeinflussung der Sinnesfunktionen durch geringe Alkoholmengen. Das Verhalten von Unterschiedsschwelle und Reizschwelle im Gebiete des Gehörsinnes (The Effect of Small Amounts of Alcohol on Sensory Functions. The Difference Threshold and the Stimulus Threshold in the Field of Auditory Perceptions), *Arch. ges. Psychol.*, 9:180–295, 1907.

Travis, L. E., and Dorsay, J. M., Effect of Alcohol on the Patellar Tendon Reflex Time, *A.M.A. Arch. Neurol. Psychiat.*, 21^1:613–624, 1929.

Vámosi, M., Ergebnisse von Blutalkoholbestimmungen bei Kraftfahrern (Results of Blood Alcohol Determination in Motor Vehicle Drivers), Z. *ärztl. Fortbild.*, **53**:635–639, 1959.

Vogel, M., Low Blood Alcohol Concentrations and Psychological Adjustment As Factors in Psychomotor Performance. An Exploratory Study, *Quart. J. Studies Alc.*, **19**:573–589, 1958.

Warren, J. W., The Effect of Pure Alcohol on the Reaction Time, with a Description of a New Chronoscope, *J. Physiol.*, **8**:311–348, 1887.

Wierenga, R., L'influenza dell'alcool sull'abilità di condurre un automobile in individui di temperamento diverso (The Influence of Alcohol on Automobile Driving in Individuals of Different Temperaments), *Arch. antrop. criminale, psichiat. e med. legale*, **56**:737–748, 1936.

Leon A. Greenberg, Ph.D.

Professor of Physiology, Rutgers University, New Brunswick, New Jersey

ALCOHOL
AND EMOTIONAL BEHAVIOR

Editor's Note   *The recognition in the experiments described by Professor Drew that different personality types react differently to the stress of driving when under the influence of alcohol, raises a more general question. How does alcohol generally affect personality? What does alcohol "do" to or for normal human emotions? Dr. Leon A. Greenberg approaches this problem from the viewpoint of a fundamental hypothesis expressed in the following question: Why have people persisted throughout history in drinking alcoholic beverages, in spite of the facts that for some people such drinking can end in the catastrophe of alcoholism, and that many grave problems have repeatedly plagued society in connection with excessive drinking behavior?*

The experimental approach described by Dr. Greenberg is concerned only with the drinking of moderate amounts of alcoholic beverage, as practiced by most people most of the time. In one series of experiments, animals were subjected to a severe stress, resulting in convulsive reactions; this result could be averted by first giving them moderate amounts of alcohol. In other experiments, with normal human subjects, electrical skin conductance was used as a measure of emotional reactivity. It appeared that moderate amounts of alcohol reduced this reactivity. From these findings Dr. Greenberg hypothesizes that the attractiveness of alcohol to man can be explained by the fact that in moderate amounts it acts as a mild emotional tranquilizer.

After I had been invited to speak at this conference and then learned of its broad make-up, I was rather gratified by the variety of disciplines represented by the participants. On arriving in San Francisco and viewing the large attendance of people from widely different areas of interest, I was even more pleasantly surprised, because this is indeed a recognition of the many facets, and the complexity of factors, with which one becomes involved in any consideration of the whole matter of drinking.

This complexity has a very wide range of manifestation. Not long ago I had occasion to participate in a two-day alcoholism program in upstate New York, and as at many such programs, one of the local church groups had its little exhibit, consisting of a bulletin board on which were cards with familiar slogans printed on them. Up in one corner was a card with a basic Christian admonition, "Make your worst enemy your best friend"; and right next to it was another card, with an equally famous admonition, "Alcohol is your worst enemy." I don't think that the inspiration for this combination of slogans was the laudatory view of the use of alcohol so eloquently articulated by Dr. Dock; I think it was really sheer accident.

The drinking of alcohol-containing beverages by man is probably older than recorded history. This use has existed in almost every society, and for many, has been one of moderation and not excess. In the United States some seventy-five million people are currently users of alcoholic beverages [Keller] and the large majority of these, perhaps over 90 per cent, drink these beverages in small and what I would call moderate amounts. A minority, less than 10 per cent, drink in excess, creating problems—personal problems and community problems.

Although the vast majority of those who drink alcoholic beverages do so in moderation and with no apparent detrimental effect on their physical, social, or economic well-being, the chief emphasis of research dealing with the effects of alcohol on man has been on its excessive and problem-provoking use. This is not surprising, because the problems arising from such excess are dramatic; they are painful, and for this reason they command attention.

MODERATE DRINKING DEFINED

It is altogether possible that the problem of deviant drinking behavior will not be solved until there is a fundamental understanding of the motivations underlying the exceedingly long persistence of ordinary drinking as a world-wide custom. In referring to drinking in moderation, it would be well, perhaps, to digress very briefly and to define this term as I shall be using it here. Drinking alcoholic beverages in moderation is drinking in such amounts and with such frequency and on such occasions as to present no threat to the health, to the welfare, and to the functioning of the individual. I think this is probably as good and as useful a definition as is possible. Such a definition of moderation, of course, precludes intoxication, and certainly precludes repeated intoxication. It is in this sense of the term that the majority of users of alcohol are said to drink in moderation, but the fact that they do not become intoxicated does not signify or mean that the smaller amount of alcohol which they drink is without any effect on their feeling or on their behavior. They may experience subjective effects such as increase in comfort, relaxation, pleasure, diminished tension or anxiety, and change of mood. They may also experience some degree of impairment of such psychological functions as sensory perception, discrimination, and judgment.

In determining and in evaluating the subjective effects of moderate amounts of alcohol, the scope has been severely limited by the available methods of observation. For the most part, such effects have remained beyond quantitative measurements, and the experiments with smaller amounts of alcohol have necessarily been concerned largely with those psychological functions in which changes could be measured, could be quantitated. Now, the interpretation of the measurement of such changes, as well as deductions from them, requires a great deal of caution, because otherwise the tendency will be to project the changes observed in one or more isolated functions into corresponding changes in total behavior, even in total efficiency. I should point out that it is not usually the experimental researcher himself who is guilty of such unscientific conclusions. He may merely report his experimental findings, but those who wish to support their own views on the use of alcohol sometimes make unwarranted deductions concerning the quality and the efficiency of total behavior from such findings.

EFFECTS OF MODERATE AMOUNTS

Such elements of behavior as speed of reaction time for coordination, sensory judgment, and discrimination are only single components of the total complexity called behavior. So also are such qualities as mood, state of tension or anxiety, and sense of comfort or relaxation. The quality of total behavior, in other words, is the result of the interrelationship, the interaction, the sum, of all of this variety of elements. And while the effects of small amounts of alcohol on certain isolated functions, if viewed by themselves, might indeed suggest inferior performance, the effects on other elements of total behavior, which by themselves sometimes inhibit maximum quality of performance, may in some situations or in some people be more than compensating and result in an improved total performance.

Although investigators in more recent years have succeeded in making finer measurements of the influence of moderate amounts of alcohol on a variety of individual functions [cf. Carpenter, 1962], the ultimate aims of these efforts, I think we would all agree, go far beyond such simple measurements. They extend to the eventual understanding of the effects of alcohol on total behavior, on the quality or the efficiency of performance in relationship to the amounts of alcohol consumed, on the psychological status of the drinker, and on the nature of the task to be performed. That scientists have not yet achieved much beyond the measuring of fragments of behavior in itself indicates the enormous complexity of this undertaking.

I mentioned earlier that moderation excludes intoxication. It is, I think, unanimously agreed that total behavior and performance is at best inferior and often destructive in the intoxicated state, and research has provided measures which give some definition to this condition in terms of the alcohol content of the blood [cf. Greenberg, 1955].

Practically all people show some degree of intoxication at alcohol concentrations in the blood of 0.15 per cent. Below this, a diminishing proportion show intoxication; below 0.05 per cent alcohol in the blood, virtually no one shows intoxication. In fact, this last value, 0.05 per cent, is the one taken commonly as prima-facie evidence of sobriety in chemical testing of motorists in this country. I shall therefore use these values in my present discussion, that is, 0.15 per cent as indicative of intoxication, 0.05 per cent as indicative of moderation. For a man of average size, 0.05 per cent alcohol in the blood is rarely exceeded by the consumption of 2 or 3 oz of whiskey, or an equal number of 12-oz bottles of American beer or about 12 oz of ordinary wine on an empty stomach, and somewhat more, appreciably more, after a meal.

The findings of psychological, pharmacological, and physiological experimentation have given the basic information that, contrary to older beliefs, alcohol is not primarily a stimulant. It is mainly a sedative, and sedatives, in general, are tranquilizers. And alcohol used in moderation is, I believe, of all the tranquilizers, probably by far the oldest, and probably, for most people, the safest.

RATIONALE FOR MODERATE DRINKING

At the very beginning, I spoke of drinking alcoholic beverages as universal behavior in antiquity. I also indicated the need for some explanation, some rationale that would explain the exceedingly long survival of this use in society. It is a basic precept of social science that no usage, no practice, persists or survives unless it fulfills some function, unless it satisfies some need. So the question—the scientific question—may then be raised: What needs might have been met by the long-continued moderate use of alcoholic beverages? I think that present knowledge of the pharmacological properties of alcohol suggests a possible psychophysiological answer. A primary effect of small amounts of alcohol is its mild sedative and tranquilizing action. Both in his physical and social environment, man has always been exposed to continuous stresses and resulting tensions. May not the action of small amounts of alcohol serve to moderate the effects of these stresses? The occasional relief of anxiety and the temporary dissipation of tension by the sedative, by the tranquilizing action of alcoholic beverages, suggests a possible rationale for its very old and persistent use in society throughout the world. These questions and this suggested rationale were put to experimental test in the researches I am about to describe briefly.

EFFECT OF ALCOHOL ON STRESS

The first group of these experiments was made with animals. The production in animals of so-called emotional responses to a variety of stressful stimuli has been studied extensively, and these stimuli range all the way from situations of psychological conflict to sensory or direct physical stimulation. The emotional responses evoked have covered the range from barely detectable to strikingly abnormal behavior. In selected albino rats, certain auditory stimuli, certain sounds, evoke an intense emotional response which manifests itself in a very dramatic manic behavior, usually terminating in convulsions, sometimes even in the death of the animal. This response is known as audiogenic seizure. The sound stimulus used in these tests in our laboratory was a loud bell. The characteristic pattern of the seizure is as follows: On hearing the bell there is at first a momentary startled reaction. After about five to ten seconds this is followed by attempts to escape from the enclosure in which the animal has been placed, and this, after a few seconds, is followed by an increasing crescendo of activities. The animal runs around wildly and rapidly and leaps into the air. This is followed by other wild activity and finally by a convulsion which terminates in rigid extension of the hind legs, followed by a state of exhaustion with a catatonia-like immobility lasting from one to three minutes.

In our studies [Greenberg and Lester] these animals were given various amounts of alcohol preliminary to exposure to the seizure-producing stimulus, and measurements of the alcohol content of the blood were made immediately following the exposure to the sound stimulus.

The results may be briefly summarized as follows: At a concentration of alcohol in the blood ranging between 0.02 and 0.04 per cent, over 40 per cent of the audiogenic seizures were averted; they didn't occur. It should be noted these were all animals that had been selected because they always gave an audiogenic seizure response.

I might point out that one does not find this response in all animals, even in all animals of one variety or one species. In the rats that we used, about one out of every three randomly picked from the stock farm would be a responder. We had an economic problem in purchasing animals that would respond without having to buy two others that didn't. I called up the rat farm and made the owner a proposition; I would send one of my people down there with our bell. He would walk through the animal room and ring the bell, and we would buy all the rats that had convulsions. This was very appealing to the rat farmer because we obviously left him with the good rats, and we took the damaged ones. It was a mutually satisfactory deal.

Now, I pointed out that with between 0.02 and 0.04 per cent alcohol in the blood, over 40 per cent of the animals no longer responded to the bell with an audiogenic seizure. This is not to say that they did not hear the bell; this is a very low concentration of alcohol. With between 0.04 and 0.06 per cent alcohol in the blood, 45 per cent of the seizures were averted; and with between 0.06 and 0.08 per cent alcohol in the blood, no seizures occurred in any of the animals. I should note that with less than 0.08 per cent alcohol in the blood there was no evidence of intoxication apparent in any of the animals. In terms of human behavior, at blood alcohol concentrations below 0.08 per cent there is little, if any, intoxication.

It was clearly apparent from these experiments that low concentrations of alcohol in the blood, equivalent to extremely moderate consumption of alcoholic beverages in man, and well below the levels of intoxication, significantly diminished the "emotional" response. I should like the record to show the word "emotional" in quotation marks—an issue may be taken with this because of what this term means to various people. In this case, it was specifically the diminished emotional response of animals to a stress that normally evokes grossly disturbed behavior.

The results observed in these studies appeared to be consistent with the hypothesis that I put forth initially, suggesting as an explanation for the sustained use of alcoholic beverage in human society the fact that it was a tension reliever. The stimulus and the audiogenic seizure evoked in the rats in these tests are obviously of severe intensity. The everyday stresses upon the normal individual are undoubtedly less intense, and I think it seems not unreasonable to speculate that with less vigorous stresses and correspondingly less intense responses, the action of alcohol in reducing the impact of the stress might be effected at even lower levels of alcohol than those used in these experiments.

Experimental studies with rats have been reported by others [e.g., Farris et al.], in which brief daily subjection of the animals to an auditory stress, such as the one that I spoke of, resulted in hypertension after long repeated exposure. It is intriguing to speculate on whether low levels of alcohol present in the blood of these animals at the time of their daily exposure to the auditory stress might have averted the resulting cardiovascular disturbances. To my knowledge this has not been tested. I think it would be worth doing.

EFFECT OF ALCOHOL ON EMOTIONAL REACTIVITY

Our experimental efforts were next directed toward the study of the effects of alcohol on—again, I would like this term in quotation marks—"emotional tension" in human subjects. In the past, experimental research involving the phenomenon of emotion in humans has been difficult because the term itself has lacked sharp definition, and because emotional tension has lacked objective and quantitative criteria of measurement. Recently, however, Lindsley proposed a useful concept in which emotion is related to the degree of activity of the nervous system, and especially to a particular complex known as the reticular system. In the presence of emotional stimuli, there is activation of the reticular system together with a corresponding increase of activity in the nervous system as a whole.

Within the framework of this concept of emotion, Woodworth and Schlosberg further proposed that this increased activity of the nervous system corresponds to "tension" or "excitement," and is accompanied by corresponding increases in the intensity of behavior. These underlying activities of the nervous system are perceptible in the measurement of such phenomena as brain waves, muscle tonus, and sympathetic nervous system activity.

The known relationship between emotional states and the activity of the sympathetic nervous system has received particular attention in recent years. The sympathetic nervous system controls the electrical conductance of certain areas of the skin, and this conductance can be measured exactly and objectively. Accordingly, skin conductance measurements would appear to offer a sensitive and objective gauge of emotional activation; at least we accepted this proposal as a definition in pursuing this particular line of research.

In our studies [Carpenter, 1957; Greenberg and Carpenter], measurement of skin conductance was therefore used as a measure of emotional activation. At the outset, two aspects of skin conductance in relation to emotion were recognized: one, the more or less sustained level of conductance associated with a correspondingly sustained state of emotional activation; and two, the sudden and rapid change of conductance of relatively large magnitude, associated with a sudden stressing stimulus. The former, the sustained level, is known as the basic conductance level; the latter, the sharp, brief one, as the galvanic skin response (GSR). To some of you this may be familiar as a device used in the so-called lie detector. The basic conductance level might be viewed as the readiness to respond emotionally, and the GSR, as the actual emotion or response to a stress situation or stress stimulus. The purpose of our study was to observe the effect of different amounts of alcohol and corresponding levels of alcohol in the blood, on the basic level of emotional activation and on the magnitude of emotional response, or GSR response, to a standard stressing stimulus.

Normal adult people were our subjects this time, and they were neither abstainers nor heavy drinkers. We had to make this distinction—and it was not too difficult, because in our country, abstainers openly declare themselves and excessive drinkers boast about their capacity, so we were able to exclude both these people. The abstainers could not be used as subjects in this experiment because for them the unusual experience of drinking an alcoholic beverage might itself have a strong emotional impact. The heavy drinkers had to be excluded because of the special emotional meaning that alcohol might hold for them if they happened to be unrecognized problem drinkers or alcoholics.

The alcoholic beverage used in these studies was one containing 12 per cent alcohol. Each subject was tested with 50 ml, slightly under 2 oz, and 350 ml, slightly under 12 oz. The smaller amount produced an average maximum blood alcohol content of 0.015 per cent, and the larger amount, approximately 0.054 per cent. These are concentrations associated with the mildest effects of alcohol and, again, substantially below the level commonly associated with intoxication. In control test sessions, water was given instead of an alcoholic beverage. No attempt was made to disguise the fact that this was water and not alcohol, because in our experiences over many years we have found that it is virtually impossible to devise a placebo for alcohol. We thought we would succeed, and almost succeeded, when we tried a near beer, beer without alcohol, and sometimes secretly added to it up to 5 per cent alcohol. Although subjects didn't detect the difference in taste, after they had a few glasses of the laced beer, something happened inside them, and they knew they had had something different from "that other beer," so that there was a built-in block against using an effective placebo. Our procedure was blind so far as the experimenter was concerned, but the subject invariably knew. In all instances, the solution was drunk at the rate of 50 ml every three minutes.

Each test session, control or experimental, was divided into three periods: (a) the predrinking period; (b) the drinking period; and (c) the postdrinking period.

In order to maintain a reasonably constant level of emotional activity and correspondingly level state of basic skin conductance, the subjects were given a relatively simple and uniform task to perform throughout the tests. We discovered after many trials that we must provide something, and something uniform, for the subjects to do. Originally we tested one of our secretaries, sat her down in a room and just gave her nothing to do; she sat there for some considerable time, was utterly bored, and tended to fall asleep. In fact, sometimes she did fall asleep, with a corresponding change in the conductance of the skin going from the waking state to the sleeping state, so that we did not have a constant state. On another trial we gave her a popular magazine, "Certified Confessions" or something like that, and during this session there were wide variations in her skin conductance. As a by-product of curiosity, I noted what pages she was reading, and it occurred to me that this might be a way of screening possible best sellers, but we didn't pursue that. We finally found that we had to present the subject with a rather monotonous, constant kind of task to perform in order to maintain reasonably constant levels of emotional activity throughout the test period. The task which worked consisted of filing in alphabetical order a randomized assortment of IBM cards with names on them. The efficiency of this performance could be scored by the total number of cards filed per unit of time and the rate of errors in the total task.

Skin conductance was recorded throughout the entire duration of the experimental session. The measurements made during the predrinking period served as a control for the daily variation in conductance level in individual subjects. Although the skin conductance was recorded during the drinking period also, the card filing task was suspended during this time. The variability of this substituted activity of drinking, together with that associated with the drinking itself, resulted in unpredictable variations in emotional activity and skin conductance during the brief drinking period; the conductance data of this period of time were therefore not used. Card filing was resumed after the drinking ceased and conductance data obtained during this portion of the experimental session provided the measurement of the effect of the test beverages on the levels of basic emotional activation.

During the postdrinking period, the galvanic skin response (GSR) to an unexpected stress stimulus was tested in the following manner. Approximately one-half hour after the beginning of this period, a startling noise from an electric horn with an intensity of 97 db suddenly sounded for ten seconds. The resulting sudden sharp change in skin conductance was recorded and served as a quantitative measure of the emotional response to this sudden stress.

Briefly, the results of these experiments are as follows: With the consumption of 50 ml of the alcoholic beverage, the average predrinking basic conductance of 19.3 micromhos fell to a postdrinking basic conductance of 16.2 micromhos, a decrease of about 16 per cent in the measure taken here to represent emotional activation. With 350 ml of the alcoholic beverage, the average basic skin conduction fell to 12.8 micromhos, a decrease of about 33 per cent.

The effects of the alcohol consumption on the GSR were also clearly apparent. The mean magnitude of the GSR evoked by the auditory stimulus during the control postdrinking period, that is, when the test beverage was water, was 12 micromhos. With 50 ml of the alcoholic beverage, this value fell to an average of 11 micromhos, a decrease of 8 per cent. With 350 ml of the alcoholic beverage, the average fell to 5.6 micromhos, a decrease of 35 per cent. On the basis of presently accepted concepts relating skin conductance to activity of the central nervous system and to emotional activation, the basic skin conductance and the galvanic skin response as measured in these experiments have been taken as measures of the levels of emotional tension. The amounts of alcoholic beverage used in these studies appeared to diminish significantly this tension state or tension response.

THE MONOTONOUS TASK

In these experiments, the largest amounts of alcoholic beverage used, 350 ml of a 12 per cent alcohol solution, had no effect on the performance of the card-filing task. In view of the common generalization that alcohol diminishes efficiency of performance, this finding deserves some comment. It is, of course, true that alcohol in the amount used here may exercise an effect on some individual functions; I am sure it does. I mentioned earlier that such functions as may be affected at lower levels of alcohol consumption are only individual factors in the complexity of total function and behavior, and that caution should be exercised in drawing any inferences about those behaviors. While large enough amounts of alcohol unquestionably cause a deterioration of all performance and function, any accurate statement concerning the effects of smaller amounts of alcohol must include consideration of such relevant features as difficulty of the task, familiarity with the task, skill and ability of the performer, motivation, and so on.

A realistic and practical understanding of the extent to which, and why, various amounts of alcoholic beverages impair, or in some instances may perhaps improve, total performance, can be gained only by taking into account the factors other than alcohol itself that are significant for the maximum fulfillment of any particular kind of performance. The card-sorting task in the present study was a very simple one. It was not complex; it offered no intellectual challenge to the subjects. That its performance suffered no impairment is, I believe, an example of the matter I have just discussed.

If in the experimental findings I have described, the audiogenic seizures in the animals and the skin conductance of the human subjects are to be taken as manifestations or indexes of emotional tension, then the relatively small amounts of alcohol used may indeed be said to diminish tension. In exercising this effect, the alcohol is, by every definition, a tranquilizer. From our research point of view, this quality is consistent with the hypothesis that I suggested earlier to explain the very long and universal survival of the moderate use of alcoholic beverages. If this hypothesis is to be strengthened, or perhaps disproved, there is certainly need for further, more definitive research in the area that I have described.

Now from the discussion you have heard so far, from Dr. Balboni, Dr. Forsander, Dr. Goldberg, and others in this conference, and from what you will hear, I believe you will appreciate that any judgments on the merits—on the assets or the liabilities—of drinking must be made with considerable circumspection. You will recognize, I am sure, that the use of alcohol may be considered to be good or to be bad, to be right or to be wrong, depending on such features as the motivation for drinking, the nature of the drinking, the amount of drinking, the purpose and the circumstances of drinking. This whole matter is remindful of the case of the young lady who came into the doctor's office complaining of increasing ill health during the past three or four months. After a thorough examination the doctor sat her down and said, "Mrs. Jones, I have some good news for you—" She interrupted, saying, "It is *Miss* Jones, doctor." He continued, "Miss Jones, I have some bad news for you."

And on this note I shall terminate.

REFERENCES

Carpenter, J. A., Effects of Alcoholic Beverages on Skin Conductance. An Exploratory Study, *Quart. J. Studies Alc.*, **18**: 1–18, 1957
Carpenter, J. A., Effects of Alcohol on Some Psychological Processes. A Critical

Review with Special Reference to Automobile Driving Skill *Quart. J. Studies Alc.*, **23**:274–314, 1962.

Farris, E. J., Yeakel, E. H., and Medoff, H. S., Development of Hypertension in Emotional Gray Norway Rats after Air Blasting, *Am. J. Physiol.*, **144**:331–333, 1945.

Greenberg, L. A., The Definition of an Intoxicating Beverage *Quart. J. Studies Alc.*, **16**:313–335, 1955.

Greenberg, L. A., and Carpenter, J. A., The Effect of Alcoholic Beverages on Skin Conductance and Emotional Tension. I. Wine, Whisky and Alcohol, *Quart. J. Studies Alc.*, **18**:190–204, 1957.

Greenberg, L. A., and Lester, D., The Effect of Alcohol on Audiogenic Seizures of Rats, *Quart. J. Studies Alc.*, **14**:385–389, 1953.

Keller, M., The Definition of Alcoholism and the Estimation of Its Prevalence, in Pittman, D. J., and Snyder, C. R. (eds.) *Society, Culture and Drinking Patterns*, New York, Wiley, 1962, chap. 17, pp. 310–329.

Lindsley, D. B., Emotion, in Stevens, S. S. (ed.) *Handbook of Experimental Psychology*, New York, Wiley, 1951, pp. 473–516.

Woodworth, R. S., and Schlosberg, H., *Experimental Psychology*, New York, Holt, 1954.

Jules H. Masserman, M.D.

Professor of Neurology and Psychiatry
Northwestern University, Evanston, Illinois

ALCOHOL
AND NEUROTIC BEHAVIOR

Editor's Note *From the effects of alcohol on normal skilled performance (Drew) to its effects on normal emotional behavior (Greenberg), this section of the symposium proceeds to the relation between alcohol and neurotic behavior. Dr. Jules H. Masserman describes an extensive series of experiments with animals which are trained to perform various tasks in order to earn their food. Suddenly, instead of receiving food when they open the feeding apparatus, they are subjected to surprising fear-producing air blasts or electric shocks. They become "neurotic"—for example, they refuse to eat even when fed by hand. Given alcohol, at this point, their neurotic symptoms are relieved, and they return to more normal ways of behaving. If alcohol is given before the traumatic experience, the neurotic response may be averted. Finally, some of the animals whose neurotic symptoms were relieved by alcohol learn to like it so well that they then preferred food or drink containing alcohol—even though originally alcohol was so distasteful that they had to be forced to take it.*

Dr. Masserman draws parallels from these experiments to human behavior in the face of irresolvable conflict situations. He infers that in the case of some neurotic individuals, once they have discovered the relief that intoxicating amounts of alcohol can give in the circumstances of a "pervasively threatening and poignantly conflictful" environment, they become attached to this effective tranquilizer and cerebral depressant, to the degree that they become addicted.

A symposium (Greek, "drink together") such as this would seem to be an excellent occasion for some sober reflection.

Man is perhaps most clearly distinguished from all other creatures by one outstanding characteristic: he alone practices the ardent art of the alibi. Ever since Adam, and undeterred by the presence of God Himself, man has brazenly blamed Eve for all his troubles, and has sought to explain away his own personal and social defalcations

122

by various and vivid verbal evasions. Historically, these take two main forms: the allegation that he is possessed by devils, or the complaint that he is the victim of mysterious physical miasmas. Currently, the most popular version of both is that he suffers from "mental diseases," purportedly caused either by uncontrollable "instinct" (again, devils) or undetectable "metabolic imbalances" (again, miasmas). It was predictable that man would try to mitigate his guilts over one of his most ancient and avid modes of social rebellion —alcoholism—on the basis that this disease, too, was either an affliction by a different kind of "spirit," or a physiological martyrdom beyond his control.

As to the second of these wishful theses, I believe I can state that, in some thirty years of intensive interest, laboratory experiment, and clinical experience, I have yet to encounter convincingly controlled evidence for any consistent genetic, constitutional, dietary, infectious, or other purely physiological causes of alcoholism, apart from the fact that an excessive intake of alcohol or any other drug in poisonous amounts can injure and destroy body and brain tissue and thereby impair resistance and judgment, thus multiplying and accelerating the adverse *effects* of alcoholism. Addiction to drink, then, is a "disease" only in the sense that excessive smoking, gambling, or wandering are also "dis-eases"—that is, partly condoned ways in which men try to haze over, compensate for, challenge, or escape from protean states of un-ease. But these statements, too, might be considered arbitrary were it not possible to support them by direct recourse to man's three principal sources of data on which to build reliable inferences: the historical, the comparative, and the experimental.

There is considerable anthropological evidence that neolithic man, almost as soon as he turned from hunting to agriculture, began to use his crops for alcoholic fermentation as well as for food. This was understandable, since he lived in an age perhaps almost as dangerous as ours. Comparative ethnologic studies of later climes and cultures have likewise revealed that man has always prepared and imbibed alcohol to an extent and persistence determined not by vectors of physical disease but by personal stress, ready availability, and cultural experience. But perhaps the least equivocal evidence has come from the animals in our experimental laboratories, where it has been possible to show (*a*) that alcohol can be metabolized as a "stimulant" only in very small doses; (*b*) that in the amounts usually imbibed, it retards perception, disorganizes memory and judgment, and impairs higher skills; and (c) that these effects may be sought by "neurotic" organisms which have been subjected to stress and therefore wish to becloud their current milieu and escape from it into a state of semiautonomous forgetfulness. A brief review[1] of these experiments on the biopsychology of alcoholism may therefore be of psychiatric interest.

EFFECTS OF ALCOHOL ON NORMAL BEHAVIOR

Experiment 1 An animal is trained in progressively more difficult tasks: First, it learns to open a box to secure a pellet of food dropped by an automatic feeder; then it is taught to delay this response until various sound or light signals have been given; next, it learns to manipulate an electric switch to work the required signals and the feeder; and, finally, it solves increasingly difficult problems of working the switch despite changes in its position and the intervention of various barriers. Now, if the animal is induced by thirst to drink a small amount of a dilute alcohol solution (0.5 cc to 1.2 cc of 95 per cent alcohol per kilogram of body weight), the most complex and recently learned adaptive patterns disappear first. For instance, the animal can no longer solve a difficult approach to the switch but can still work the switch if it is made more easily available, after which the animal responds to the signals and opens the box with only a minimal loss of efficiency. However, if progressively larger amounts of alcohol are given and absorbed, the animal gradually loses the capacity to work the switch in any position. Next, the discriminated "meaning" of the signals becomes impaired; then the animal can no longer find or open the food box, although it may avidly take food offered directly. Finally, the animal enters into an alcoholic stupor in which all stimuli—even the food itself—cease to have any apparent significance. Conversely, as the animal recovers from the drug, its responses return in reverse order: First, it begins to take food from the box; then, to respond to the feeding signals; next, it recovers its ability to work the switch in simple position; and,

[1] Adapted from my text book, *Principles of Dynamic Psychiatry*, 2d ed., Philadelphia, Saunders, 1961. These experiments are illustrated by photographs included in that volume, and by two motion-picture films entitled, "Alcohol as a Preventative of Experimental Neuroses" and "Neurosis and Alcohol, An Experimental Study," prepared by the author and distributed by the Psychological Cinema Register, Pennsylvania State University.

finally, it regains its capacity to solve increasingly complex approaches to the switch and food box. In short, alcohol in sufficient amount apparently disorganizes learned skills until only the most elementary associations remain; conversely, as the animal recovers, it regains its abilities in their order of learned complexity and efficiency.

PRODUCTION OF AN EXPERIMENTAL NEUROSIS

Experiment 2 A cat (or a rat, dog, or monkey) is first trained to respond to the flash of a light or the sound of a bell, or to both signals together, by opening a box to secure a pellet of food. It is then further trained to depress a switch to operate these feeding signals at will. During the period of its training the animal is friendly to the experimenter, enters the training cage eagerly, and operates the switch readily and effectively; indeed, the animal sometimes continues to do so even after its hunger is satiated.

If, however, on several irregularly spaced occasions the animal is permitted to work the switch and reach for the food but is at that moment subjected to a mild, physiologically harmless, but unexpected air blast or electric shock, the situation obviously becomes motivationally conflictful. The switch-signal configuration still represents the possibility of satisfying hunger, provided the animal responds with its learned adaptive behavior of taking the food deposited in the box. But the same situation now also threatens the animal with an unpleasant experience which can be avoided only by an exactly opposite pattern of behavior. In effect, then, urgent needs and their incompatible patterns of expression are in conflict. Under these circumstances, remarkable changes in the total behavior of the animal occur along lines that so clearly correspond to neurotic patterns in the human being that, for purposes of comparison, the two may be described under the following headings.

Anxiety The animal crouches and trembles with hair erect and dilated pupils; it breathes rapidly, shallowly, and irregularly and has a fast, pounding pulse and a markedly increased blood pressure. Special studies reveal other bodily changes indicative of the mobilization of various physiological resources and "emergency mechanisms" which parallel those that accompany the subjective experience of normal and neurotic anxiety in the human.

Phobias and startle reactions The manifestations of anxiety increase markedly when the light or bell signals are given, when the animal is forced toward the food box by a movable barrier, or when, though hungry, it is offered food pellets similar to those that it formerly secured in the box. Moreover, these aversions quickly become more generalized: the animal resists being put into the experimental cage and immediately attempts to escape from it; it avoids the experimental room and, in many cases, the experimenter himself. Similarly, even when it is replaced in its accustomed home cage, it shows severe startle reactions to, and fear of, sudden lights or sounds, constricted spaces, or restraint.

ALCOHOL AS A PREVENTIVE OF NEUROSES

Experiment 3 A normal animal, trained as in Experiment 1, is given 1 cc of ethyl alcohol per kilogram of body weight and, while mildly intoxicated, is subjected every second day over a period of months to various intensities of unexpected air blasts or electric shocks or both at the moment of food-taking, as in Experiment 2. These ordinarily "neurotigenic" traumas, if sufficiently severe and frequent, may induce mild and transient hesitation in feeding, but the animal develops none of the dramatic and persistent symptoms of the usual neurosis. However, if the preventive doses of alcohol are discontinued and the animal is subjected to the same conflictful experiences for a few more days, a full-blown neurosis develops.

The analogy with human experiences hardly needs elaboration. Wine was the first anesthetic—a nepenthic administered to cloud the imminence and mitigate the horrors of primitive surgery, and some of us still are inclined to take a "bracer" before asking for a raise, proposing marriage, or undertaking some other presumably dangerous experience.

EFFECTS OF ALCOHOL ON NEUROTIC BEHAVIOR

Experiment 4 A sober animal is permitted to work the switch for food and is then made neurotic as in Experiment 2. As described, the animal develops a highly complicated set of behavioral aberrations: various inhibitions, aversions, phobias, compulsions, regressions, etc. Now, if the animal is again forced by thirst to drink a 10 per cent solution of alcohol at a dose of about 1 cc per kg of body weight, these complex reactions are also partially disintegrated as described in Experiment 1, this time permitting earlier, simpler, and more directly goal-orientated (i.e., more "normal") responses to break through.

Thus, when a neurotic animal is mildly intoxicated, its phobic aversions are sufficiently diminished so that it may spontaneously work the switch and feed on signal, and may thereafter be more easily induced to do so when sober.

Of course, the alcohol has no specifically selective effect on the neurotic symptoms; on the contrary, all behavior patterns are affected. As a result, intoxicated animals, whether normal or neurotic, show ataxia, confusion, repetitious movements, fragmentation of whole responses, and disturbances in goal-orientation. Nevertheless, along with these general effects there occurs a particular disorganization of the highly complex neurotic patterns themselves, so that, with small doses of alcohol, more nearly elementary and better-established reactions such as dominance-assertion or simple feeding on signal remain relatively intact and reappear in overt behavior.

NEUROSIS AND ALCOHOL ADDICTION

Experiment 5 Of all the animals who experienced an alleviation of neurotic symptoms during repeated mild intoxications, about half apparently associated the smell or taste of alcohol with this relief from tension, fear, and inhibition and began to prefer food or milk containing alcohol to plain food or milk; that is, they showed behavior characteristic of "alcohol addiction" until their underlying conflicts were alleviated by various means analogous to those used in the treatment of human neuroses.

HUMAN PARALLELS IN MOTIVATIONAL CONFLICT

Can these "hothouse" observations in the laboratory be meaningfully compared with human experiences? Possibly so. Let us consider a military trainee who, without adequate preparation or "seasoning," is suddenly subjected to the carnage, destruction, and immediate personal danger attendant on front-line combat. All his motivations are, of course, self-preservative; but he cannot implement them through immediate escape because, at the same time, deeply ingrained and contrary patterns of self-preservation through patriotism, group loyalties, hostility against a common enemy, and considerations of his social safety confine him to the battlefield. He is, therefore, torn between insistent but apparently mutually exclusive patterns of adaptation which make it impossible for him to resolve the situation by the usual devices of compromise, flight, or fight. If, then, his integrative capacities are further weakened by illness, fatigue, thirst, starvation, etc., he becomes incapable of handling the disruptive internal stresses so engendered and begins to suffer overwhelming anxiety accompanied by severe physiological dysfunctions such as tachycardia, tremors, gastrointestinal dysfunctions, motor disturbances, alterations of consciousness, etc. At this point he may actually welcome even a moderately serious wound, or inflict one on himself, and feel elation instead of pain while being evacuated. Thereafter, any threatened return to the site of his traumatic experiences, actual or fancied, induces a recurrence of his anxiety to the point of panic; and even in the relative safety of the base hospital he shows hypersensitivity and phobic reactions to any event symbolic of these experiences. For instance, bedrails cannot be tolerated because they are reminiscent of the inescapable confinement of the fox hole, and the buzz of a fly, or the striking of a match, produces reactions comparable to those produced by the dive of a strafing plane or the explosion of a mortarshell. Would he not welcome any surcease from this nightmare memory and harrowing experience, including that offered by drugs?

CLINICAL OBSERVATIONS

Objective studies have shown that from a psychiatric and psychoanalytic standpoint, the intake of alcohol or other hypnotic drugs clouds attention and perception, ameliorates tension by partially dissolving repressions and inhibitions (i.e., unconscious fears of the consequences of an act), and thereby permits previously repressed drives to find release in action. Many of the behavior patterns that thus find expression are, as may be suspected, also regressive in nature: the alcoholic titillates his "oral" desires with his bottle, becomes maudlin and sentimentally dependent while drunk, and may continue to intoxicate himself into a dreamy torpor which, unfortunately, the toxic effects of the drug may change into delirium. In many cultures, behavioral aberrations under such circumstances receive some measure of social sanction, in that alcoholism is accepted to a considerable degree as a mitigating circumstance for the expression of erotic (including homosexual), aggressive, or destructive behavior that would be severely condemned in the completely sober individual. Small wonder, then, that a neurotic who has found these escapes from intrapersonal and social conflict—however illusory and evanescent such escapes may be—should continue to misuse the drug to the point of becoming addicted.

GENERAL SIGNIFICANCE

There is little doubt that alcohol, morphine, the barbiturates and bromides, and most of the so-called "tranquilizers," act as cerebral depressants, causing impairment of finer perceptions and discriminations, constriction of thought, and progressive disorganization of adaptive responses. As has been seen, however, these effects, once experienced, would continue to be "desired" by a neurotic individual to whom the environment had become pervasively threatening and poignantly conflictful, since under such circumstances, transient but welcome relief would be afforded by ingesting a drug that blurred and disorganized anxiety, diminished inhibitions, and facilitated a regression to a relatively elementary need-fulfilling behavior.

As already indicated, mankind has nearly always and everywhere concocted and consumed various nepenthics (such as volatile ethers and alcohols, and substances allied to mescal, marihuana, and the opiates) to guard or to release him from real and fantasied threats of disappointment or injury. Physicians therefore have a long experiential precedent for prescribing, under proper conditions and adequate controls, sedative or hypnotic drugs in measured doses to troubled patients to dull their perceptions, blunt their fears, and give them temporary but welcome surcease from anxiety until their underlying conflicts can be resolved. However, we must recognize that drug therapy is inextricably associated with (a) each patient's unique fantasies of dependent allegiances ("my doctor's special remedy," or "a toast to the Queen"); (b) group-belongingness through social drinking; and (c) superordinal and mystic connotations (religious rituals, "miracle drugs," etc.); indeed, these may far overbalance the pharmacological actions of the drug itself. Because of such symbolisms, and because of the availability of many drugs, neurotics readily become habituated. There are possibly five million alcoholics, and uncountable numbers of addicts to barbiturates, ataractics, and opiates, in the United States alone.

Franz Alexander, M.D.

Director, Psychiatric and Psychosomatic Research Institute,
Mount Sinai Hospital, Los Angeles, California

ALCOHOL
AND BEHAVIORAL DISORDER
—ALCOHOLISM

Editor's Note   Dr. Franz Alexander delivered his presentation in the section on The Social Implications of Alcohol. His thesis, however, follows so logically upon the preceding presentations, that it has been deemed appropriate to include it here. Dr. Alexander, from the viewpoint of clinical psychiatry—as Dr. Masserman did from the viewpoint of experimental psychiatry—deals with the question of causality and alcoholism. He discusses types of alcoholism as reported in the older psychiatric writings; then, from his own contemporary viewpoint, he relates the origin of alcoholism to psychodynamic concepts derived from psychoanalytic theory. In this light he also explains the therapeutic effectiveness of such a fellowship as Alcoholics Anonymous. Nevertheless, Dr. Alexander warns against monocausal explanations of alcoholism. He believes that a genetic constitutional factor may be necessary, and that the cultural milieu too must contribute its share before an individual will choose alcoholism as the way of responding to his emotional troubles.

Alcoholism offers a paramount example of the need for a comprehensive multidisciplinary approach in psychiatry. Man is a complex biochemical machinery, an individual person with a unique family history, and also a member of a cultural system. All these three parameters, the biological, the individual-psychological, and the sociological, are necessary to describe alcoholism, to understand it, and to approach it therapeutically. Arguments that it is primarily a biochemical or a psychological or a sociological problem are meaningless and defeat our aim to control this vital problem. The proper planning of a conference like this requires an orderly division of the problem into its different aspects, and their assignment to different persons who have an expert knowledge of biochemistry, psychology, and sociology. These three aspects of the problem are, however, so intertwined that anyone who would attempt to restrict his contribution entirely to one of these avenues of approach would give not only a one-sided but a distorted picture. Bearing this in mind, I shall focus my presentation on the individual-psychological approach, but I shall try to discuss the psychological in its relation to biological and sociological considerations. In fact, my emphasis is to show that the psychological-motivational, the biological, and the sociological factors are highly interdependent.

Generally, the consumption of alcohol is condoned in our culture, is in certain subcultural groups enthusiastically approved; in others, looked upon with reservation; and again in others, frowned upon; among certain minorities it is strictly outlawed. This variance in cultural acceptance makes a medical definition of alcoholism difficult. The answer to the question, when should it be considered a medical or a psychiatric problem, depends to a high degree upon culturally determined value judgments. Is the member of the fashionable cocktail set, who practically every evening returns in his chauffeured car to his home in a semistuporous state, less a medical or a psychiatric problem than the inhabitant of skid row who has developed his own system to reach his flophouse bed in a drunken state? The main difference is that the latter constitutes a public charge, the former not at all. The liver cells, however, do not care whether their owner is a socialite or a day laborer. The medical sequelae in both cases may be identical; the social consequences, however, are substantially different. The socialite is likely to land in a private sanatorium, or at Alcoholics Anonymous, or in the office of a psychoanalyst; the man from skid row—at best, in a county hospital, more likely in a jail. Unfortunately, reliable statistics to show which of the two has a greater chance for ultimate recovery are lacking.

CRITIQUE OF OLDER CLASSIFICATIONS

Classification based on description of overt, directly observable behavior of large numbers of cases is of little value for meaningful definition or etiological understanding or treatment. Only intensive study of the multiplicity of etiological factors in individual cases can give us an understanding of alcoholism as a medical and social problem. The descriptive behavioral and statistical approach has been long dominant in clinical psychiatry, as best exemplified by Kraepelin's treatment of this subject. From this we learn about the frequency of alcohol abuse in different psychiatric diseases in the early part of this century. Kraepelin found it in over 40 per cent of epileptics and patients with traumatic neuroses, very commonly among arteriosclerotics, but much less frequently among dementia praecox patients, hysterics, and manic-depressives. The meaning of these correlations, whether etiological or secondary, remains completely unclear. From the studies of Kraepelin and his followers we also learn that alcohol abuse was more common among men than among women, and among the Germanic nations than among Mohammedans, Buddhists, or Mormons. Statistical findings of older clinicians seemed to indicate that alcoholism has an effect upon descendants; that stillbirth and miscarriage were more prevalent in the families of alcohol abusers; and that the occurrence of idiocy was more common in children who were conceived during intoxication. A genetic factor in alcoholics was postulated based on such findings as those of Bonhoeffer that 35 per cent of beggars and vagrants and 44.7 per cent of prostitutes come from "alcoholic families" [Kraepelin]. The social, psychological, and biological factors were never clearly differentiated in this type of crude statistical investigation. It can be safely stated that this chaotic uncritical correlation of highly undifferentiated and heterogeneous variables threw little light on this complex problem but caused a great deal of confusion and faulty conclusions. The same can be said for the improved and somewhat more critical statistical studies of recent times. The greatest emphasis in research has been on the secondary effects of alcohol upon brain and other body functions, as well as on the clinical, particularly psychiatric sequelae of chronic excessive alcohol consumption, of which delirium tremens and Korsakoff's psychosis are outstanding examples.

In my presentation I shall restrict myself to etiological considerations, to the discussion of factors which lead to continued excessive consumption of alcohol.

PSYCHODYNAMIC FORMULATIONS

Since drinking is a voluntary act which has both conscious and unconscious motivations, the psychological approach offers itself as a natural point of departure for systematic analysis of the etiological variables involved in alcoholism. Most psychiatric authors differentiate between two types of alcoholism, between a less and a more malignant form. Knight, who approached the problem by means of psychoanalytic observation and therapy, distinguishes three kinds of alcoholics: the "symptomatic drinker," who coincides with what colloquially is called "social drinker"; the "reactive alcoholic"; and the essential alcoholic. Reactive alcoholism, however, is only the secondary incidental result of some underlying psychopathology and is not a primary symptom. Accordingly, Knight's classification deals primarily with two groups: a more and a less severe form of alcoholism.

Early psychoanalytic authors, such as Freud, Abraham, Ferenczi, and others, drew their conclusions from more or less incidental observations of individual cases. Theirs were not systematic clinical studies of serial cases, but observations of random patients who incidentally came to their attention in private practice. This was a fortunate beginning, showing the value of the intensive study of a small number of cases in contrast to statistical observations made on large numbers. The paramount questions—how an individual person actually becomes a confirmed alcoholic, what function alcohol plays in his emotional household, what perpetuates the habit—cannot be resolved by the superficial study of overt behavioral manifestations and their statistical correlation. Such correlations may be most useful in raising questions, but these questions can be answered only by the intensive study of individuals. The statistician may find that orthodox Jews drink less than Irish Catholics, but only the intensive biographical study of representatives of these two groups will reveal the basis of this statistical correlation. In the light of the psychodynamic findings of the early psychoanalytic authors, these types of statistical distributions may become meaningful.

These early psychoanalytic authors stressed the disinhibiting effect of alcohol, which reduces repressions and permits a freer expression of ego-alien, mostly infantile, cravings. Under the effect of alcohol certain controls of behavior acquired during the process of biological and social maturation, cultural standards superimposed upon a more primitive state of organization, are reduced in their effectiveness. Moreover, speech becomes less coherent, muscle coordination diminishes, and thinking regresses in the direction of the primary process. All the shackles of the progressive organization of behavior, the adaptation to increasing biological independence and to cultural standards, are loosened, and the happiness of the less responsible, less self-reliant state of childhood is temporarily recaptured. Isolated observations of this kind are so numerous that it would be pointless to refer to authors.

Alcohol obviously favors the ever-present regressive trend to escape from the hardships of the relentlessly recurring adaptive tasks, which is an integral part of the serious business of living.

Among the repressed tendencies which can be mobilized by alcohol, oral-dependent and passive homosexual cravings were observed by the early psychoanalytic investigators. Since passive homosexual trends are as a rule superimposed upon oral trends, the latter seem to be the more specific psychological factor in alcoholism. Also, repressed or inhibited heterosexual and hostile impulses are mentioned by several observers. Radó postulated that alcohol intoxication allows a regression to a very early quasi-orgastic sensation in which the whole alimentary tract is involved; he referred to this phenomenon as alimentary orgasm. The "narcotic super-pleasure," according to Radó [1957], is "a derivation of alimentary orgasm."

In my own observations I was impressed—as were Knight [1937b] and Radó [1957]—by the cyclic effects of excessive drinking, as practiced in alcoholism, which constitute a vicious circle consisting of three phases. The first phase consists in elation, lack of inhibitions, and freer expression of inhibited or repressed trends. Then follows the second, the depressive phase, obviously resulting from the gradually increasing paralyzing effect of alcohol. Finally, after sobering up, the original emotional stressful situation from which the patient tried to get relief by drinking returns with an added stress, namely, the sense of guilt and shame with which the patient reacts to his alcoholic excess. This is the hangover, which induces the patient to seek again temporary stimulation from alcohol, which at the same time relieves his self-accusations by dulling higher discriminatory judgment.

Most psychodynamic studies found, as the paramount underlying motivational factor in alcoholism, the oral-incorporative urge, the trend toward returning to the earliest form of gratification in the nursing situation. Knight [1937b] believes that this oral fixation is due to a specific family configuration: an indulgent mother married to an inconsistent father. The orally indulged child does not learn self-control and reacts with rage to every frustration. The inconsistent father aggravates the emotional instability by his unpredictable—now indulgent, now tyrannically forbidding—attitude. Mother and father's characteristic behavior mutually reinforces the child's intolerance of frustration and favors his oral fixation. One has to discriminate in the motivational dynamics of the alcoholic two distinct factors: (1) escape from stress; and (2) seeking the regressive gratification of repressed or inhibited impulses.

The *escape factor* is less specific. Alcohol may serve to relieve almost any kind of emotional stress, be it anxiety, shame, guilt, or feelings of insecurity in general. Different psychiatric and psycho-analytic authors convincingly described these different kinds of emotional inducements to drink to excess, such as inferiority feelings resulting from excessive inhibitions and manifesting themselves in great shyness, in pent-up and never expressed resentments, and also in inhibition of sexual cravings. Such observations were so widespread that it would be pointless to quote special contributions. When such an inhibited person discovers the magic effect of alcohol, which makes him feel self-confident, daring and enterprising, the experiential basis is set for recurrent indulgence to the point of relief. Whenever adverse turns of events in life—such as failures in professional ambitions and in love relations—increase these emotional frustrations, the lure of alcoholic indulgence may become irresistible. Although this experience of freedom from emotional restrictions in itself is highly gratifying, the essential attraction consists in the relief from self-defeating inhibitions and their emotional consequences.

The *gratification component* derived from drinking appears to be more specific: the reestablishment of the bliss of an oral-dependent satiation, as well as of infantile omnipotence, which in Radó's concept of alimentary orgasm appears in the purest form, and which later he called also "narcotic elation" and "narcotic super-pleasure."

According to Knight, the prevalence of the urge to gratify oral cravings differentiates the malignant cases, which he calls essential alcoholics. In the reactive alcoholic this oral fixation is less significant; he drinks to escape from current stress situations occasioned by traumatic turns of events in his life.

On the basis of my own clinical observations, I think it is justifiable to distinguish between two groups of alcoholics. In the first group the *escape from an emotional stress situation* of no specific nature is the main issue, an escape which is achieved by the pharmaco-psychic effects of alcohol which cloud the highest discriminatory and self-critical functions and relieve the emotional distress caused by external vicissitudes. This group can well be contrasted with the second one, in which the element of *regressive gratification* prevails, primarily the gratification of oral impulses. However, this feeling of gratification is more complex than the mere satisfaction of an isolated drive.

Radó well characterized the gratification the alcoholic experiences as the bliss derived from the reestablishment of the omnipotent feeling of the infant not yet hampered either by recognition of the hard facts of the external world nor by the self-critical faculties which gradually, in the course of life, inexorably whittle down the illusion of infantile omnipotence.

Lolli describes the emotional content of the alcoholic's gratification in quite similar terms—the satisfaction of the longing for "physical warmth," "pleasurable skin sensations," "maternal coddling," "liquid and warm feelings in his stomach," which are differentiated from longings for security, reassurance, self-respect, independence, and, at times, omnipotence. He sees the essence of the alcoholic's fulfillment in the experience of an undifferentiated pleasure of body and mind in union. These blended pleasure sensations which the alcoholic cannot achieve in any other way are believed by Lolli to be at the root of the addiction.

Although these reconstructions of the psychodynamic background of alcoholism, particularly the differentiation between the escape and the gratification component, are well established, yet they do not sufficiently account for the entirety of the problem. These psychodynamic factors can only be evaluated properly in the light of sociological and biological considerations.

SOCIOLOGICAL COMPONENTS

In order to demonstrate the interrelatedness of the psychological and sociological factors, I shall refer only to a few examples of the steadily growing literature on this subject. Abraham Myerson many years ago called attention to the relative infrequency of alcoholism among certain ascetic Protestant sects, such as Christian Scientists, Mennonites, and Quakers, as well as among orthodox Jews, in contrast to its relative frequency among nonascetic Protestants and Irish Catholics. Isidor Thorner attempted to account for these differences by indicating differences in group values as well as in child-rearing practices. The supreme social ideal of self-control, together with contempt for uninhibited indulgences, is inculcated in the members of these ascetic social groups through lifelong education. It appears, though this is not yet demonstrated, that the psychodynamic mechanism responsible for the high frequency of abstinence in these societal groups consists of successful repression. An added psychological factor among orthodox Jews is the strong internal solidarity prevailing in this minority group, which makes it resistant to the mores of the majority group.

Of course such group influences in themselves are of a psychological nature, just as are the individual influences prevailing in each family, depending upon the idiosyncratic qualities of the parents. Since families belonging to the same cultural group share the same group ideals, their attitudes toward their children necessarily will have common features. This explains the statistical frequency of certain types of behavior in members belonging to the same culture. As to their psychological mode of action, there is no difference between cultural and individual influences upon personality development. The origin of group ideals itself is, however, no longer a purely psychological problem. They can only be understood in the light of the total social structure of the prevailing social institutions—all this viewed, of course, from an historical perspective. Group ethos is the result of the history of a culture, just as individual personality is the outcome of the person's life history. The topic, how group ideals develop, is beyond the scope of the present discussion. Their influence upon the individual in possibly preparing the soil for alcoholism, however, is a psychological problem which must be studied by the same methods as the influence of such an incidental combination as an indulgent mother married to an inconsistent father.

Alcoholics Anonymous. The influence of the group can be aptly observed in the singular therapeutic successes of Alcoholics Anonymous. The study of Alcoholics Anonymous offers a suitable approach to the appraisal of etiological factors, because it is open to the psychoanalyst who frequently has opportunity to study members of this organization under the psychological microscope.

Identification with a group which does not condone drinking by its members and yet is neither punitive nor contemptuous toward the alcoholic allows him to gratify his dependent needs without inner conflict, something he never could do in the past. This gratification of dependency needs is not interfered with by shame or by rebellion toward the person or persons upon whom the patient depends. Moreover, the member of Alcoholics Anonymous is not only a recipient of help but becomes a helper himself. This restores his internal equilibrium by elevating his self-esteem, by eliminating the shame for his childish dependency. As a member of the group he can receive help without shame because at the same time he gives help; he need not feel such a helpless and worthless being. Also, his guilt reactions are reduced because he is not censored. This eliminates reactive hostility and rebellion, which is the main source of guilt feelings. He finds emotional support which is not personalized but is distributed among the whole group and emanates eventually from a Supreme Being. By giving help to fellow sufferers with whom he can identify himself to a high degree, he receives vicarious gratification for his dependent needs. Above all, in the spirit of the group there is no place for hostility or rebellion because there is no censorship or scorn.

THE PHYSIOLOGICAL COMPONENT

Focusing our interest exclusively on the psychodynamic factors—both on individual and culturally shared influences—should not make us forget an important biological factor which may be decisive in the most malignant cases. I mean the physiological constitution. There are reliable clinical observations indicating a striking difference in susceptibility toward alcohol in different persons. These differences do not seem to be fully explainable as differences in personality structure resulting from postnatal experiences. Moreover, in advanced cases, another physiological factor, which is more important in other drug addictions, is indicated, namely, the physiological adaptation of the organism to the drug. This may be partially responsible for the uncontrollable power of the craving. It can be safely assumed that not every person who comes from a family with an indulgent mother and inconsistent father will necessarily become an alcoholic. Knight assumes that the oral fixation and lack of self-discipline can be traced back to early experiences in the family. The family constellation of indulgent mother and inconsistent father is, however, much more common than the occurrence of the malignant form of alcoholism. It is strongly indicated that in addition to family influences, oral fixation may be the result of a nutritional deficiency related to a type of metabolic block attributable to a specific enzyme structure of the individual, as assumed by Roger Williams in his genetotrophic theory of alcoholism. Williams observed, in experiments with rats, that the tendency of the animals to consume alcohol was increased by certain nutritional deficiencies in their food supply and could be reduced by supplying the omitted nutritional components. Furthermore, he also observed a native difference among different strains of rats in their tendency to consume alcohol. His critics, such as Popham, and Lester and Greenberg, have pointed out that his observations did not prove at all that a specific craving for alcohol is increased in these animals through nutritional deficiencies. The specific nature of the craving, however, is not essential and does not contradict the gist of Williams's hypothesis. The animal experiments show an increase of an incorporative urge due to metabolic factors. It is quite consistent with our present knowledge of conditioning that if this undifferentiated craving becomes coupled through repetition with the pleasurable sensation following the ingestion of alcohol, a specific craving for alcohol might develop.

Although the conclusion of Williams, from his study of a relatively small group of human subjects, that the alcoholic has a specific metabolic individuality distinguishing him from the nonalcoholic has been challenged, yet on the basis of common clinical and everyday experiences, its validity appears highly probable. Full experimental proof, however, still remains to be furnished.

A similar assumption has been made by I. Arthur Mirsky, who collaborated with Therese Benedek in a psychoanalytic study of diabetics conducted at the Chicago Institute of Psychoanalysis. In these patients, from the early beginnings of life, an extreme oral-demanding attitude can be observed, an attitude which may not be fully explained by psychological experiences within the family. Mirsky suggested that, in addition to early oral frustrations, diabetics may have defective physiological constitutions contributing to their oral insatiability. This is indicated by the familial nature of the disease. A child with this strong physiologically determined oral demandingness is likely to provoke in the mother defense reactions which, in turn, reinforce the oral cravings of the child.

Masserman and Yum have thrown light not so much on the gratification factor as on the escape factor involved in alcoholism. They succeeded, by the administration of alcohol, in abolishing conditioned responses in cats and also in protecting them from developing experimental neurosis. By its distintegrating effect on behavioral patterns acquired through conditioning, alcohol in these animals disintegrated also those neurotic patterns which they acquired through conditioning. In other words, the animals experienced a relief from neurotic patterns by the ingestion of alcohol, which they developed from conditioning. In experiments by Conger, albino rats under the effect of alcohol overcame their fear of approaching the feeding box which gave them electric shocks whenever they came in contact with it. These rats became more daring under the influence of alcohol, just as humans do who take alcohol to overcome their lifelong inhibitions which they acquired through the interpersonal experiences of their past history.

All that has been said speaks against a monocausal explanation. It is most probable that the genetotrophic factor alone in most cases would not lead to malignant forms of alcoholism without additional interpersonal experiences which further contribute to the development of oral fixation and to the lack of internal discipline postulated by Knight and, before him, by others. Moreover, both the genetotrophic factor and early interpersonal experiences may be counteracted and neutralized by cultural influences which introduce into the child's personality in his early years a value system which emphasizes self-control and aversion against indulgences.

The complexity of the problem should warn us against trying to isolate one single category of factors in the etiology of alcoholism.

The implications of such a multifactor position for therapy and prevention are obviously far-reaching.

REFERENCES

Alexander, F., Remarks about the Relation of Inferiority Feelings to Guilt Feelings, *Int. J. Psycho-Anal.*, 19:41–49, 1938.

Alexander, F., *Fundamentals of Psychoanalysis*, New York, Norton, 1948.

Alexander, F., "Views on the Etiology of Alcoholism: The Psychodynamic View," Conference on Alcoholism as a Medical Problem, New York, N.Y. Acad. Med., October 7, 1954.

Conger, J. J., The Effects of Alcohol on Conflict Behavior in the Albino Rat, *Quart. J. Studies Alc.*, 12:1–29, 1951.

Knight, R. P., The Dynamics and Treatment of Chronic Alcohol Addiction, *Bull. Menninger Clin.*, 1:233–250, 1937a.

Knight, R. P., The Psychodynamics of Chronic Alcoholism, *J. Nervous Mental Disease*, 86:538–548, 1937b.

Kraepelin, E., *Psychiatrie* (Psychiatry), 8th ed., Leipzig, Barth, 1910, vol. 2.

Lester, D., and Greenberg, L. A., Nutrition and the Etiology of Alcoholism, *Quart. J. Studies Alc.*, 13:553–560, 1952.

Lolli, G., Alcoholism As a Disorder of the Love Disposition, *Quart. J. Studies Alc.*, 17:96–107, 1956.

Masserman, J. H., and Yum, K. S., An Analysis of the Influence of Alcohol on Experimental Neuroses in Cats, *Psychosom. Med.*, 8:36–52, 1946.

Mirsky, I. A., Emotional Factors in the Patient with Diabetes Mellitus, *Bull. Menninger Clin.*, 12:187–194, 1948.

Mirsky, I. A., Physiologic, Psychologic, and Social Determinants in the Etiology of Duodenal Ulcer, *Am. J. Digest. Diseases*, 3(N.S.):285–314, 1958.

Myerson, A., The Treatment of Alcohol Addiction in Relation to the Prevention of Inebriety, *Quart. J. Studies Alc.*, 5:189–199, 1944.

Popham, R. E., A Critique of the Genetotrophic Theory of the Etiology of Alcoholism, *Quart. J. Studies Alc.*, 14:228–237, 1953.

Radó, S., The Psychic Effects of Intoxicants: An Attempt To Evolve a Psychoanalytic Theory of Morbid Cravings, *Int. J. Psycho-Anal.*, 7:396–413, 1926.

Radó, S., Narcotic Bondage, *Am. J. Psychiat.*, 114:165–170, 1957.

Thorner, I., Ascetic Protestantism and Alcoholism, *Psychiatry*, 16:167–176, 1953.

Williams, R., *Nutrition and Alcoholism*, Norman, University of Oklahoma Press, 1951.

PANEL DISCUSSION

THE EFFECTS
OF ALCOHOL ON BEHAVIOR
AND EMOTION

Moderator Dr. Karl H. Pribram
Participants Prof. George C. Drew, Dr. Leon A. Greenberg, and
Dr. Jules H. Masserman

Dr. Pribram I thought I would begin by reversing the order
of the presentation and get Dr. Masserman to tell us what he didn't
get a chance to tell us before.

I have two questions for him. First, the question he raised himself: the problem of individual differences. Have you an idea, Dr.
Masserman, why some of the cats did take to alcohol to alleviate
their neuroses and others did not?

Dr. Masserman We only have half an hour for the entire
panel, and this is a question that has agitated psychiatrists and all
thinking humans from time immemorial! I can tell you some of the
vectors that need analysis, and the first, of course, is genetics. It is
perfectly possible to demonstrate, for example, that closely allied
species of monkeys will respond quite differently to the exact same
stress. Given the same stressful experience, the cat monkey will
develop sexual aberrations that are peculiar even in a monkey; the
spider monkey will become exceedingly dependent, whereas other
monkeys will become homicidal. I know that these monkeys are
slightly different genetically; and I know it certainly has much to do
with very early postnatal experiences. It is possible, and it is a little
troublesome to me, to demonstrate that if you take a very young
cat monkey home and raise it among devoted foster parents—
human foster parents—who don't happen to be afraid of snakes, it
grows up so that it will pick up a snake and is not particularly afraid
of snakes; if, however, the same monkey is raised by its monkey
mother, who presumably is afraid of snakes, she somehow transmits
this to her offspring. Postnatal experiences later on in life certainly
also have much to do with this.

There are, moreover, some indications that the mother's own life

142

experience may have some effect on the behavior of her offspring. This is because of the effects of the mother's experiences on her own metabolic, physiological, and psychological make-up—three of the major influences on later behavior.

Dr. Pribram The second question I had was that you characterize neurotic behavior, or even behavior which looks psychotic, as the more complicated or more complex type of behavior. Would you mind telling us a little bit about that? I think people as a rule have been unaware of the notion that the neurotic type of behavior is the more complicated type.

Dr. Masserman This is in line with what I said, neurotic behavior being the last and most difficult. We have some experimental observations on this. For example, you train an animal to push a switch three times to get a food pellet, which is a fairly complex thing to do. Then you change the training so that the animal need push it only once, and you keep the one-time push over a period of months. Now if you give the animal a large dose of alcohol, it will go back to the three-time push. This has been noted by a good many people who have investigated the effect of electro-shock at a surgical operation. In the field of languages, for example, a person with brain trauma might go back to a highly complex language he used formerly, such as Arabic. It is not necessarily a question of the most complex that is disrupted but the most recent.

Dr. Pribram Thank you. Now we will take off on something else that you mentioned with regard to the problems of expectation: that unless the fear-like behavior has been produced by a change in the expectation, it does not produce neurosis. And I should like to go to Dr. Greenberg's paper with regard to this problem.

Dr. Greenberg, you used galvanic skin response as an index of what you call emotionality. Alcohol is known to cause dilatation of blood vessels. Do you think that perhaps some of your findings could be due to the fact that vasodilatation was produced by the alcohol rather than any change in the emotionality?

Dr. Greenberg If one measures skin temperature, you would expect that the vasodilating effect of the alcohol would be indicated by a change in the temperature of the skin. But in the areas of the skin that were measured, the vasodilatation, or the sweating processes going on as a result of this, were not evident.

Dr. Pribram Have you done any work with the habituation of these changes in the GSR? As you know, the Russians, Sokolov and Lurya, have shown very nicely that GSR and other physiological indexes change after repeated stimulations. These changes, that is, the lack of response that occurs after the stimulants are repeated over and over again, have been found to be not a dropping out of the response system so much as a build-up of some kind of neuronal model, or an expectation, which is used by the organism to match the incoming stimuli; in other words, he does just the kind of thing Dr. Masserman mentioned, "represses the incoming stimuli." Have you, perchance, been working at all with habituation?

Dr. Greenberg   No, we have not, but this perhaps may, in the minds of some of us, bear some relationship to the question of adaptation, or learning a response, and I think we are fairly successful in such learning. We tried to *avoid* the anticipation of the stimulus, in our experiments. We did not introduce the GSR-providing stimulus at any regularized time, so that there was a minimum possibility for the subject to anticipate when it was going to happen.

Dr. Pribram   I wonder if anyone on the panel knows of any experiments on the effects of alcohol on habituation?

Prof. Drew   You mean in the sense of habituation to alcohol?

Dr. Pribram   The Russians use it—not habituation to alcohol but habituation to an incoming stimulus.

Prof. Drew   There has been some work done by the Russians indicating that as the blood alcohol rises, though they don't know specifically what the blood alcohol deals with, so does the habitual response; with dishabituation, the original response to a stimulus comes back again.

Dr. Pribram   The situation is difficult.

Prof. Drew   They have done it in two ways: one, the elimination of a stimulus during the situation; and two, with alcohol. They have also done it in situations of positive conditioning, where you get the disappearance, for example, of the initial response to sounds, the startle response to sound stimulus. Using sound as a conditional response, you get disappearance of the startle response. There is some evidence, but it is not very good, that as the blood alcohol rises, the conditional response drops out.

Dr. Masserman   May I cite what might be a relevant observation of our own. At the University of Chicago we had indexes of so-called emotional reaction. Emotion is a very simple term—it simply means *a motion*; you move, you are doing something. We were interested in determining also whether key stimuli would agree in an individualized way. I remember a typical experiment: A young girl who had some separation anxiety that had existed since childhood was brought into the laboratory, and we were determined to show that we could measure this physiologically. We took her GSR, breathing rate, brain waves, and then talked to her about her past separation from the family, and so on, with no effect whatsoever. We pursued it by hypnotizing her, telling her to relive this particular episode of her past. She did have a minimal reaction such as we expected, but the physiological indexes were neutral. There were no signs of any particular emotional disturbance. Then we showed a film in which such scenes as a child being torn from his mother were presented. She looked at them blandly without any kind of response. At this point I had to leave the room, and as soon as I did so, her GSR went way up, and both her brain waves and breathing showed a measurable increase. In other words, it is the *meaning* of the situation, however subliminal in perception to the individual, that seems to come with these indexes, rather than what we set up for our particular purposes as being meaningful. Would you agree with that?

Dr. Greenberg Yes. I think the whole phenomenon that you have described of effects of alcohol on different kinds of learning depending on whether they were recent learnings or old learnings, or whether they were easy or hard, pleasant or unpleasant—I think this might fit very well into an explanation of the remarkable phenomenon that the alcoholic takes one or two drinks and then goes whole hog and loses all control.

There has been a proneness, and I still think there is, to look upon this phenomenon as some kind of very special quality that *alcohol* has, or some very special quality that the *alcoholic* has. I think it might be rather explained in the terms you spoke of, Dr. Masserman. We have a man with a history of alcoholism. At some earlier period of his life he found a great deal of gratification in his drinking—this is old learning, and it was a very gratifying learning. Then the problems of his alcoholism close in on him, and he reaches a point where at last he relearns—he now learns not to drink. This is painful learning, and it is more recent learning. And one may assume that for the alcoholic, or recovered alcoholic—the man who can never drink without risking loss of control—actually all that may happen when he takes that first drink or two is that he unlearns the more difficult, the more recent learning, and moves back to the earlier and the more pleasant learning. I think this offers a reasonable explanation of why the alcoholic can't take just a drink or two.

Prof. Drew It seems to fit it. I personally wonder about alcoholics, whether anybody has ever investigated whether it is true that they can't take one or two drinks. My own feeling is that to some extent they are always placed in a situation where having a drink, once they have been cured, is an exceedingly tension-producing situation because they have been told that if they have one, they've had it. So, if they do take a drink, the obvious response is, "I am sunk, I might as well go on." And I wonder, has anybody ever investigated what happens to an alcoholic who has in effect been indoctrinated that one drink will bring his downfall?

Dr. Masserman The case you described, of course, means a person who, when taking a drink, and having learned the effects before, is simply reasserting his right to drink as much as he wishes. In that case the first drink is simply the harbinger, or the herald, of a great many more he has already decided will follow. Certainly there are a great many people for whom this symbolic eventuality does not follow at all. I have treated many alcoholics who have now reverted to drinking mildly, without the necessity of continuing what used to be called dipsomania.

Dr. Greenberg There are many factors involved. For example, the alcoholic can be brought into something of a laboratory drinking scene that is entirely different in its content and purpose from the drinking scene and purpose that was involved in his problem-drinking situation. He then need not go overboard.

Dr. Pribram This morning, Dr. Masserman spoke of "decision," and you, Dr. Greenberg, referred to "situation expecting," and so on. Perhaps Professor Drew would assert that the tracking and the skilled performance in his experiments is really a matter of decision process made on the basis of the expectation that the organism, the subject in this case, sets himself up in a situation, and then tracks the expectation, so that in a way what we have here is a living phenomenon of these expectation-decision processes which Dr. Masserman so nicely pointed out to us.

Prof. Drew I suspect that the two main elements in a tracking task which show deterioration with alcohol are first of all the perceptual. There is a very severe restriction of information. I don't believe that this is actually a sense-organ deficit. I suspect it is what

Foreman calls the single-channel analyzer, sort of a reduction in capacity, in this organizing channel; and I suspect that the difficulty arises then in what you call the decision-taking period. This seems, to me, to fit in with a number of other kinds of data which don't fit in any sort of way.

Dr. Greenberg referred to the fact that familiar tasks, whether they be tracking tasks or nontracking tasks, showed less detriment than unfamiliar tasks. We got rather strange results with intellectual function—problem-solving activities showed less deterioration in what would appear to be simpler tracking tasks. The problems seemed to me to show some signs of being put into a kind of order by the subjects, if you regard an order of decision-making tasks to exist where you get a difference in the degree to which the rules are clearly defined, as in mental arithmetic. There you don't get deterioration as quickly—not until the blood alcohol is considerably higher —as you do in situations where the rules are less highly defined. In a tracking task which is unfamiliar, although you have the general set of rules you have to respond to, they are not as intimately known as the rules in a familiar tracking task, and similarly you find then that the familiar one does not deteriorate and the unfamiliar one does.

I expect that looking at them all from the point of decision-making might well be an extremely interesting way of doing it.

Dr. Greenberg I am reminded of the work done in our laboratory by Carpenter and colleagues on the effect of alcohol on higher-order problem solving.[1] They too have run into this enigma of improved performance with alcohol, at least up to some considerable level.

Dr. Masserman Professor Drew, you indicated as much when you mentioned the lady who slowed down to 8 mph. It is perfectly possible that internal action becomes circumspect and care is increased, thereby improving performance. This might be a factor.

Prof. Drew It may well be. There are two things involved here, I think. First of all, this factor that you referred to, the compensating response, which, if our results are reliable, and I personally believe they are, is related to personality variable. Some personalities are better able to do this than others. But I think it is also a function of

1 J. A. Carpenter, O. K. Moore, E. S. Lisansky, and C. R. Snyder, Alcohol and Higher-order Problem-Solving, *Quart. J. Stud. Alc.*, 22:183–222, 1961.

the difference that occurs between subjective judgment, the ability to respond, the ability to criticize one's own performance, and one's actual level of performance.

I don't believe this is again anything which is specific for alcohol. This is something that happens whenever you put an individual in a stressful situation. If you merely make him carry on one of these tracking tasks for a couple of hours, so that he gets fatigued, you find the same kind of difference taking place. You find, on the one hand, the kind of fatigue arising from a competitive, highly concentrated task wherein, after a two-hour period of controlling a fairly unstable machine, you can measure a very serious deterioration in the actual objective accuracy; and at the same time, coincidental with this, there is an increased belief on the part of the subject that he is doing better.

When we asked our subjects how they felt about their performance, they constantly reported that the task they had done was difficult at first and then it became simpler and they were better at it; but, in fact, the exact opposite was true of their performance. I suspect this is a fairly standard stress performance. When our critical judgment goes down—and this is speaking exceedingly anthropomorphically, but descriptively—it is as though we had some internal standard of judgment against which we were controlling our performances; under stress conditions we lower this standard more rapidly than we actually do deteriorate, and hence we get the feeling of doing better. I think it is a very common experience with fatigue. I expect that the judgment that many of us have that we drive better after a cocktail is a combination of the two.

3

SOCIAL IMPLICATIONS
OF ALCOHOL

Dr. Lucia *Any substance, such as fermented beverage, which has had continuous use in all civilizations from the earliest recorded history to the present time . . . has in its own right achieved a validity which places it among the truly cultural attributes of history in evolution.*

Dr. Lolli *It should be evident by now that the value of alcohol depends primarily on who drinks it, and on when, how, how much, why and in what form.*

Salvatore P. Lucia, M.D.

Professor of Medicine and Preventive Medicine
Chairman, Department of Preventive Medicine
University of California School of Medicine
San Francisco, California

THE ANTIQUITY
OF ALCOHOL IN DIET
AND MEDICINE

Editor's Note   A *fermented beverage—of grapes, grains, or other plants, and even of milk and honey—has played an important part in the social, festive, religious, and domestic life of the historical civilizations. The following presentation recounts systematically the ancient uses of alcoholic beverages, particularly in diet and medicine. After noting the legends which refer back to the dawn of civilization, the recorded history of fermented beverages in ancient Mesopotamia, Egypt, the land of the Bible, China, Persia, India, Greece, and Rome is reviewed.*

This is one of those fortunate occasions when a symposium, in the classic Greek tradition, is attended by a discussion of the significance of dietary beverage alcohol. The symposium was an esteemed social function in ancient Greece in which wine played an important and often rigidly prescribed role. I will defer a discussion of the symposium itself and devote myself to establishing the fact that wine, or some other beverage alcohol, occupied a prominent place in ancient civilizations.

When discussing beverage alcohol in the ancient world, we must keep in mind that we are talking about the naturally fermented juice of the grape, and a limited number of other fruits, grains, and, occasionally, even flowers. In no instance are we dealing with the yet to be isolated chemical substance ethanol.

The discovery of fermented beverage is lost in the darkness of prehistory. There are two sources through which we may gain requisite clues: one derives from the legends, tales, and folklore of various civilizations; and the other deals with inscriptions, scrolls, hieroglyphs, tablets, and other archaeologic devices.

Among mythological tales—our heritage and legacy—are many relating to fermented beverage. One tale, probably of Babylonian origin, stems from the epic of Gilgamesh, in the "Creation of the World." In it, the forces of evil are combating the forces of righteousness for possession of the earth. And as in any legend, the benevolent deities emerge victorious. But in the actual fray, they suffered many losses. Wherever the gods fell, the soil in which their bodies rotted spawned the vine. This is offered in explanation of the appearance of the vine and its subsequent significance and distribution over diverse areas of the earth. Herodotus speaks of the Egyptians, who tenderly and assiduously cultivated the grape, as having "divinities spring up in their gardens." The fruit of the vine gave forth the blood of the grape—symbolically the blood of the gods, and whosoever drank of it became imbued with divine spirit. Thus, this symbolism became entrenched in early religions, and it has survived into relatively modern times.

Then, there is the Biblical story. Some are of the opinion that the tree of knowledge was the vine. We may assume that with the fall of Adam man lost this knowledge and that not until after Noah had salvaged his people from extinction by building the Ark was the viticultural concept reinstated. Back on dry land, the Lord ordered Noah to plant a vineyard, and what happened to him in consequence is common knowledge.

Of course, these stories do not really illustrate the discovery of fermentation. They merely report the significance of the vine. Undoubtedly fermentation occurred as a natural phenomenon in distant geologic ages. In warm climates the gathered fruit would ripen and ultimately rot, thus initiating the transformation of fruit sugars into alcohol and its congeners. The following tale illustrates the accidental discovery of alcoholic fermentation.

In legendary times, when lives were more dear than money, there lived in Persia a prince named Djemsheed who had an insatiable love of the grape, to the extent that he would mourn the passing of each vintage harvest. One autumn, when his vines were heavy with luscious fruit, he stored some for future use. Accordingly, the grapes were gathered in jars and properly sequestered. His disappointment must have been great when several weeks later, having gone to fetch some grapes, he encountered instead a murky seething liquid. A ready explanation that some evil spirit had poisoned his treasure was proffered. So he labeled the jars "poison" and departed to drown his sorrows in his harem. The prince, as befitted a man of his standing, had a harem composed of exquisite creatures, and some intelligent. One of them, obviously maladjusted, had lost the glow from her cheeks, the pallor extending to rob her eyes of their luster. In her depression, she wandered through the palace and happened upon the jars labeled poison. This offered her a chance to resolve her problems. She filled a cup and courageously quaffed it in a single gulp. Great was her amazement when, instead of the pains of death, there appeared glimmers of the joy of life. She drank another cup. Life was even better. After a third cup, she could not resist informing Prince Djemsheed of her discovery. And to this day, wine is known in Persia as "the delightful poison."

These legends constitute a rather elaborate and quite charming explanation of the natural occurrence of fermentation. They are perfectly logical and even make good sense. I can almost visualize a Tartar housewife collecting the daily supply of mare's milk in her leather bottle. The bottle was not very clean, but then her own person too was wanting. By the time her mate came home to quaff his milk, the heat and the contaminating bacteria had done their work. What he got was not mare's milk, but *koumiss*. He must have liked it at the first try, since no drink has ever replaced it.

MESOPOTAMIA

The following discussion will present in chronologic order the significance of fermented beverages in ancient civilizations. The earliest records extant of the Mesopotamian civilization date from the third millennium B.C. These, inscribed on unbaked clay, dealt mostly with the glory of kings and gods, some commercial contracts, and a few esoterica, among which occurs the recipe of a physician detailing a prescription of medicinal agents mixed in wine. Apparently wine was the menstruum then current, and it has persisted as such these past forty centuries.

Among the fermented beverages of Mesopotamia will be found a beer made of barley, and wines made of the date and crushed sesame seed. Grape wine was imported into Mesopotamia, since the native vine had incurred the curse of Dionysus whose frustration at the hands of the Mesopotamians turned him away in anger [Lutz].

The Mesopotamians were a chameleonic people—on the one hand, they were capable of tremendous achievements, and, on the other, they seemed to lack the simplest of knowledge. Man was but a child, with everything yet to learn. They had fire, but were ignorant of ovens; thus, the basic elements of their diet were not baked, and bread was poured from a vessel, since it had the consistency of a modern thin polenta [Contenau]. During the dynasty of Ur, the registered citizens of Assyria received daily, from official hands, a gallon of bread and a gallon of fermented beverage—barley beer being the most prevalent. The drinking cup was a significant possession of these peoples, somewhat like the *tastevin* among modern Burgundians. At death, the personal cup was placed in the coffin, which was then burned in the funeral pyre. Indiscriminate drinking of alcoholic beverages was discouraged, although taverns for the commercial procurement of beverages were available, and these were tended by women, mostly of ill repute. Furthermore, money was not the medium of exchange in the purchase of beverages; this was accomplished by barter, and any deviation from the going rate incurred the penalty of death [Meissner].

In the religious sphere, fermented beverages were in common use. For libations, the expensive imported grape wines were offered. Wine was poured in the consecration of ground before building a temple or a house, and it was sprinkled upon the embers of the funeral pyre. Upon the sacrificial altars were placed three different offerings: one consisted of four jars of wine; another, three measures of bread; and the last, a jar of honey and milk [Meissner].

Fermented beverages were important in entertainment, since the official cupbearer and official chief brewer were prominent members of the court of the kings. Feasts to celebrate the victorious return of the kings were signalized by a service of wine to all concerned. In the third tablet of the Creation series, the one great literary achievement of the Babylonians [cited by Lutz], Anshar says to his minister: "Let the gods, all of them, prepare for a feast, let them sit at a banquet, let them eat bread, let them mix wine!"

This résumé epitomizes the broad usage of fermented beverages for domestic, religious, festive, and medicinal purposes in Mesopotamia 4,000 years ago.

EGYPT

In Egypt, the fermented beverage in common use was a beer made from barley—a drink enjoyed mainly by the common people. A discreet amount of palm wine and date wine was also used, as well as a restricted amount of grape wine. The significance of grape culture is not too clearly understood, although Herodotus reported the presence of extensive vineyards in early Egypt. The vineyards in general were the gardens of the pharaohs. The grape itself was used as an article of diet, since its pips, seeds, and stems have been recovered from pre-Nubian tombs. Pictographs on the walls of Theban caves demonstrate the complexities of the grape harvest, wine presses, and the making of wine [Reed].

Among the religious uses of fermented beverages, the libation commanded the greatest respect since it was a common ceremony throughout all Egypt, and it was usually performed with wine. There is a legend that tells that only bronze vessels were used for libations until the reign of the twelve kings, instituted at a time when Egypt became divided into twelve provinces. At that time, the oracle had predicted that the one among the twelve kings who should offer a libation from a bronze vessel at the temple of Hephaestus would unite Egypt under his sole leadership. From then on all libations were performed with gold and silver vessels. But at one ritual in the temple of Hephaestus, the presiding priest brought only eleven goblets, and the last in line took off his bronze helmet and offered his libation from it. This was Psammethicus, and just as the oracle had predicted, after a short lapse of time, he united all of Egypt and became the pharaoh. At this point it is important to record that the priests of Egypt, in order to establish a closer relation with the gods, always drank a part of a libation. This is of particular importance since in later civilizations, libations contained, in addition to a fermented beverage, the blood of human or animal sacrificial hostages. The Egyptian religion was polytheistic; many of the gods were worshiped singularly by tribes and family units, not unlike the household gods of later Rome. However, the gods Isis and Osiris were worshiped in common by all Egyptians, Osiris being the wine deity, the precursor and counterpart of the Grecian Dionysus [Herodotus].

Among the dietary usages of fermented beverages, a distinct division is made in that beer was the beverage of preference in the corn country, and wine the table drink of the grape country.

As to medicinal uses, we have abundant evidence from the medical papyri that beer and wine were the common menstrua for medicinal agents. Although Egyptian medicine was theurgic, it was based on rational understanding of the specific problems involved.

In the papyrus Ebers [Bryan's translation], it is specified that the fruit of the vine also was used medicinally; the grape itself therefore was included in the materia medica.

As to entertainment, there were elaborate formulas and rituals for the blending and service of wines which, at feasts, were offered in silver and gold goblets. By the nature of the rivalry exercised among hosts, it is obvious that entertainments were common in which wine was served in abundance.

In closing these remarks on Egypt, I think it would be fitting to tell the story [from Ferval] of a famous banquet which arose out of Cleopatra's desire to impress Mark Antony. It came about that after one of Antony's sumptuous affairs, Cleopatra, not to be eclipsed, told him that she would present him with a banquet costing 10,000 sesterces. Antony was irked at the suggestion that a banquet surpassing his could be accomplished. He smiled indulgently, and they agreed to a wager of a kingdom—Phoenicia—if Cleopatra won. When the occasion arrived, the banquet proceeded at a fairly monotonous pace, and Antony began to feel secure of his prize. Just then, Cleopatra beckoned to one of the slaves, who brought her a cup of deep dark wine, whereupon she detached with care and deliberation one of the two perfectly matched black pearls that she wore and dropped it into her cup. She made ready to detach the other one, saying to Antony, "When I have drunk this, my wager will have been won." But Antony stayed her hand and admitted his defeat. Thereafter, Cleopatra wore the single black pearl around her neck, whence it was recovered after her death.[1]

THE HEBREWS AND THE BIBLE

The fermented beverages in common use among the ancient Hebrews were predominantly wine of grapes, some date wine, and a lesser quantity of palm sap liquor. Wine played an important part in their rituals as well as in their daily life. There were eight clearly defined types of wine in common use—among them *yayin*, a strong red grape wine, frequently diluted with water and used at sacrifices, and *mesek*, a true mixed wine mingled with water and aromatic substances reminiscent of spiced or mulled wine. These beverages were singled

[1] Pliny, in his rendition of this story, states that Cleopatra was served a strong vinegar in which to dissolve the pearl.

out for special purposes, and they were served in a distinctly ceremonial fashion [Kitto; Patton].

The most important use of wine among the Hebrews was for
religious purposes, especially for the celebration of special religious
days, and for purposes of libation—a ceremony common to their
culture.

As dietary beverages, wines of all types were used, more often
as drinks following meals and feasts rather than as accompaniments
of food. It is stated that Moses introduced wine in the dietary pattern
of these people after their exodus from Egypt, when he laid down
the details of their daily regimen.

The Bible is replete with references to the medicinal uses of
wine. The Hebrews were specific as to its antiseptic value, and they
used wine to wash the wounds at circumcision. Furthermore, a
relationship was noted between the consumption of sweet wine
(*hasis*) and obesity [Brim].

Among their ritual and festive uses occurs an important custom
of offering soldiers bread and wine on their return from maneuvers.
An extension of the libational use was placing bread and wine on the
table of the new home which a family was to occupy. Throughout
the Bible, wine is referred to as cheering, nourishing, and stimulating.
And, I presume, in some recondite passages one may find allusions
to its use as a tranquilizer—"Give wine unto those that be of heavy
heart."

At folk festivals, banquets, and other forms of communal entertainment and relaxation, wine flowed freely as it had in Egypt. Yet
one must admit that the Hebrews were temperate drinkers, and
drunkenness was severely discouraged.

CHINA

The types of fermented beverages common in China were "wine"
from millet and from rice, and an ill-defined wine derived from the
native grape. It is doubtful that wine of the *Vitis vinifera* was available in ancient China, excepting perhaps by importation. Among the
uses of fermented beverages are many which follow the patterns
already established by other cultures.

The most important uses of fermented beverages were related
to religious practices. The Chinese resorted to libations of all types

and for many different occasions. In pre-Christian times the libational vessels were of massive volume and were usually filled with two liquids: one described as a clarified liquid red in color, the other, murky—possibly because it had been mixed with bone marrow in the androphagous ritual. Human sacrifice was common in ancient China and during these times the earth was fed with the "spirit of life"—wine and blood, most likely. Wine was used at the worship of ancestors, and during the Shang dynasty wine was the only product of the soil offered to the gods [Ackerman].

In entertainment, wine was the beverage of banquets and official occasions. These were often aromatic wines, as is stated in an inscription on an early Chou vessel. Such wines were offered at the command of the king and, as described by Marco Polo [Yule's translation], were served at the fabulous feasts of the Great Khan.

Among the ancient Chinese, references to the use of wine as a dietary beverage are indeed scanty; however, records of medicinal uses are abundant. Wines of many types were used in the materia medica and there is some controversy as to the varietal grape sources of these wines. In general, wine—of whatever type—was used as a menstruum for what at times appears to have been a conglomeration of organic and inorganic medicinal materials [Hübotter].

PERSIA

There are very few evidences extant of ancient Persian culture. Most of the information we have comes from archeologic fragments and legendary tales. The available references to the domestic use of wine among the Persians are not very edifying. The rulers and noblemen of ancient Persia drank phenomenal quantities of grape wine. In addition, a beverage was used called haoma, fermented from the flowers of the *Asclepias acida*. Its identity is much like the soma of ancient India, and it was probably used for religious ceremonies and libations [Herodotus].

The uses of fermented beverage were many. In the religious sphere, as in other parts of the ancient world, wine was a prerogative for libations and sacrifices.

Among the dietary uses the wine of dates mixed with spices was a relatively common article, and references to the Persians' great love of wine, especially among the poets, probably referred to a spiced date wine—else, how could one explain the Ghazals, whose words and expressions are not only intellectually perfumed but morally intoxicating.

In entertainment the prerequisite was wine served in lavish quantities. And although viticulture was advanced in ancient Persia, and a great deal of wine was produced, an appreciable amount was imported. Xenophon tells us that at one time the Persians used to eat and drink but once a day and work the rest of the day, but after the advent of Cyrus the Great, they still ate and drank but once a day, indulging in one continuous feast from early morning until late at night.

There is considerable ambivalence about the use of wine after the spread of Mohammedanism in Persia. However, the kings continued to use wine openly and the presumption is that everyone else did likewise, but surreptitiously—else, how could a poet like Omar Khayyam have said what he said to inflame a whole nation and, incidentally, other nations as well.

Among the medicinal uses of fermented beverages the most common was as a stomachic. The haoma was more general in its use since by inference it conferred longevity and good health to him who partook of it.

INDIA

The claims that fermented beverages, as we know them in the western world, had their origin in India are not sustained. If one were to make a statement of universal conclusion referable to fermented beverages, one could say that no area of the world in which fruits, or plants containing natural sugars, growing in a soil supporting the parasitic mycoderma, was ignorant of fermented beverages. This extends back, deep into geologic ages. All one needs is the opportunity to allow the sequestered fruit carrying the mycoderma to disintegrate, as well as a little bit of patience before sampling the residual mash, to discover that the result is an alcoholic beverage.

The Indians used a relatively large series of fermented beverages in their daily life and for their religious rituals: soma, from the *Asclepias acida*—a substance whose name presaged our modern tranquilizer; *modaka*, a "wine" made from rice; *prashanna*, made from grain flour; *asaya*, made from sugar; *maireya*, from molasses; and *madhu*, from honey [Bose]. Madhu ties in with the universally fermented beverage made from honey of many other civilizations.

In religious usage the fermented beverage, soma, was so highly revered that it was worshiped as a god in its own right. Kings requisitioned and recommended the use of fermented beverage among their peoples and offered it in libations to the gods. Even the hermits in India used soma, and in the Tantric ritual wine is a prerequisite.

As a dietary beverage the various Indian tribesmen used different types of fermented beverage, depending upon the caste to which they belonged.

For entertainment wine was commonly used at banquets, and exclusively by men and their mistresses, but it was strictly tabu to the wives, although they were allowed to smell the wines!

The concept of soma as a medicinal agent enjoys a universality second to no other medicinal substance recorded in human history.

An interesting sidelight derives from the persistence of a fermented beverage made from the mahuda flower (*Bassia latifolia*) and its common use among the Bhils, a tribe of Indians living in a sequestered area. The Bhils have been using mahuda liquor continuously from ancient times to the present. It was the Mother Goddess who taught the Bhils how to make mahuda—a ritual which they follow to this day. Some thirsty Bhils drink other liquors, which are labeled for profane uses, but in times of stress, or tribal and religious needs, they return to the mahuda [Pertold].

GREECE

Wine of grapes was the choice and preference of the ancient Greeks, although some beer may have been used among the northern tribesmen who were considered to represent a coarser element among the Greek nations. It was they who introduced the *rhyton*, the horn for drinking purposes, a word which persists in our time and implies immoderate drinking.

The ancient, polytheistic Greeks endowed their gods and goddesses with liberal license. Details of the prowess of some of their deities are nothing short of fantastic. They are understandable if one subscribes to the concept that the mind of man is a remarkable instrument and that life is but an attitude of mind. We shall refer to the one unique god, the god of the vine and wine—Dionysus.

Dionysus represents the enigmatic duality: the god who by his gift of wine had the power to drive man to madness, but who, also by this same gift, was able to teach man a deeper appreciation of beauty, of pure enjoyment, and of life itself. This is also demonstrated by the close association between Dionysus and Orpheus, to both of whom mystic rites were dedicated.

Wine was of such general and universal use in Greece that it would be difficult to single out religious libations and festive occasions in which it was not used. It was essential in all rituals and obviously was the beverage used in libations. Although we are apprised that the Greeks were temperate users of wine, a purview of their history reveals that they enjoyed a highly sophisticated and complicated knowledge of grape culture, wine types, and wine production. And, for a people who took every license to drink a libation, it goes without saying that they must have developed gargantuan tolerances.

In entertainment wine was the most important element. In support of this statement stands the *Deipnosophistae* of Athenaeus, in which all matter of specific detail referable to wine, physically and spiritually, is brought out. In the course of the discussions, great men and their philosophies are brought to light, in perhaps the most unique repository of such information in the Western world. The symposium, the signal for a social and intellectual gathering, has been the Grecian legacy to the civilized world at large. And it is common knowledge that in the time of ancient Greece, men had many opportunities to meet at table and enjoy the *deipnon*.

The *deipnon*, the dinner, consisted of two main courses: the first of meats, vegetables, and fish; and the second devoted to the presentation of sweets, desserts, and fruits. The *deipnon* was followed by the *potos*—the drinking of wine according to rigidly defined laws which were set and determined by the symposiarch, the master of ceremonies for the occasion. At times, the philosophical discussions of the symposium gave way to the more profane social arts of man. But no matter what the occasion for the symposium, it was always opened with a libation of wine [Athenaeus].

One need hardly dwell on the importance of wine as a dietary beverage, a medicine, and a menstruum for medicinal agents in the life of the ancient Greeks. From Hippocrates to Galen, physicians have written tracts on wine—altered and unaltered. There was a school of physicians called *physikos oinodotes*, who prescribed wine of various kinds and in varying doses for different diseases. The antagonists to this school shunned the use of wine and the names of their leaders are almost lost to history. Only the names and deeds of the wine-prescribing physicians have survived these many centuries. And when one analyzes the writings of the prescribers of wine, one is surprised at the accuracy of their advice—some of which is currently being unraveled in the university laboratories of the Western world, thanks to the assembled scholars among us who represent this vanguard.

ROME

The sublimity of the Grecian worship of wine as exemplified through the cult of Dionysus became in part profaned by the Romans when Dionysus changed his garb for that of his Roman counterpart, Bacchus. Rome offered a more favorable soil and climate to the culture of the grape, and the best document of this is the tract on wine of Claudius Clarissimus Galen, in which very careful descriptions are given of soil, terrain, grape varieties, wine qualities, and medicinal and therapeutic uses in relation to quality and age of the various regional wines. By contrast with previous civilizations, Rome was a world of relative leisure, ostentation, orgy, and extravagance. The quantity of food and wine presented and consumed at festivals was conspicuously wasteful.

Among the religious uses of wine in ancient Rome the most important one, perhaps, was the libation. Originally milk was used for libations, but after the Latins became a successful agricultural people, wine was requisitioned for the task [Fowler]. The original god of wine was Liber, who later became identified with Dionysus and ultimately Bacchus. The wine used for libations and other religious rituals was carefully made, and it was derived from pruned vines uncontaminated by proximity to anything unclean [Pliny]. These rituals set the lore of wine deep in the hearts of a people who, in their use of it, often lapsed into orgy. Thus the tradition was forged which has persisted for the many ensuing centuries. Rome set the pattern for the modern world relative to the dietary, festive, and medicinal uses of wine. Wine was also an important element in the burial rituals; it was used to quench flames into dying embers; and the cremated remains of Roman citizens were often washed in wine [Ramsay], for what reasons is not clear.

As for the use of wine for entertainment, the lighthearted and gay element of ancient Rome ensured for the Romans a plethora of festivals, most of which were proclaimed days of rest, and in which the consumption of wine, often in large quantities, played an important part. There were festivals dedicated to the vine as well as to wine.

The sublimity of the symposium of ancient Greece often degenerated in Rome. Again, the dinner—the *cena*—was patterned after the Greek *deipnon*. However, the profusion of viands was incredible and beyond the imagination of modern man. The *commissatio*, or drinking ceremony, which followed the dinner, more often became profaned into a drinking round. In its minor details, too, the Roman symposium closely followed the forms adopted by the Greek, but it never reached the heights of the latter. It was often not an intellectual gathering of the best available talent but an opportunity to indulge in sensualities. The most florid example of the symposium in Rome is depicted in the *Satyricon* of Petronius, where the detailed description of the banquet of Trimalchio transcends the imagination of modern man and certainly his capacity for orgy.

The use of wine as a medicine was frequent and often unconsciously artful. Specific varieties were assigned for the most delicate nuances of disease, a trait still characteristic of the modern descendants of ancient Rome. Also, with the new and rapidly evolving knowledge of medicinal plants, the galenicals, the most adequate menstruum for their portage was wine.

As a dietary beverage wine was overtly as common as bread and so recognized. The poorer people lived on a fare as simple as that of the banquets was lavish. The diet of the poor people was bread and wine—a hard, wholesome bread soaked in wine to reduce its coarseness and increase its palatability. As one became affluent and his fortune allowed for indulgences, the basic dietary was embellished by an *obsonium*—any comestible which would blend appropriately with the basic bread and wine, such as meat or cheese [Prentice]. Bread and wine were cardinal elements of the diet in pagan times, and they ultimately became the all-embracing symbols of Christianity and survival. We can look upon bread and wine as the staple foods of men anywhere and everywhere in the ancient as well as in the modern world.

DISCUSSION

This brief historical review illustrates that fermented beverages were universally known and used in the ancient world for a variety of cultural, religious, and festive ceremonies. Fermented beverage, whether grape wine, palm wine, or one derived from whatever the land might furnish (cereals, grains, fruits, or flowers) was put to many uses, not the least of which was as a dietary adjuvant. In the struggle for survival, men learned from experience that these beverages had more than nutritional value. They made the water more potable, as well as safe; they were effective medicines, and they could be relied upon to ensure the tranquility essential to a state of well-being. The more intellectual and more cultured people used fermented dietary beverages with temperance and moderation, permitting themselves more liberal digressions only as prescribed by tradition and their religious beliefs.

In the primitive polytheistic religions of early civilizations wine played an important role—its use as well as its abuse (such as in the Dionysian rites) being rigidly defined. Wine had universal acceptance in libations, some civilizations requiring natural wine, others an admixture with blood, while still others permitted the addition of spices and aromatic substances. In fact, so strong was the symbolism of wine that it retains its aura of romance and fathomable mysticism to this day.

Aside from its role in religion, wine—or any other fermented dietary beverage—was an element of significance on all festive occasions: at banquets and at birth, marriage, and death celebrations. On these occasions, too, its use was carefully prescribed. In the symposium, the consumption of wine was defined by a tradition which required strict adherence. On certain occasions, especially in the religious festivals and often in celebration of a military victory, wine was used to the point of excess.

Another important use of fermented beverages was in medicine —mainly for its intrinsic values as a diuretic, a tonic, or as a sedative, and often as an agent to carry other medicinal substances. It was the only reliable medicinal menstruum available to the ancients, and in this guise it has persisted to this day—at times with stealth, unfortunately.

Any substance, such as fermented beverage, which has had continuous use in all civilizations from the earliest recorded history to the present time despite the fact that it may have waxed and waned in popularity has in its own right achieved a validity which places it among the truly cultural attributes of history in evolution. Fermented dietary beverage, and especially wine, was so common an element in the various cultures that it was taken for granted as one of the basic elements of survival and self-preservation.

REFERENCES

Ackerman, P., *Ritual Bronzes of Ancient China*, New York, Dryden Press, 1945.
Athenaeus, *Deipnosophistae* (Gulick, C. B., transl.), in Loeb Classical Library, London, Heinemann, 1927.
Bose, D. K., *Wine in Ancient India*, Calcutta, Connor, 1922.
Brim, C. J., *Medicine in the Bible*, New York, Froben Press, 1936.
Bryan, C. P., (transl.), *The Papyrus Ebers*, New York, Appleton, 1931.
Contenau, G., *Everyday Life in Babylon and Assyria* (Maxwell-Hyslop, transl.), New York, St Martin's, 1954.
Ferval, C., *Cleopatra* (Poindexter, M.E., transl.), New York, Garden City Publishing Company, 1926.
Fowler, W. W., *The Roman Festivals of the Period of the Republic*, London, Macmillan, 1899.
Herodotus (Godley, A.D., transl.), in Loeb Classical Library, Cambridge, Harvard, 1930–1938.
Hübotter, F., *Chinesisch-Tibetische Pharmakologie und Rezeptur* (Chinese-Tibetan Pharmacology and Prescription), Ulm, Haug, 1957.
Kitto, J., *A Cyclopaedia of Biblical Literature*, Edinburgh, Black, 1876, vol. III.
Lucia, S. P., *A History of Wine as Therapy*, Philadelphia, Lippincott, 1963.
Lutz, H. F., *Viticulture and Brewing in the Ancient Orient*, Leipzig, Hinrichs, 1922.
Meissner, B., *Babylonien und Assyrien* (Babylonia and Assyria), Heidelberg, Foy's Kulturgeschichtliche Bibliothek, 1920, vol. I.
Patton, W., *The Laws of Fermentation and the Wines of the Ancients*, New York, National Temperance Society, 1871.
Pertold, O., The Liturgical Use of Mahuda Liquor by Bhils, *Arch. Orient*; Praha, 3:400–407, 1931.
Petronius, *Satyricon* (Heseltine, M., transl.), in Loeb Classical Library, London, Heinemann, 1913.
Pliny, *Natural History* (Bostock and Riley, transl.), London, Bohn, 1855.
Prentice, E. P., *Hunger and History. The Influence of Hunger on Human History*, New York, Harper, 1939.

Ramsay, W., *A Manual of Roman Antiquities*, London, Griffin, 1859.

Reed, H. S., *A Short History of the Plant Sciences*, Waltham, Mass., Chronica Botanica, 1942.

Xenophon, *Cyropaedia* (Miller, W., transl.), in Loeb Classical Library, London, Heinemann, 1914, vol. II.

Yule, H. (transl. & ed.), *The Book of Ser Marco Polo*, 3d ed., London, J. Murray, 1929.

Berton Roueché

Author

ALCOHOL
IN HUMAN CULTURE

Editor's Note   *Like Dr. Lucia, Mr. Berton Roueché chose the historical perspective; and though in the first part of his presentation some of the same very early ground is covered, there is no actual duplication, owing to the different selection of illustrative material.*

While Dr. Lucia was interested in showing the history of fermented beverages particularly in diet and medicine, Mr. Roueché was concerned with the history of alcoholic beverages as drinks fascinating to man specifically for their alcoholic effects. His special contribution is in tracing the story of developments after distillation became known, first in Europe and later in the New World. He thus takes us on a journey through aqua vitae, brandy, gin, whiskey, scotch, rum—right up to the modern cocktail—showing where and how and under what circumstances each came into being and gained its adherents and made its particular mark in the affairs of men.

When man first encountered alcohol is not known. That epochal hour, like so many beginnings, is lost in the deeps of time. About all that can be said with any certainty is that it occurred in his earliest infancy, and that the meeting was entirely fortuitous. For alcohol, in contrast to most of our cultural acquisitions, owes nothing to man's creative hand. It comes to us as a triumph not of human imagination but of human curiosity. Like fire, it is a natural phenomenon that man stumbled upon and gratefully bent to his use. It also shares with fire a genealogy of superhuman length. The origin of alcohol probably goes back at least two hundred million years, to the late Paleozoic era. By then, as far as science can determine, the materials that its generation requires—water, plant sugars or starches, and yeast—had all appeared on earth.

The form in which man first discovered alcohol, though a matter of some debate, is less perplexing a question than when the discovery was made. Only three possibilities are seriously regarded as likely. One is fermented fruit juice, or wine. Another is fermented

grain, or beer. The third is fermented honey, or mead. Most pre-
historians, at least at the moment, are inclined to favor the last.
Their inclination is largely based on a single thread of etymological
evidence. In both Sanskrit and Greek, "mead" is a root whose range
of meaning embraces "honey," "sweet," "intoxicating drink," and
"drunkenness." This generic association of honey, rather than grain
or fruit, with the concept of intoxication suggests its superior antiquity as a source of alcohol. If so, it is possible to suppose further that
beverage alcohol in the form of mead was known to Paleolithic, or
Old Stone Age, man, for there is an abundance of evidence that his
Neolithic descendants were acquainted with wine and beer.

That acquaintance was intimate and deeply cherished. It was
not, however, casual. The role of alcohol in Neolithic culture has
been defined by various investigators, and there is general agreement
that its use was essentially ritualistic. Primitive man, there can be no
doubt, drank hard, but the time, the place, and the manner of his
drinking seem always to have been rigidly determined by custom.
And, it seems equally certain, he always drank in company. Donald
Horton noted that "The individual inebriate is conspicuous by his
absence from most primitive communities." At the Neolithic level,
drinking was invariably a communal rite.

THE OLDEST RECORDS

The casual use of alcohol, like the individual inebriate, is a product
of civilization. It made its first appearance in Mesopotamia about
five thousand years ago. The oldest known examples of cuneiform
writing—a collection of clay tablets recovered from the third-
millennium (B.C.) temple at Erech, near the head of the Persian
Gulf—clearly demonstrate that while beer was brewed in quantity
for sacramental purposes, it was also drunk for pleasure. One of the
Erech tablets consists of a wage list with a series of entries—
presumably personal names—followed by the indication, "beer and
bread for one day." And the anonymous author of the somewhat less
ancient Mesopotamian account of the Flood, which was unearthed
at Nineveh in 1926, thoughtfully included alcoholic beverages among
the comforts taken aboard the Ark. "For our food," the passage reads,
"I slaughtered oxen, and killed sheep day by day, and with beer, oil,
and wine I filled large jars." (The Old Testament, of course, goes
considerably further in attributing to Noah a familiarity with alcohol:

"And he drank of the wine, and was drunken.") Another Ninevite tablet, which is thought to have been inscribed around 2300 B.C., contains an allusion to a *bit sikari*, or tavern. Within two hundred years, resorts of this type had become so prominent in Mesopotamian culture that Hammurabi found it necessary to devote 2 of the 282 paragraphs of his monumental Code to their regulation.

Mesopotamian civilization also produced the earliest clinical description of intoxication on record, and the first attempt at an antidote. "If a man has taken strong wine," the account [cited by Sigerist] reads, "his head is affected and he forgets his words and his speech becomes confused, his mind wanders and his eyes have a set expression; to cure him, licorice, beans, oleander (and eight other unidentified substances), to be compounded with oil and wine before (sunset), and in the morning before sunrise and before anyone has kissed him, let him take it, and he will recover."

One of the few surviving relics of the seventeenth Egyptian dynasty, which roughly coincided with the reign of Hammurabi, is a hieroglyphic outburst by a female courtier. "Give me eighteen bowls of wine!" she exclaims. "Behold, I love drunkenness!" The inclination, though expressed with uncommon candor, is not an unusual one in the annals of ancient Egypt. "Drunkenness . . . seems to have occurred in all layers of society, from the farmers to the ruling class," Sigerist remarks. "Banquets frequently ended with the guests, men and women, being sick, and this did not in any way seem shocking." It was, in fact, considered a suitable subject for art. A recovered fresco of the second millennium B.C. shows a woman banqueter turning from the table to vomit into a bowl held by a servant. A mural found in a tomb at El Kab, near Luxor, depicts a tavern proprietor welcoming a patron. According to an accompanying legend, his greeting is "Drink into rapture!" The customer's reply is equally vigorous. "I will drink till I am happy," he says, "and the mat under me is a good straw bed upon which I can sleep myself sober."

In addition to its distinctive distaste for sobriety, dynastic Egypt has the understandable distinction of having invented the temperance tract. A work called *Wisdom of Ani*, written around three thousand years ago, is perhaps the first of the genre. "Take not upon thyself to drink a jug of beer," its author begins. He then enumerates the consequences of ignoring his advice. "Thou speakest, and an unintelligible utterance issueth from thy mouth. If thou fallest down and thy limbs break, there is none to hold out a hand to thee. Thy companions in drink stand up and say: 'Away with this sot.' And thou art like a little child."

The later civilizations of the ancient world took a less tempestuous view of alcohol. In the Orient, its double-edged powers were assayed with characteristic calm. The *Rig-Veda* refers to soma, a popular infusion of fermented grain and honey, as "poison suspended in a leather bottle," but nowhere explicitly condemns its use. The Chinese position was formally fixed, around 650 B.C., in the *Shu Ching*, or *Canon of History*. "Men will not do without beer," an entry entitled "The announcement about drunkenness" reads. "To prohibit it and secure total abstinence from it is beyond the power even of sages. Here, therefore, we have warnings on the abuse of it." The warnings recommended moderation. A Japanese poet carved them into an instructive epigram. "At the first cup," he wrote, "man drinks wine. At the second cup, wine drinks wine. At the third cup, wine drinks man." The Jews, possibly because of their youthful exposure to Egyptian culture, filled the Old Testament with denunciations of drunkenness, but they held alcoholic beverage in good esteem and at times even prescribed it. "Give strong drink unto him that is ready to perish," the Book of Proverbs proclaims, "and wine unto those that be of heavy hearts. Let him drink, and forget his poverty, and remember his misery no more." The "strong drink" of the Bible, most authorities believe, was merely undiluted wine. A mixture of wine and water was the usual Jewish drink.

The Greeks, and eventually their cultural heirs in Rome and elsewhere around the Mediterranean, also embraced this gentle custom, though for rather different reasons. To drink undiluted wine, they felt, was a sign of barbarism. In addition, they thought it was dangerous, and could permanently ravage the mind. The accepted ratio was one part wine to two parts water, and thus fashionably modified, it was considered both safe and salutary. "Wine," Euripides enunciates in *Bacchae*, "removes the cares pressing upon the minds of sorrowing mortals, who, when filled with this juice of the grape, no longer need sleep and no longer remember their daily miseries. There is no other like cure for all their troubles." One of the few still audible Grecian voices to question the habitual use of wine was that of the early poet Alcaeus, and he contented himself with a word on habitual excess. "One that hath wine as a chain about his wits," he warned, "such a one lives no life at all." Even Plato, the leading ascetic of his time, went no further. "To drink to the degree of drunkenness is neither becoming anywhere," he declares in *Laws*, his final masterwork, "except perhaps in the days of festival of the god who gave men wine for their banquets." The poet Martial, a mirror of Roman rationality in the first Christian century, includes among the ingredients of a sensible life "not drunken nights, yet loos'd from care." With this cheerful philosophy his influential contemporary Pliny the Elder was in sufficient accord to devote the whole of the fourteenth volume of his majestic *Historia Naturalis* to wine and viniculture. He also, in a companion volume, discusses at sympathetic length the preference of some races for mead, and adds that others—notably the Egyptians and the peoples of Spain and Gaul—find adequate comfort in beer. "Indeed," he concludes with satisfaction, "in no part of the world is drunkenness ever at a loss."

THE DISCOVERY OF DISTILLATION

Although, as Pliny rightly reckoned, drunkenness has never been at a loss, its vehicles lacked variety in the ancient world. They were also, being confined to the muted products of natural fermentation, relatively deficient in vigor and impact. It was not until around A.D. 800, when human ingenuity evolved the process of distillation, that a livelier choice became possible. An Arabian alchemist named Jabir ibn Hayyan and known to the West as Geber is generally credited with this resounding feat, and it may have been he who suggested the name for its most effective result. "Alcohol" is, at any rate, a word of Arabic derivation. It stems from "alkuhl." The latter originally referred to the eye cosmetic made of powdered antimony, but with time and use it came to mean any fine-ground substance, then "essence," and, ultimately, the essential spirit of wine.[1] A dissenting opinion advanced by nineteenth-century temperance leaders held that the proper root of "alcohol" was the Arabic "alghul," meaning "ghost," or "evil spirit."

How Geber was led to accomplish the isolation of alcohol is uncertain. His writings on distillation, which reached medieval Europe under the title *Liber Investigationis Magisteri*, gave only a rambling account of his aim and general technique. Indeed, his style was so elaborate and loitering that it persuaded Samuel Johnson to record in his *Dictionary of the English Language* that the etymological seed of "gibberish" was "Geber." Nor is there any evidence that

[1] Or "finely divided spirit," as Dr. Leake notes (see p. 8).

Geber saw in alcohol a liquor of much practical value. That discovery was made by Arnaldus de Villanova, a professor of medicine at the University of Montpellier, toward the end of the thirteenth century.

THE "WATER OF IMMORTALITY"

Arnaldus' conception of alcohol was practical in the extreme. It solved before his dazzled eyes the problem that was then the chief concern of European science. It was the philosopher's stone, the universal panacea, the key to life everlasting. "Limpid and well-flavored red or white wine," he wrote in announcing his find, "is to be digested twenty days in a closed vessel, by heat, and then to be distilled in a sand bath with a very gentle fire. The true water of life will come over in precious drops, which, being rectified by three or four successive distillations, will afford the wonderful quintessence of wine. We call it aqua vitae, and this name is remarkably suitable, since it is really a water of immortality. It prolongs life, clears away ill-humours, revives the heart, and maintains youth." Raymond Lully, another Montpellier savant, is sometimes linked with Arnauld in this equivocal triumph. His works contain not only an equally gripping testimonial to the virtues of aqua vitae but a ready designation of their source. They came, he said, as "an emanation from the Deity." Both Arnaldus and Lully lived to be well over seventy, a considerable age for that time, and it is possible that their example was taken as convincing confirmation of the emanation's worth. It is certain that it was rapidly elevated to a place of sovereign prominence in the Christian medicine chest.

"Aqua vitae is commonly called the mistress of all medicines," Hieronymus Brunschwig, the titan of fifteenth-century German medicine, surgery, and pharmacology, proclaimed. "It eases the diseases coming of cold. It comforts the heart. It heals all old and new sores on the head. It causes a good color in a person. It heals baldness and causes the hair well to grow, and kills lice and fleas. It cures lethargy. Cotton wet in the same and a little wrung out again and so put in the ears at night going to bed, and a little drunk thereof, is of good against all deafness. It eases the pain in the teeth, and causes sweet breath. It heals the canker in the mouth, in the teeth, in the lips, and in the tongue. It causes the heavy tongue to become light and well-speaking. It heals the short breath. It causes good digestion and appetite for to eat, and takes away all belching. It draws the wind out of the body. It eases the yellow jaundice, the dropsy, the gout, the pain in the breasts when they be swollen, and heals all diseases in the bladder, and breaks the stone. It withdraws venom that has been taken in meat or in drink, when a little treacle is put thereto. It heals all shrunken sinews, and causes them to become soft and right. It heals the fevers tertian and quartan. It heals the bites of a mad dog, and all stinking wounds, when they be washed therewith. It gives also young courage in a person, and causes him to have a good memory. It purifies the five wits of melancholy and of all uncleanness." Brunschwig's proclamation included, however, a cautionary note. "It is to be drunk by reason and measure," he warned. "That is to understand, five or six drops in the morning, fasting, with a spoonful of wine."

BRANDY AND GIN

In its original manifestation, aqua vitae was the liquor now known as brandy. The latter term, which derives from the Dutch *brandewijn*, meaning burnt (or distilled) wine, came into use around the middle of the seventeenth century. It was a distinction inspired by necessity. After nearly four hundred years of solitary eminence, Arnaldus' quintessence of wine was no longer the only aqua vitae on the European market. Human ingenuity had produced another, distilled from grain, which contained the quintessence of beer. Exactly who was responsible for this procrastinated revelation is unclear, but the best evidence points to Franciscus Sylvius (or Franz de la Boe), a seventeenth-century professor of medicine at the University of Leyden. If so, it is probable, since Sylvius was a dedicated investigator, that his discovery was an accident of pure scientific research. At any rate, in making his novel aqua vitae, he carried the distilling process to its ultimate. Nothing remained of the original beery ferment but its essence—alcohol.

It is also probable that Sylvius called his new liquor simply "aqua vitae." Before his death in 1672, however, convenience had found a more specific name. In Leyden and the rest of Holland, it was known as *junever*, the Dutch for "juniper," the herb with which it was generally flavored to mask the taste (then considered objectionable) of raw spirit. The French soon altered this to *genièvre*. It received its present, and practically universal, name in England, where the characteristic British impatience with foreign words corrupted *genièvre* to "geneva," and then, as characteristically, truncated this to "gin." In Russia, a stricter xenophobia discarded the foreign flavor along with the foreign name, and the new spirit was called "vodka," or "little water." By the time of Sylvius's discovery, Geber's wine-derived aqua vitae, despite its classic depiction as a celestially potent medicine, had long since emerged from the sickroom. An increasing desire for a degree of young courage and purified melancholy unobtainable from wine or beer had swept it into daily domestic use. "The use of *aqua vitae* has grown so common in Nether Germany and Flanders," a Dutch physician named Laevinius Lemnius reported around 1550, "that freelier than is profitable to health, they take and drink it."

Elsewhere in northern Europe, it was taken, if anything, even "freelier." The first brandy aqua vitae reached England by way of troops returning from an expedition to the Low Countries in 1585. Eight years later, according to Stephen Dowell, it had all but supplanted beer. "In their endeavors to meet the increasing demand for cheaper spirits," Dowell recounted, "our distillers now began to use, in lieu of wine or wine lees, hog's wash and such articles for making *aqua vitae*, and they continued to do so until 1593, the year of the plague. In former ages, it had been usual to attribute a visitation of the plague to the Jews, who were said to have poisoned the wells, or, indeed, to any source other than filth and their dwellings that fostered it. On this occasion, the distillers were accused of having, in effect, poisoned the *aqua vitae*." The plague may have forced an improvement in the quality of aqua vitae, but it did nothing to improve its supply. That, for all the exertions of viticulture, continued inadequate until Sylvius opened the distillers' eyes to the limitless possibilities of grain.

The change, especially in England, where in 1690 a kindly government passed "An Act for the Encouraging of the Distillation of Brandy and Spirits from Corn," was galvanic. Within four years the annual production of distilled liquors, mostly gin, reached nearly a million gallons. By 1714 the output had been doubled. By 1733 the output had increased to 11 million gal. In 1736 the government, sensing that its encouragement had gone too far, attempted to moderate the consumption of spirits by prohibiting their sale in quantities of less than 2 gal. Six years later, in 1742, the production of English spirits reached 20 million gal. The government repealed the 2-gal law in 1743. Then, setting an example that all governments have since been happy to follow, it increased the traditional nominal tax on spirits to the limit of public endurance. In addition, it encouraged, at least implicitly, a fledgling temperance movement. One of the first to respond to this encouragement was a London clergyman named James Townley. His response, which took the form of a poem, was published in 1751:

> Gin, cursed fiend, with fury fraught,
> Makes human race a prey;
> It enters by a deadly draught,
> And steals our life away.
> Virtue and Truth, driven to despair,
> Its rage compels to flee;
> But cherishes, with hellish care,
> Theft, murder, perjury.
> Damned cup, that on the vitals preys,
> That liquid fire contains;
> Which madness to the heart conveys,
> And rolls it through the veins.

The madness, however, continued to roll.

THE ORIGIN OF WHISKEY

Gin was not, as it happens, the first spirituous liquor to be distilled from grain. It was merely the first that came to the receptive attention of the civilized world. The original grain spirit was whiskey. Despite its subsequent universal identification with Scotland, it is probable that whiskey made its first appearance in Ireland. Its name alone would suggest that it came into being there. "Whiskey" derives from *uisgebeatha* (or usquebaugh), the Irish-Gaelic equivalent of aqua vitae. But when whiskey first appeared and by whom it was introduced are questions whose answers are lost beyond recall. The best that even Irish legend can do is to number its invention among the many good works of St. Patrick. Since St. Patrick died in 461, this is generally considered an unconvincing, as well as a lamely unimaginative, attribution. Nevertheless, it cannot be doubted that whiskey is very old. Most authorities, including Sir Robert Bruce Lockhart, whose work on Scotch, published in 1951, is the most recent word on the subject, are satisfied that it was widely distilled,

highly admired, and heavily consumed in Scotland at least as early
as the late fifteenth century. Documentary evidence, cited by Lockhart, establishes that James IV, who died at Flodden Field in 1513,
was only too familiar with its existence, and there is no reason to
believe that it was a novelty in his time. In addition to tracing its
age, Lockhart provides an arresting illustration of the esteem in
which whiskey was held. At the Battle of Culloden, in 1746, he
relates, "John Maitland, a Presbyter of the Episcopal Church of
Scotland, administered the Holy Eucharist to the mortally wounded
Lord Strathallan with oatcake and whisky, 'the requisite elements not
being obtainable.' " It is equally certain, however, that the whiskey
of Scotland (and its Irish counterpart) was long confined to its
native hills and glens. It was unknown in England even by name
until the middle of the eighteenth century. Dr. Johnson, in his
dictionary, which appeared in 1755, refers to it only obliquely. After
defining usquebaugh as "a compounded distilled Irish spirit, being
drawn on aromaticks," he adds, "The Highland sort is somewhat
hotter; and, by corruption, in Scottish they call it *whisky*." Dr.
Johnson encountered whiskey personally for the first time in 1773,
during his much-publicized tour of the Hebrides. His opinion of it,
which is one of the earliest on record by an Englishman, could
hardly have delighted his hosts. "I never tasted whisky," he noted in
his published version of the jaunt, "except once for experiment at
the inn in Inveraray, when I thought it preferable to gin." What
Dr. Johnson thought of gin may be deduced from his famous utterance on the acceptable varieties of drink: "Claret is the liquor for
boys; port for men; but he who aspires to be a hero must drink
brandy."

His judgment was, if nothing else, prophetic. Brandy, for those
who could afford it, remained the European choice in spirits until
the nineteenth century was well advanced. "My father," Sir Winston
Churchill has noted in a memoir, "could never have drunk whisky
except when shooting on a moor or in some very dull chilly place.
He lived in the age of brandy and soda." He also lived to see its
end. In 1849, when Lord Randolph Churchill was born, whiskey—
Scotch whiskey—was still confined not merely to Scotland but
largely to the Scottish Highlands. By the time of his death, in 1895,
it was everywhere known and respected. The general acceptance of
Scotch reflected to some extent a change in general taste. But only
in very small part. It was chiefly brought about by a change in the

taste of Scotch. In Dr. Johnson's time, Scotch whiskey (as well as that native to Ireland) was distilled from a mash, or cereal base, composed entirely of malted barley. The manufacture of malt whiskey involves three major steps. As in the standard brewing process, the barley is first malted—that is, steeped in water, allowed to sprout, and then slowly heated until dry. The next step, induced by the addition of yeast and hot water is, of course, fermentation. When fermentation has ceased, the resulting beerlike liquor is pumped into a pot, or simple retort-type still, and its alcoholic essence is vaporized, condensed, and recovered by distillation. A second distillation and a period of aging (three years or more) in sherry casks complete the process. In making Scotch, the malted barley is heated in peat-fired kilns, and the pungent odor of the burning peat is what gives the liquor its distinctive smoky flavor. It is also, however, what principally caused its long unpopularity beyond its Highland home. Although the smoky flavor of pure Scotch malt whiskey is often praised by kilted connoisseurs, less cultivated palates have usually found it dense to the point of strangulation.

THE RISE OF SCOTCH

The sudden ascendancy of Scotch was an accident of technological progress. Aeneas Coffey, an early-nineteenth-century tinkerer at the Dock Distillery in Dublin, is usually acknowledged to have been the inadvertent pioneer in its emancipation. It was Coffey's good fortune to invent the prototype of what is now known as the continuous still. His still, which a trade historian has crisply described as "an affair of two tall columns, heated by steam, into which fermented mash is poured at one end and out of which practically pure alcohol pours at the other," was patented in 1830. A year or two later, a group of Lowland entrepreneurs, inflamed by its millennial promise, introduced it into Scotland. The virtues of the Coffey still were conspicuous enough. Its operation was cheap and its production was high. That it had its drawbacks was less immediately apparent, but they presently came into view. The whiskey produced by the early Coffey still seemed all but impervious to aging. It emerged from the cask only a little darker than pure alcohol, and almost as raw and flavorless. For the next twenty years or so, this light and unappealing distillate, which now goes under the name of grain spirits (or, in the United States, grain neutral spirits), found its only reliable market among the gin rectifiers of London, who distilled it further, added juniper to it, and then bottled it as gin. The salvation of the Lowland distillers, and the ultimate triumph of Scotch, can be laid to an act of desperation by an Edinburghian named Andrew Usher. Usher was a grain-whiskey distiller, but he also handled, as a sideline, the rugged output of a Highland malt-whiskey distillery. In 1860 he conceived the revolutionary notion of blending these disparate whiskeys. Precisely what Usher hoped to achieve—a tastier grain or a blander malt—is not a matter of record, but the wisdom of his hunch has never profitably been challenged.

"RUM-BULLION ALIAS KILL-DEVIL"

The first spirituous liquor to be manufactured in what is now the United States was made on Staten Island. A distillery was established there by William Kieft, the predecessor of Peter Stuyvesant as director-general of the New Netherlands, around 1640. Until 1664, when, along with all other Dutch possessions in America, it was taken over by the British, the Kieft distillery seems to have concentrated on brandy aqua vitae and gin. The new owners converted its facilities to the distillation of rum.

Rum—or rumbullion, the name by which it was originally known—is the alcoholic essence of fermented molasses. It was introduced to the world, and probably invented, by the first European settlers in the West Indies. An anonymous seventeenth-century manuscript entitled A *Brief Description of the Island of Barbadoes*, now in the possession of Trinity College, Dublin, contains perhaps the earliest surviving reference to its name and origin. "The chief fuddling they make in the island," the author reports, "is rum-bullion, alias kill-devil, and this is made from sugar-canes distilled, a hot, hellish, and terrible liquor." According to the records of the General Court of Massachusetts, a rum distillery supplied with molasses by West Indian planters was operating in Boston as early as 1657. Its success was instantaneous, and fatefully far-reaching. Within a generation, the manufacture of rum had become (as it continued to be throughout the Colonial era) New England's largest and most profitable industry. It was also its most unsavory. For the profits in rum, unlike those acquired by the London gin distillers, derived from more than a lively demand for cheap domestic spirits.

"In whatever branch of trade we find ourselves," the nineteenth-century historian W. B. Weeden noted, "we are impressed by the prevalence and moving power of rum. Negroes, fish, vessels, lumber, intercolonial traffic in produce, all feel the initiative and moving impulse of rum." By "Negroes," Weeden meant slaves.

RUM AND SLAVES

The New England distillers were the bankers of the slave trade. They provided an international currency that made the commerce possible. Slavers of all nations used New England rum as a means of filling their holds from the slave pens on the Guinea coast. The slavers then headed for the West Indies. There they sold their slaves (for later resale in the islands and elsewhere) and took on a load of slave-produced molasses. The molasses was then brought to New England and traded for another cargo of rum. "Out of the cheap molasses of the French Islands," Woodrow Wilson once remarked, "New England made the rum which was the chief source of her wealth— the rum with which she bought slaves for Maryland and the Carolinas, and paid her balances to the English merchants." It is probable that it was this intimate association with slaving, as much as its own hot, hellish, and terrible powers, that inspired the use of "rum" as a deprecatory term for all spirituous liquor. New England rum and the Guinea trade both reached their apogee in the eighteenth century. They declined together early in the nineteenth. Slaving was crushed (though it struggled fitfully on almost to Appomattox) by an Act of Congress in 1807 that prohibited the importation of additional slaves. New England rum received a double blow. The overnight loss of the African market was merely the first. The second fell less abruptly, but its impact was even more shattering. It took the form of a revolution in public preference. The domestic supremacy of rum was founded on a demand for cheap and abundant spirits. It was toppled by an inundation of cheaper domestic whiskey.

RYE AND BOURBON

The beginnings of American whiskey are obscure. There is no clear record of either the time or the place of its birth, and even what

grain was first used in its manufacture has yet to be firmly established. The only certainty is that its production, if any, was insignificant until after the Revolution, and that it first came into
prominence as a backwoods substitute for rum on the hill farms and
keelboat landings of western Maryland, western Virginia, south-
western Pennsylvania, and eastern Kentucky. It was introduced there
by a postwar wave of Scotch-Irish settlers to whom the making of
pot-still whiskey was a natural phase of farming. At first, in all
probability, they were only concerned with providing for the family
circle. Circumstance, however, soon turned the production of whiskey
into an economic necessity. "There were no roads in the new terri-
tory," H. F. Willkie has noted, "and most of the trade was by pack-
horse. It cost more to transport a barrel of flour made from the grain
which was the principal product of that region than the flour would
have sold for on the eastern markets. If the farmer converted the
grain to whiskey, a horse, which would carry only 4 bushels in solid
form, could carry 24 bushels in liquid form. Practically every farmer,
therefore, made whiskey. So universal was the practice that whiskey
was the medium of exchange." The medium of exchange in Maryland and Pennsylvania was rye. In Virginia and Kentucky, it was corn.
Monongahela rye, a Pennsylvania product, was among the hardest of
these frontier currencies. The hardest of all was a distinctive distillate of corn produced in Bourbon County, Kentucky.

The first Kentucky whiskey was made by a Baptist clergyman
named Elijah Craig at Royal Spring, near Georgetown, in the fall
of 1789. Since Georgetown was then in Bourbon County (it is now
the Scott County seat), he thus became the inventer of Kentucky
bourbon. Tradition also credits Craig with the discovery that whiskey
stored in a charred-oak barrel eventually loses much of its natural
pallor and acquires a more pleasing taste. His eminence as Kentucky's
only distiller was not of long duration. By March 17, 1792, he had
sufficient competition to prompt the publication in a Lexington
weekly of a notice headed, "To the Distillers of Spirits in the District
of Kentucky." The notice, signed by Thomas Marshall, a revenue
inspector, announced the imposition of a federal excise tax on "Stills
and Distilled Spirits." It read, in part: "Some of the distillers, I am
informed, pretend to say they are taught to believe that the excise
is not to be collected in this district. From whence they derive their
information I cannot conceive; but do hereby inform them that the
collectors will shortly be with them in order to collect it." Six years

later, according to Marshall's records, the delinquent distillers in Kentucky alone numbered nearly two hundred. By 1810, the total of the known distillers in the state was 2,000, and their output exceeded 2 million gal. There are far fewer distillers in the entire United States today. Nevertheless, they manage, through the operation of a mere eighty-six licensed distilleries, to produce around 160 million gal of whiskey a year.

The age of alcoholic innovation expired with the nineteenth century. Its final accomplishment was the application of the Scottish principle of blending to Kentucky bourbon and Pennsylvania rye. By 1900, all the forms of alcohol now known had been discovered, tried, and appraised. The impact of the twentieth century on alcohol is difficult to chart. Its paths lead in a diversity of directions.

THE CURRENT SCENE

This is the century in which for the first time the nature of alcohol and its effect on the human mind and body has been scientifically investigated and, to a large extent, illuminated. It is the century in which for the first time an attempt was made by civil authority in Western countries to prohibit the use of alcohol. It is the century in which the nature of chronic drunkenness has been objectively examined, and the drunkard has been accepted as a sick man rather than a sinner. It is the century in which alcohol has emerged from the saloon and the stag party to the cocktail lounge, the parlor, and the family picnic—in which the ladies' entrance of the bar has become the front door. It is the century in which drinking has become a social obligation—in which to decline a drink is to invite suspicion not that one is a teetotaler but an Alcoholic Anonymous. It is the century in which the proportion of drinkers to nondrinkers has steadily increased—and in which the per capita consumption of alcohol in the United States has dropped from nearly 3 gal to only a little more than one. It is the century in which beer has lost much of its alcohol content and most of its flavor, and in which the strength of spirits has generally been reduced from the once standard one-hundred proof to eighty-six or eighty or even less. It is the century of the nursery drink—of rum and Coca-Cola, of whiskey and 7-Up, of vodka and tomato juice, of gin and consommé. But it is also the century of the eight-to-one martini, and the telltale glitter of the beer can on the highway.

REFERENCES

Arnaldus de Villanova, *The Earliest Printed Book on Wine, Now for the First Time Rendered into English and with an Historical Essay by H. E. Sigerist, with Facsimile of Original Edition*, 1478. New York, Schuman's, 1943.

Brunschwig, H., *Liber de arte distillandi: de simplicibus*, Strasbourg, 1500.

Dowell, S., *A History of Taxation and Taxes in England from the Earliest Time to the Present Day*, London, Longmans, 1884.

Horton, D., The Functions of Alcohol in Primitive Societies: A Cross-cultural Study, *Quart. J. Studies Alc.*, 4:199–320, 1943.

Johnson, S., *Journey to the Western Islands of Scotland*, Dublin, Williams, 1775.

Lemnius, L., *De miraculis occultis naturae, libri IV*, Antwerp, 1561.

Lockhart, R. H. B., *Scotch: The Whisky of Scotland in Fact and Story*, London, Putnam, 1951.

Roueché, B., *The Neutral Spirit: A Portrait of Alcohol*, Boston, Little, Brown, 1960.

Sigerist, H. E., *A History of Medicine*, New York, Oxford University Press, 1951.

Weeden, W. B., *Economics and Social History of New England, 1620–1789*, Boston, Houghton Mifflin, 1890.

Willkie, H. F., *Beverage Spirits in America: A Brief History*, New York, Newcomen Society of England, American Branch, 1947.

Giorgio Lolli, M.D.

*President, International Center for Psychodietetics
Rome, Italy, and New York City, New York*

THE COCKTAIL HOUR:
PHYSIOLOGICAL, PSYCHOLOGICAL, AND SOCIAL ASPECTS

Editor's Note   *Dr. Giorgio Lolli brings a new perspective on the function of that most modern use of alcoholic beverages—the cocktail hour. He sees it as possibly fulfilling a need in the contemporary way of living, as a help in shifting gears between the life of the large workaday world and that of the small private world. But he sees it as misused if divorced from food or if the drinking is carried to the point of inebriety. He refers to new research which demonstrates the great differences in the effects of alcohol when taken with or without food and whether taken as alcohol or as wine. And he urges that the only approach to the prevention of alcoholism is to prevent the repeated behavior that must precede it—inebriety.*

I accepted the invitation to attend this symposium with great pleasure. I find the topic assigned to me most interesting, and I welcome the privilege and the opportunity to discuss an aspect of our way of life which seldom has been mentioned in the scientific literature and which never, as far as I know, has attained the dignity of multidisciplinary discussion.

This attempt at a scientific approach to the realities of the cocktail hour stems in part from another, and not too different, endeavor. About two years after the opening of the Yale Plan Clinics for alcoholics, of which I was then the medical director, as a result of the experiences gathered from patients, I wrote a paper on the medical, psychological, and social aspects of the hangover. This was fifteen years ago, in 1946. It was a topic which some scientists and many pseudo-scientists considered with frigidity, or abhorrence, or perhaps personal and distressing memories.

Today we are considering not hangovers—which often are the sad outcome of having attended a cocktail party without knowing whether, how, how much, when, and why one should drink—but the phenomenon of the cocktail hour itself.

For me, both the topic and the situation are far happier. We all know more than we did fifteen years ago about the effects of alcohol on body functions, on mental activities, and on men and women themselves while they participate in social functions. At the same time, the attitudes of most scientists have altered from feelings of repugnance to demonstrations of keen interest in all aspects of alcohol.

Over these fifteen years, my interest in this fascinating area has remained high, but my focus has changed to some degree. Personally, to borrow from a political columnist, my own viewpoint toward alcohol is now that of the extreme center. I do not agree with either those at the extreme left or extreme right. There are, of course, no political implications here—with either the unrealistic "drys" who insist that alcohol is always dangerous for everyone, or the equally unrealistic "wets" who emphasize that alcohol is dangerous mainly for the rare alcoholic. My extreme center view is that alcohol is neither "good" nor "bad."

It should be evident by now that the value of alcohol depends primarily on who drinks it, and on when, how, how much, why, and in what form. I am confident that we already know a good deal about who should drink, and under what conditions; and that we will learn much more if, liberated from abstract generalities and illogical premises, we will try not to ask impossible questions but to reply to those which can be answered.

A study of the cocktail hour offers such a possibility. It is an ideal natural experimental situation in which body, mental, and social effects can be measured with precision. It is a situation in which the beneficial effects of alcohol as well as the detrimental ones can be assessed.

DEFINITION OF INEBRIETY

The detrimental effects can best be grouped under the label of inebriety, or what might better be termed—and so I shall define it—alcohol-induced inefficiency. And I submit that inebriety—not alcoholism—represents the fundamental alcohol problem. So-called alcoholics may be "sick" or "diseased"—society has not yet agreed on the proper descriptive term. Still, they are commonly classified as alcoholics only if, and when, they become inebriated inappropriately, frequently, and intensely. Without inebriety there is no alcoholism. I submit, also, that the prevention of those excesses labeled "alcoholism" can be achieved only by the prevention of inebriety.

Naturally, not all forms of inebriety originate from the cocktail hour. And, certainly, not all cocktail parties lead to inebriety. Most participants in such affairs do not demonstrate the detrimental effects of alcohol but rather appear to show definite benefits.

These benefits of the cocktail hour have been variously described as relaxation, socialization, a respite from the cares of the business day. In my mind, the institution of the cocktail hour is important because it represents for the individual an interlude between his participation in the activities of what we may term the "large" society and his participation in the activities of the "small" society.

SHIFTING GEARS BETWEEN TWO LIFE STYLES

By large society, I mean the contacts established by the individual during working hours. The large society encompasses a wide range of actions and reactions for the executive, the farmer, the teacher, the bus driver, and almost everyone else who must spend his eight hours a day coping with the problems, vexations, and other phenomena inextricably involved with the production of goods or of services of all kinds. The large society includes, of course, the activities of the housewife at home in her contacts with the grocer, the school teacher, and the next-door neighbor.

By small society, I mean those activities which take place in the family and are of concern to the members of a family nucleus only. There are problems and vexations here, too, but they are different from those of the large society, and the individual brings a different set of attitudes to the handling of them.

The cocktail hour is neither large nor small society. The former has just been left behind and the latter has still to be faced. The attitudes of the individual at cocktail time are neither those he wears at work nor those he wears at home. He is in a fluid state, emotionally, socially, and chemically—even before he ingests any alcoholic fluids. If he can understand this significant situation, he can be helped greatly toward understanding the real role—or the nonrole—of alcohol in his life.

The cocktail hour itself—this shifting of gears from large-society living to small-society living—is deceptively easy to describe. It may last from a few minutes to a few hours. It may be attended by an individual once in a lifetime or every day of the year. Its time is, to a large extent, optional, with middle or late afternoon preferences during weekdays, and often earlier hours during holidays. The place may be the bar or the individual's home, the train, the airplane, a friend's home, or a hotel lounge. The participants, ranging from one to several hundred individuals, may or may not move from one gathering to another and thus face different kinds of opportunities and dangers. These opportunities and dangers vary tremendously—and include many more than the opportunity of making romantic overtures, or the danger of saying the wrong thing to the wrong guest. But behind this easily depicted institution are other factors which are more significant, and which can be described only in the languages of physiology, psychology, and sociology.

Let us consider the United States, which has been widely honored or attacked as the birthplace of the cocktail hour and certainly of the cocktail party. It has been stated often, and by many, that ours is a pluralistic society. Many religious, ethnic, and national groups have brought different cultures to this country. They have withstood the impact of the melting pot and made impossible, fortunately, any monolithic vision of man and of the world. The understanding, tolerance, and utilization of cultural variety is the source and, at the same time, the result of our kind of democracy.

Yet, notwithstanding pluralism, our institutions are cemented by some fundamental ideals and goals shared by all. These are: the pursuit of excellence, the idolization of efficiency, and the passion for education as a means to achieve efficiency and excellence.

Our attitudes toward alcohol have been molded by these ideals and goals which already were part and parcel of the basic structures of the earliest American family and religious life. There is no question that enthusiasm for science and emphasis on method as a means to approach both spiritual perfection and material success have greatly contributed to the formulation of the American vision of life since Colonial times.

Method, education, excellence, and efficiency are the words of the American dream which the unceasing activities of the citizenry bring into concrete being. They are the words applicable to the work of the clergyman, the carpenter, the sailor, the jazz musician, and the physician. All these words convey, among other things, the message that no matter what we do, it is our duty and responsibility to do it well. And, this includes drinking or abstaining from drinking.

NEED FOR EFFICIENCY AND INEFFICIENCY

Let us look more closely at this word "efficiency." It is the hallmark of living and working in the large society and also in the small. It means the individual's ability and willingness to maintain already acquired knowledge, to acquire new knowledge, and to utilize his potentialities, physical and mental, to the fullest. Efficiency, likewise, represents the individual's freedom in the three main areas of self-realization, self-perfection, and self-determination.

But it also appears significant that each individual needs some inefficiency, and that each individual has his own optimum ratios of efficiency to inefficiency. For example, sleep is a state of inefficiency but requisite for greater efficiency in the day to come. A person who suffers from insomnia may thus use small amounts of alcohol at night in order to achieve a state of much needed inefficiency. For all of us, the adequate rhythms of active wakefulness and restful sleep are vivid examples of an adequate ratio of efficiency to inefficiency in one important personality area.

It becomes more and more apparent that the proper indications and contraindications for the uses of alcoholic beverages stem from the evaluation of their effects on the ratio of efficiency to inefficiency of the individual.

This ratio is a viewpoint more than a formula; its facets are as many as the infinite facets of the individual's psychological and physiological personality and vary from individual to individual according to age, state of health, occupation, and so on.

This ratio, when applied to the study of the cocktail hour, calls for replies to two questions: (1) Does ethyl alcohol contribute favorably or unfavorably to an individual's efficiency when he needs efficiency? (2) Does ethyl alcohol contribute favorably or unfavorably to an individual's inefficiency when he needs inefficiency in order to foster greater efficiency to come?

In the so-called well-adjusted individual, inefficiency occurs at the proper time and with the proper intensity to meet the demands of efficiency at a later time. In the neurotic and, even more, in the psychotic, inefficiency takes over and overwhelms efficiency. For instance, we can observe the results of inefficiency in the individual who compulsively washes his hands a hundred times a day or who cannot cross a street in fear of an automobile which is not there.

But, although excessive inefficiency is obviously undesirable, we should keep in mind the fact that inefficiency is not always excessive and not always undesirable. I have already intimated that neurotic or even psychotic behavior is only and exclusively inefficiency at the wrong time, at the wrong place, and for the wrong reasons. I would like to add now that inebriety, from its mildest manifestations to the extremes of stupor, is only and exclusively an alcohol-induced form of inefficiency at the wrong time, at the wrong place, and for the wrong reasons.

As with inefficiency in general, alcohol-induced inefficiency is not always and everywhere undesirable. Remember, if you will, the surgeons who, in the centuries before the discovery of ether and chloroform, gave large amounts of alcohol to their patients in order to protect them from pain.

The difference, then, between neurotic or psychotic behavior on the one hand and inebriated behavior on the other is mainly that the former may be observed in alcohol-free states while the latter is alcohol-induced at all times.

Some so-called neurotic or psychotic individuals drink; others don't; some use alcohol toward and others against an optimum ratio of efficiency to inefficiency. A poet may use moderate amounts of alcohol to tame some unrealistic anxieties which thwart his creative efforts. He thus widens and heightens his efficiency; he might accordingly create great poetry. Yet the very same poet would enhance his inefficiency if he drank shortly before driving his automobile. Is this poet a neurotic? Yes, because some unrealistic anxieties hamper his efficiency when he writes poems and when he drives a car. Yes, because all human beings are neurotics in the sense that neurosis, and psychosis too, is only and exclusively inefficiency—a hurdle on the road to knowledge of ourselves and of the world in which we live. Of course, there are differences, but quantitative differences only, between the mild inefficiencies of the majority of "functioning" individuals and the utter sterility of the relatively few men and women who are psychotic to the point of an almost total unawareness of reality.

ALCOHOLISM — NOT A DISEASE

Here, the matter of definitions becomes important. I most emphatically agree with the statement of a contemporary poet, C. E. Eaton,[1] that

> there should be sanctuaries
> if for nothing but the refuge of exhausted words.

A sanctuary is especially needed for the words "neurosis" and "alcoholism," both of which have become particularly exhausted. To paraphrase C. S. Lewis,[2] they have exhibited a peculiar tendency to become less descriptive and more evaluative. The consequence of this tendency is that both the "neurotic" and the "alcoholic" now are undefinable individuals who can only be labeled as "sick." The original meaning of both "neurosis" and "alcoholism" has been killed, or to use C. S. Lewis's expression, "verbicide" has been committed.

This situation becomes apparent when we examine what has been done so far in the prevention and treatment of alcoholic excesses. We have tried to count the heads of "alcoholics" without being able to define them with precision. We have carefully avoided testing the definitions of alcoholism with the tools of logic. We have squandered energies, and we have been profligate with commonplaces in futile attempts to find the very early cause—if there is such a thing—for a very late effect. We have entered controversies about the body or the mental or social causes of this effect as though the emphasized distinctions between these supposed causes were concrete realities and not convenient devices for the description of what, in all likelihood, is only one world—a world which, because of our inadequacies, we must temporarily describe in more than one scientific language.

Our failures, however, involve more than semantics. Contrary to all public health principles, after having proclaimed that alcoholism is a public health problem, we have cavalierly overlooked the early signs and symptoms of the so-called disease and rapturously trained our guns only on the saddest end products of faulty drinking habits. Of course we have failed, just as we would have failed in

[1] C. E. Eaton, Artists' Anonymous, *Northwest Review*, 4:19, Summer, 1961.
[2] C. S. Lewis, *Studies in Words*, London, Cambridge University Press, 1960, p. 7.

eradicating malaria or smallpox by displaying concern only over the final manifestations of these diseases. Many of us have failed to recognize that the addictive drinker does drink, not because he suffers from a disease, albeit he may become diseased as a result of too much drinking. The sad results of our alcoholism programs indicate the difficulties inherent in achieving a separation—legal or otherwise —between the inveterate excessive drinker and his bottle. And finally, the very good results which can be achieved in preventing inebriated behavior and in favoring wholesome drinking habits are constantly overlooked by those who are emotionally blind to the realities of the alcohol situation.

THE OTHER SIDE OF ALCOHOL

Those who have such emotional blind spots seem to ignore the end-less instances where alcohol has proved helpful over scores of cen-turies, and instead have concerned themselves—and attempted to concern us—only with alcohol problems. It is much as if a group of high-minded individuals limited their attention only to the harm which milk may cause to some people. Of course, quite a few persons are allergic to this much revered food item, and many more probably are damaged by it because of its content in fats; yet, these actual or suspected liabilities do not blind us to the realities of the great nutritional value of milk.

Those who have considered only the marriages which have been wrecked by alcohol at the cocktail hour, or the fights which have been started, or the business decisions clouded, might look also at the many marriages which may well have been saved, at the fights which may have been averted, and at the business decisions which may have been clarified by this ceremony.

Of course, alcohol has created some problems, notably here in America. But ours is a civilization of problems. According to one well-known literary critic, problems are mass-produced in this country. They represent America's most popular industry, the fatal corollary of our achievements and of their intricacies. It should not be for-gotten that alcohol also solves or alleviates many of these difficulties. It should not be forgotten that, in these tense years, alcohol can help man not just to escape from reality, but to live with it.

The view that alcoholic beverages can help in our attempts to live realistically is neither fantasy nor wishful thinking. It is based on numerous research projects carried out by my associates and myself over a number of years. The results of these investigations already point to what can be done in order to offset the dangers of drinking and to widen and deepen the advantages of the cocktail hour.

IMPORTANCE OF EATING WITH DRINKING

Some of our most important and practical findings have come from a broad inquiry on the eating and drinking habits of Italians living in Italy and Italian-Americans living in this country. The total consumption of alcoholic beverages, we found, was far higher among the Italians than among the Italian-Americans. Wine represented for the Italians, but not for the Italian-Americans, a part of the normal daily diet. Most of the Italians, but less than 10 per cent of the Italian-Americans, drank alcoholic beverages exclusively with meals.

Yet the occurrence of inebriety or intoxication among the Italians was relatively uncommon. But, in striking contrast, the Italian-Americans—who consumed less alcohol—reported a more frequent occurrence of episodes of excessive drinking.

I feel that the custom of using alcoholic beverages with food protects the individual to a large extent from some untoward effects of alcohol. Conversely, I stated at the time of the study that the cocktail hour should be watched as a possible source of difficulties.

I wrote then [Lolli et al., 1958]: "Customarily scheduled late in the afternoon, the cocktail hour comes at a time when the individual's general resistance, and specifically the resistance of his central nervous system, are usually at their lowest ebb during the day. Fatigue is the theme of the hour. This fatigue is partly the result of the day's work. It is, however, enhanced by dietary habits followed by many Americans—certainly by many of those who adhere to the cocktail custom. Their noontime meal is usually small, and sometimes omitted. In addition, the type of noon meal consumed by the majority of Americans includes only small amounts of slowly absorbable carbohydrates. Instead, it generally includes swiftly absorbable carbohydrates which lead to high blood sugar levels soon after lunch, followed by a reactive and marked hypoglycemia at the time of the cocktail hour. Thus the individual begins this hour in a state of general starvation plus a specific starvation for sugar—an internal environment which provides the central nervous system with little protection against the toxic effects of excessive amounts of alcohol. During the cocktail hour itself, the individual drinks on an empty stomach. As a result, the alcohol is absorbed rapidly from the digestive tract, high blood alcohol levels are produced, and the alcohol is oxidized slowly."

I was not planning at that time a huge job of social engineering, a crusade against the cocktail hour. I saw then and still see some dangers in it—dangers which to a large extent can be avoided if some of the facts mentioned above are kept in mind.

The dietary heresies of a hasty and unsubstantial breakfast, of an irrational luncheon preceded by, rather than eaten with, a drink, and of an oversized late dinner are all matters which can and should be corrected.

During the cocktail hour itself, food should be presented and should be consumed—whether this be the pretzels or crackers and cheese at the neighborhood tavern or the more or less complex hors d'oeuvres of the hostess at home.

Our research indicates the high incidence of unusually low blood sugar values in many uninformed eaters who turn into uninformed drinkers in the late afternoon. It should be borne in mind that, with equal amounts ingested, the effects of alcohol are more pronounced, more sudden, and more hazardous when blood sugar values are low [Serianni et al.]. Given an adequate breakfast and an adequate lunch —the latter may be eaten with a drink, but certainly should not be preceded by one—the individual will approach the cocktail hour, the interlude between his large society and his small society, with less fatigue, less anxiety, and less need for sudden and deep personality changes.

NEW AND OLD WAYS IN ITALY

It is interesting to note that the cocktail hour has now been exported to Italy. Among the Italians, it is still true now, as it was decades ago, that the incidence of serious alcoholic excesses is one of the lowest in the world, and that this partial immunity is due mainly to the widespread custom of drinking wine almost exclusively and of drinking it at mealtime. But the swift changes of the age, the complications of a problematic and mechanized life, are modifying the drinking habits of the Italians and their attitudes toward drinking.

For example, the automobile has come to Italy, and there are millions of Italians who drive cars. The Italian can no longer doze off any mild inebriety while holding the reins of his horse. He is now faced with the problem of being alcohol-free rather than care-free.

Unquestionably, with the dawn of universal history and related universal problems, Italians have been searching for chemical comforts with increasing zeal. Among them, and among many other rapidly evolving groups in the world, the cocktail hour gathers growing numbers of votaries. There are problems associated with this trend, but I venture to say that the cocktail hour, rather than being the main cause of these problems, is one of the consequences of the difficulties of our times—difficulties which the individual seeks to alleviate by means of alcoholic beverages.

Italians are still faithful to wine, but they have started the use of other beverages. They, too, as a result of prosperity, can afford a more diversified use of alcoholic beverages. Some comparative studies of drinking habits carried out a few months ago simultaneously among Americans and among Italians indicate a growing tendency toward uses of alcohol motivated by an acute need for relaxation and reduction of fatigue—a need which finds its fulfillment in the cocktail hour.

BLOOD ALCOHOL LEVELS AND PSYCHOLOGICAL EFFICIENCY

We are engaged in another research project now which is casting still more light on the bodily and mental effects of cocktail-hour drinking—an attempt to correlate the effect of certain doses and certain blood levels of alcohol with the physiological and psychological efficiency of healthy human beings.

Seemingly, this is not at all a new area of research. Many studies have been conducted here by many competent workers. Usually these investigations have been planned with the goal of finding whether, when, and how alcohol does harm—not finding what alcohol does or whether, when, and how alcohol may help. And, in attempting to find whether alcohol does produce harm, most scientists—I do not know whether consciously or unconsciously—have planned and carried out research mainly with large doses of pure ethyl alcohol dissolved in the appropriate amount of water.

The results of this earlier research are generally clear. It is evident that alcohol in such forms and in such amounts—for example, enough to produce blood alcohol levels of 0.15 per cent or more—is usually harmful. To use my terminology, it tips the ratio of efficiency to inefficiency unfavorably in the majority of individuals.

But the majority of individuals who attend a cocktail party, rarely, if ever, drink pure ethyl alcohol in water. They drink sherry or whiskey or gin or vodka or beer or vermouth or mixtures, each containing different chemicals which may modify the rate of alcohol absorption and perhaps of its burning. And, the majority of individuals who attend a cocktail party seldom, or never, drink such large amounts; their blood alcohol levels rarely reach 0.15 per cent and usually are much below this point.

This level of 0.15 per cent is of strategic significance to many leaders both in and out of medicine. I am convinced, as are most research workers in the field, that—with many exceptions due to individual variations in tolerance to alcohol—there is a fairly close relationship between blood alcohol levels above 0.15 per cent and the degree of alcohol intoxication.

"UNDER THE INFLUENCE"—A MUDDLED CONCEPT

But, I am also convinced that an equally close relationship between blood alcohol levels which are considered presumptive of being "under the influence" (0.05 to 0.15 per cent) and clinical behavior does not exist. This is not surprising. The concept of "under the influence" as distinct from the concept of "intoxication" is a muddled one. Even experienced clinicians, policemen, social workers, probation officers, and, in general, people whose occupations call for skill in evaluating human behavior, often disagree in their estimation of who is and who is not under the influence. To decide empirically and unanimously who is and who is not under the influence at a cocktail party is a well nigh impossible task, especially if the people observed drank only a few drinks. These discrepancies in judgment stem in part from the fact that, at reasonably low blood alcohol levels, only some functions are involved in under-the-influence states. Moreover, some observers are likely to minimize the significance and to overlook the impairment of functions which other observers consider of paramount importance. Thus a person may or may not appear to be under the influence according to the observer's specific moral standards or practical concerns. Besides, the concept of under the influence overlooks the possibility that, while some functions may be impaired, others may be favored by the presence of small amounts of ethyl alcohol in the body systems and organs.

The combination of some functional impairment in some facets of the personality with some improvement in others—often vaguely sensed but seldom rationally analyzed—is puzzling to the observer. It is a common feature of the cocktail hour and a neglected source of diagnostic discrepancies. It has led to a bewildering situation and to an almost blind reliance on blood alcohol concentrations as unequivocal touchstones of under-the-influence states. Because it is difficult to evaluate these states clinically, blood alcohol concentrations are burdened with the diagnostic task.

Scientists and legislators may legitimately advise judges to consider blood alcohol levels between 0.05 and 0.15 as suggestive of under-the-influence states. The mere presence of alcohol in the blood, no matter how low its concentration, probably should carry the connotation of under the influence because there is evidence that ethyl alcohol, even in minimal amounts, "influences" psychological or physiological functioning or both. But this influence is not necessarily damaging. A few cubic centimeters of a water solution of ethyl alcohol may increase the flow of stomach juices and an ounce of whiskey may favor some psychological performance. It is unfortunate, however, that the label "under the influence" should have acquired the meaning of "under the bad influence."

In this puzzling and controversial area, we are now entering the third of three historical periods of alcohol research. The first was highlighted by strivings to correlate physiological and psychological changes with amounts of alcohol ingested. The second was marked by attempts to correlate physiological and psychological changes with blood alcohol levels. The blood alcohol level is by no means the same as the amount of alcohol consumed, for it is significantly affected by such factors as the form of the alcohol, whether it was consumed as beer or wine or distilled spirits, and whether it was consumed with meals or on an empty stomach. The third phase, in which we are now involved, has started with studies of individual tolerance to small quantities of ethyl alcohol—the amounts actually consumed by nonproblem drinkers—and of the effect of variables other than blood alcohol concentrations.

BLOOD ALCOHOL LEVELS AND NUTRITIONAL CONDITION

Our own studies in this third phase were prompted partly by the scanty and often contradictory nature of the information now available on the effects of small amounts of alcohol, as well as by the growing concern in most civilized countries over the effects of such small amounts on individual efficiency—a concern which is mirrored not only in research projects but also in legislative proposals and actions. Although our results are still unpublished, some of the data from the first year of work are so clear-cut, and seem to have such a definite bearing on the problems of the cocktail hour, that they may be mentioned here.

Starting with an earlier but unconfirmed impression that, for example, 6 oz of whiskey on a full stomach may cause less reaction than 2 oz of whiskey ingested at the cocktail hour by a half-starved individual, we first set up a testing procedure with all the standard clinical and statistical controls. Healthy subjects were tested on an empty stomach with no alcohol, on an empty stomach but with alcohol added, and after a standard 1500-calorie mixed meal with alcohol. The alcoholic beverages included a dry red wine containing 12 per cent alcohol and a 12-per-cent solution of ethyl alcohol as a control.

By adjusting the dosages, it was possible to produce the same blood alcohol levels under different conditions. For instance, to duplicate the blood alcohol concentration produced by 5 oz of wine on an empty stomach, it was necessary to administer 10 oz—a double dose—with meals. These were the amounts of wine given to subjects weighing approximately 150 lb—amounts which were proportionately increased or decreased with heavier or lighter subjects.

The subjects then underwent a battery of standard psychological and physiological tests to measure blood pressure, pulse rate, eye-to-hand coordination, flicker fusion frequency, time perception, form perception, bimanual coordination, and other functions.

A comparison between the empty-stomach tests and the empty-stomach-plus-wine tests showed that some of the functions had been improved while others had been impaired by wine.

More significant was the comparison between the empty-stomach-plus-wine tests and the meal-plus-wine tests. Here the dosage of the beverage had been adjusted to give the same blood alcohol level. But only the performance with wine on an empty stomach showed any significant interference with function. Test performances with wine given with a meal, and given in a double dose, demonstrated essentially no differences from the scores obtained on an empty stomach without wine.

DIFFERENCE BETWEEN WINE AND ALCOHOL

It was also observed that the results under these different conditions with wine could not be matched by similar tests with plain alcohol. Alcohol taken as a water solution produces much higher blood alcohol concentrations than alcohol taken in equal amounts as wine. This may be due to the faster rate of absorption and perhaps also to the slower rate of burning of alcohol taken as a water solution.

We likewise have some preliminary evidence that alcoholic beverages other than wine may produce significantly different blood alcohol curves and perhaps cause different reactions. A careful study of these other beverages is urgently needed.

Let me note again that these investigations were conducted with relatively small amounts of alcohol and with relatively low blood alcohol concentrations. These concentrations were far below the 0.15 per cent level which is of such importance to judges and police officers, but they were nevertheless in the range which occurs commonly in the lives of normal drinkers, of men and women who use alcohol but have no alcohol problems, of most people who participate in the cocktail hour.

A tremendous amount of work remains to be done by all of us before we will be able to remove all the vague beliefs and all the weird hearsay from this field. But already we can do a great deal. We already can supply drinkers with factual information—quantitative data—which can help them toward excellence and protect them from inadequacy.

Strivings toward excellence and protection from inadequacy are ideals shared by us and by those who so far have been against the use of even moderate amounts of alcoholic beverages. Of course, we do not want to force teetotalers into drinking. But, I am confident that we will be able to prove that excellence can be pursued effectively by individuals who use alcoholic beverages rationally. As for the extremes of alcohol excesses, we are far more radical in our approach than even those individuals who are concerned with "alcoholism" almost exclusively. Our goal is to prevent any form of inebriety, any form of unjustified alcohol-induced inefficiency. It is much easier to prevent inebriety than to prevent the extremes of alcohol addiction. And with the prevention of inebriety, prevention of alcohol addiction follows by itself.

As a conclusion, I should like to emphasize that the thoughts which I have presented and the results of these thoughts stem from a lifelong interest in nutritional habits, studied not only in their physiological and biochemical but also in their psychological and social aspects. Nutritional habits include eating and drinking habits.

A study of the uses of alcohol belongs to the broad and rewarding field of nutrition. A combined medical, psychological, and social approach to the problems of alcohol understood as a special problem of nutrition offers the best hope of success.

After so much insistence on the scientific approach, you will allow a physician, born to medicine at a time when medicine was still considered an art more than a science, to quote from a poet who did not have the cocktail hour in mind when he wrote in 1839:[3]

> Life's more than breath and the quick round of blood.
> 'Tis a great spirit and a busy heart;
> The coward and the small in soul scarce do live.
> One generous feeling, one great thought, one deed
> Of good, ere night, would make life longer seem
> Than if each year might number a thousand days
> Spent as is this by nations of mankind.
> We live in deeds, not years; in thoughts, not breaths;
> In feelings, not in figures on a dial.
> We should count time by heart-throbs. He lives most
> Who thinks most, feels the noblest, acts the best.

Rather than hinder, the cocktail hour can favor our efforts to attain these ideals, still shared by all of us.

REFERENCES

Lisansky, E. S., Golder, G., and Lolli, G., Relationship of Personality Adjustment to Eating and Drinking Patterns in a Group of Italian Americans, *Quart. J. Studies Alc.*, 15:545–561, 1954.

Lolli, G., The Hang-over in Relation to the Theory and Treatment of Alcohol Addiction, *Quart. J. Studies Alc.*, 7:193–213, 1946.

[3] Bailey, Phillip James, "Festus," 1839.

Lolli, G., *Social Drinking. How to Enjoy Drinking without Being Hurt by It,* Cleveland, World Publishing, 1960.

Lolli, G., Serianni, E., Banissoni, F., Golder, G., Mariani, A., McCarthy, R. G., and Toner, M., The Use of Wine and Other Alcoholic Beverages by a Group of Italians and Americans of Italian Extraction, *Quart. J. Studies Alc.,* **13**:27–48, 1952.

Lolli, G., Serianni, E., Golder, G., Balboni, C., and Mariani, A., Further Observations on the Use of Wine and Other Alcoholic Beverages by Italians and Americans of Italian Extraction, *Quart. J. Studies Alc.,* **14**:395–405, 1953.

Lolli, G., Serianni, E., Golder, G. M., and Luzzatto-Fegiz, P., *Alcohol in Italian Culture. Food and Wine in Relation to Sobriety among Italians and Italian Americans,* Glencoe, Ill., Free Press, and New Brunswick, N.J., Rutgers Center of Alcohol Studies, 1958.

Lolli, G., Serianni, E., Golder, G., Mariani, A., and Toner, M., Relationship between Intake of Carbohydrate-rich Foods and Intake of Wine and Other Alcoholic Beverages. A Study among Italians and Americans of Italian Extraction, *Quart. J. Studies Alc.,* **13**:401–420, 1952.

Luzzatto-Fegiz, P., and Lolli, G., The Use of Milk and Wine in Italy, *Quart. J. Studies Alc.,* **18**:355–381, 1957.

Serianni, E., Cannizzaro, M., and Mariani, A., Blood Alcohol Concentrations Resulting from Wine Drinking Timed According To the Dietary Habits of Italians, *Quart. J. Studies Alc.,* **14**:165–173, 1953.

ALCOHOL IN
CONTEMPORARY CULTURE

Moderator   Dr. J. Anthony Deutsch
Participants   Dr. Franz Alexander, Dr. Giorgio Lolli, Dr. Salvatore
P. Lucia, and Mr. Berton Roueché

Dr. Deutsch   I should like to open this panel discussion with
Dr. Lucia's definition of alcoholism. I believe he has a great many
things to say on the subject, and I think it will help clarify some of
the questions we are at a loss here to answer.

Dr. Lucia   I should say that this symposium has been conspicuous by the apparent deletion of any discussion of alcoholism. Also, I
should say that we have not mentioned the situation in which mankind finds itself—a situation in which the need to escape, or to find
some mechanism of release, has been considered to require more than
a compatible dose of alcohol.

Now about alcoholism: From the very beginning, and I think
everyone knows this, alcohol is a depressant; therefore, one can anticipate a degree of alteration in the psychobiological reaction of the
imbiber, depending upon his tolerance, depending upon the way he
would react to it, and to a lot of other things, too.

One says, "it gives me a lift," but it does not give him a lift.
That "lift" is due to a state called euphoria which, in turn, is due to
a lack of inhibitions. When someone is attracted to the use of an
agent capable of inducing such a state, and if the agent happens to
be alcohol, he very soon learns to feel the need for it, and when he
feels this need, he is habituated; and, when his drive for the satisfaction of this habituation leads to intemperate use, and if withdrawal
symptoms appear when he cannot obtain this agent, that, to my
point of view, constitutes alcoholism. It is the habituation to a
chemical agent which interferes with normal functioning of the body
in its absence.

Dr. Deutsch   Thank you very much indeed. There is, however,
one question which arose in my mind: Dr. Lucia stated that alcohol
is a depressant, but some of Dr. Alexander's remarks made it ap-

parent, to me at least, that alcohol seems to have an uneven or selective action. Dr. Alexander said that certain pleasurable sensations are unaffected or may even be enhanced by the use of alcohol, whereas certain sensations or feelings of the opposite variety, those arising from noxious stimulations, general feelings of guilt and anxiety, seem to be reduced. This would tend to argue for some kind of selective action by the alcohol on those centers in the nervous system which tend to affect the centers more concerned with unpleasant effect.

I was wondering whether any of the speakers would like to comment on this?

Dr. Alexander I think what one should consider, in evaluating the effects of alcohol, is the time element. The statement that alcohol is a depressant is true if one wants to evaluate the end effect or the total effects of alcohol. But one can also refer to alcohol as a stimulant, when you consider a certain time element—namely, the initial effect of the alcohol. In this case it is a stimulant because it inhibits inhibitory functions.

When the effects of the alcohol extend over a period of time and the lower centers too become involved, then the overt manifestation will be that of a depressant. The most common observation is that after the first drink the person is exuberant, talks more, is louder; certainly he does not appear depressed; if anything, "stimulated." But if he continues drinking and time passes, he might drink himself into a stupor. Obviously, then, you get an entirely different picture if you study the initial effect of alcohol, say the first half hour, or the effect five or six hours later.

For most people, the early effect of alcohol produces greater exuberance, an elated mood, a feeling of light, carefree daring; a shy person becomes more daring and more stimulated sexually, but if he goes on drinking, he can drink himself into complete impotence. Obviously, then, a statement that alcohol is a depressant must be qualified as to when it is a depressant. Is it a depressant all the time? It changes the equilibrium of the inhibitory and the excitatory process: initially, it cuts out certain inhibitions and the person becomes more excited; later, when the deeper centers are also affected, the paralyzing effect starts.

Dr. Lucia You are discussing something which is a compensatory mechanism, a very complicated piece of engineering, the human brain. If one takes alcohol and applies it to a single cell, it is a depressant. When you have a highly organized unit, it is also a depressant, if you admit—and I use your own words now—that it produces excitation by virtue of the euphoria. A person's adrenal activity is then interfered with, and you can interpret this as stimulation, if you wish, but to me it is a release of a tremendous amount of energy that happens to be disorganized. It is the end result of a basic, cellular depressant reaction.

Mr. Rouché   I wonder if the effect of a drink or two might not give a truer picture, a truer image of the individual, than the one he might present of himself when sober and bound by established inhibitions or restrictions?

Dr. Lucia   It is an artificial device.

Mr. Rouché   He is really more himself.

Dr. Lucia   No, I wouldn't say he was more himself; he would censor himself less. By removing this censor he might make himself less attractive as a citizen, by and large.

Mr. Rouché   That is true.

Dr. Lolli   I don't agree with either. We are dealing with a semantic problem here. We apply the word "depressant" to two different things. With the exception of one research worker who is here present, alcohol is considered by practically everybody as a depressor of the central nervous system. However, just because this depression moves gradually from the highest to the lowest centers of the central nervous system, it might result in behavioral stimulation. Pharmacologically, I am quite certain, alcohol is a depressant—unless some experiments which I think Dr. Masserman carried out many years ago[1] with very minute solutions of alcohol have been confirmed recently; I don't know about that. Anyway, the majority of investigators think about it as a depressant of the central nervous system, which doesn't mean a depressant of behavior at all times.

Dr. Alexander   I think that to compare the effects of alcohol on a single cell with its effects on a mechanism as complex as the brain is wrong. I would accept that the basic effect of alcohol on cellular activity is depressing; but if we deal with the total central

[1] J. H. Masserman, Experimental Psychopharmacology and Behavioral Relativity, in P. H. Hoch and J. Zubin (eds.), *Problems of Addiction and Habituation*, New York, Grune & Stratton, 1958.
J. H. Masserman, J. Beal, and R. Sanders, Stimulant Effects of Ethyl Alcohol in Corticohypothalamic Functions, *J. Pharmacol.*, 70:450–453, 1940.

nervous system, not the single cell, alcohol depresses "depressing" influences—in other words, it has a cortical inhibitory function. The effect has to be judged as it extends over the total nervous system. If you have a complex system of cells and some of these cells inhibit other cells, let us say cortical cells inhibit hypothalamic cells, then, if you depress the cortical cells, the hypothalamic centers are more active—or less inhibited—because the inhibitory effect is depressed. We are not interested in single cells, but a system of cells—the central nervous system.

Dr. Lucia I incorporated in my statement, in the very beginning, that the manifestations of the effect of alcohol are characteristic of the individual, the way an individual responds to a stimulus— whether it is a depressive stimulus or what you may interpret as an excitatory stimulus. This involves a mechanism over and above the single statement I made that we are dealing basically with a depressing agent, a cellular depressant.

How you may react to a cutting statement may be quite different from the way I would react, but we cannot say that the statement itself has the venom in it; it depends on our interpretation of it. The fact is that alcohol is a depressant, and how a person reacts to it at the psychic level and the higher levels, rather than some of the intermediary levels, is not the point of issue, because that is not predictable.

Dr. Alexander It is a depressant with a stimulating effect.

Dr. Lucia If the concept of stimulation means removing inhibitions, then I agree.

Dr. Deutsch I think this has been a very amusing and enlightening discussion. I am just wondering what grounds there were for certain assumptions made by the speakers—for example, that the inhibitory effect of alcohol is primarily a cortical spreading-downwards effect.

I seem to remember that some of the work pioneered by Dr. Masserman suggested at least the possibility that alcohol may not primarily be working on the high centers, but may have some kind of selective action on other, lower centers.

Dr. Lucia There is one point which might be brought up and which, I think, has practical significance. There are certain people who do not like gin, and others who do not like rum, for very definite reasons. I am talking about the effect of the aromatic constituents of some drinks on certain highly organized functions, like equilibration, hearing, nystagmus, gait. These things are extremely delicate, but they can be measured and they show different reactions to a like dose of alcohol in different individuals. And to get these things mixed up with higher and lower nervous system centers— though I appreciate that we have to take that into consideration—or to draw universal conclusions aside from what one can measure, is, I think, ridiculous.

Dr. Deutsch   We were mainly discussing alcohol and not the various substances mixed with it.

Dr. Lucia   They play a role in alcohol—unfortunately.

Dr. Lolli   We see in hangovers different reactions to different beverages; there is no question about that.

Mr. Roueché   It has been pointed out that nobody drinks alcohol, pure alcohol.

Dr. Alexander   They do have different effects. If we speak of alcohol, that is one thing; if we speak of drinking the commercially available drinks, then we don't study the effect of alcohol but alcohol plus all kinds of other substances, among them some which have stimulating effects.

Dr. Deutsch   This one seems to be a field for Mr. Roueché, trying to advocate the devising of new forms of alcohol admixtures —an art which unfortunately has died out. It seems to me that with the present scientific potential and biochemical knowledge, we might be able to advance better mixtures which wouldn't have the unfortunate effects Dr. Lucia complained of.

Dr. Lucia   This is not an unfortunate effect; this is just life. It just happens to be a product which has been created, given to the public, and the people have learned to tolerate it; that is the important thing. We all are aware that the noxious influence may be neutralized by increase in tolerance—from the psychological level right on down to the biological and chemical level—and we should not ignore that.

I should like to come back to a point I made in the beginning, that some of these things we have been discussing, which may have an unpleasant connotation as applied to human behavior, are the result of forces which have driven man into a situation where he has to have release of some type or other. Let us define that, along with our definition here of social uses of the cocktail hour. I think a cocktail hour is an insult to an intelligent human being.

Dr. Deutsch It seems to me that Dr. Lolli has already gained a convert.

Dr. Lolli In what sense?

Dr. Deutsch As far as I understood you, you were saying that the cocktail hour as it was presently constituted led to serious types of excessive use of alcohol which could perhaps be avoided if the alcohol were consumed under different circumstances.

Dr. Lolli I said that the cocktail hour has some assets and some liabilities and that it is up to us to decide which are the assets and which are the liabilities in a given individual. I think it has to be individualized a good deal; I don't think we can generalize.

Dr. Alexander A statement was made, and I think it is a very fine global statement, but as every such statement, it must be qualified: Humanity is driven by civilization to some kinds of relief measures like drinking. I should like to rephrase this and state that some of humanity is driven more and some is driven less, and this is what makes the difference between the alcoholic and the social drinker.

Dr. Lucia Dr. Lolli, do you think that our American habits have contaminated the Italians?

Dr. Lolli No, I think their new ways are better than their old ways, but I am not against the old drinking habits. I also think that huge jobs of social engineering are very difficult. Americans are learning from the Italians and from the Europeans a good deal in the use of alcoholic beverages with meals. It is a sign of sophistication now to drink wine with meals. However, I am not convinced that they are going to give up distilled spirits or beer, and I am not convinced that they should do so, because these also fulfill some need.

Mr. Roueché I think Dr. Lucia goes too far in denying our friends a more stimulating depressant spirit than wine.

Dr. Lucia I don't deny it to them. I think there is nothing on earth finer than a really magnificent spirit taken straight.

Dr. Deutsch I should like to know if the panel would like to make any further statements, or raise any further questions?

Dr. Lucia I should like to make a statement now that if anyone were to apply to me the term "sophisticated," I should like him to define this term. To me it implies something very superficial—it has breadth, thinness, but no depth.

Dr. Lolli What I meant was that people open to artistic

expressions and experiences——who enjoy with a good meal also
some of the artistic quality the setting has—— now use wine, which
they would not have done in this country some years ago. Isn't
the increasing acceptance of wine an amazing phenomenon in this
culture?

Dr. Alexander Wine also can be drunk in a very unsophisti-
cated way. The worst cases of alcoholism are the wine-drinking
alcoholics.

Dr. Lolli My colleagues and I have carried out a rather careful study of this whole story. We studied Brazilians, Italians, New
Yorkers, Californians, French, and Swiss,[2] and we found the following: In Brazil there is a very good distilled spirit, very tasty,
called *cachaca*. It is very inexpensive, whereas wine is very expensive there. All real problem drinkers drink *cachaca*; they don't
use wine.

In Italy the few inveterate alcoholics use wine, because they
don't have anything else available.

In New York and to a certain extent in San Francisco, the use
of fortified wine by problem drinkers and advanced problem
drinkers is definitely linked with economics. As long as an ounce
of alcohol as fortified wine costs much less than an ounce of
alcohol as distilled spirits, when money is not available, they drink
that wine. But practically all of the winos that we studied showed
preference for other alcoholic beverages. They use wine because it
costs less; in other words, it is the chemical comfort which can be
achieved at a cheaper price. So we have, on the one hand, the
civilized, cultured consumer of wine, and on the other, the most
destitute penniless problem drinkers.

[2] P. Devrient and G. Lolli, Choice of Alcoholic Beverage among 240 Alcoholics
in Switzerland, *Quart. J. Studies Alc.*, 23:459–467, 1962.

G. Lolli, G. M. Golder, E. Serianni, G. Bonfiglio, and C. Balboni, Choice
of Alcoholic Beverages among 178 Alcoholics in Italy, *Quart. J. Studies Alc.*,
19:303–308, 1958.

G. Lolli, E. Schesler, and G. M. Golder, Choice of Alcoholic Beverage
among 105 Alcoholics in New York, *Quart. J. Studies Alc.*, 21:475–482, 1960.

D. Parreiras, G. Lolli, and G. M. Golder, Choice of Alcoholic Beverage
among 500 Alcoholics in Brazil, *Quart. J. Studies Alc.*, 17:629–632, 1956.

R. Sadoun and G. Lolli, Choice of Alcoholic Beverage among 120 Alcoholics
in France, *Quart. J. Studies Alc.*, 23:449–458, 1962.

J. Terry, G. Lolli, and G. Golder, Choice of Alcoholic Beverage among
531 Alcoholics in California, *Quart. J. Studies Alc.*, 18:417–428, 1957.

Dr. Deutsch Would you say that wine, with economic incentive being equal, is less likely to lead to alcoholism?

Dr. Lolli I would not like to generalize, but if you drink too much wine, you get some horrible hangovers, so in general it is conducive to moderate drinking.

Dr. Lucia Did I understand that there was a disparaging note in the fact that the American public had rediscovered the value of sequestering a bottle behind the faggots somewhere? I think it is a sign of civilization that we can give the right place to a good dietary beverage and to select beautiful samples of it and divide them and share them with our friends at the table. This, to me, is civilization. We should cultivate it; it is the only road to temperance, because as soon as you say "thou shalt not," you're in trouble.

Dr. Lolli I agree with you.

4

ALCOHOL
IN OUR SOCIETY

Dr. Straus   *The press reflects a popular tendency to assume that almost any anti-social behavior involving young people is usually due to their drinking; such assumptions are sometimes made in the face of clear evidence to the contrary.*

Judge Murtagh   *I want to emphasize the fact that we should not assume, because we have a chronic excessive drinker on skid row, that he is an alcoholic. . . . He probably has a much more deep-seated pathology of which the excessive drinking is symptomatic.*

Robert Straus, Ph.D.

Professor and Chairman, Department of Behavioral Sciences
University of Kentucky Medical Center, Lexington, Kentucky

TO DRINK
OR NOT TO DRINK

Editor's Note   The effects of drinking on society and society's influence on drinking are topics which have only lately come under the
formal consideration of the scientific disciplines. As yet only a few
studies furnish concrete information in this realm. In his introduc-
tory presentation Dr. Robert Straus calls attention to the fact that
in American culture a great number of individuals, especially young
people just emerging into maturity, have to make individual decisions about drinking. With insight derived from original research,
Dr. Straus describes the plight of adolescents of high school and
college age. The laws of most states seem to expect them to practice abstinence until their twenty-first birthdays. Most of them,
however, are introduced to drinking, often in their families, long
before this, and many of them become simultaneously acquainted
with the conflict around drinking. It is forbidden, but it is needed
—for example, to prove one's manliness or to get dates. Because
adolescence is a crucial period for the socialization of the individual in our culture, Dr. Straus suggests that the need for a more
rational approach, based on research within a holistic frame of
reference, is especially acute in this connection.

Most references to the problems associated with the drinking of
alcoholic beverages focus on a consideration of alcoholism. Less
attention is given to the many additional problems, including
other forms of pathological drinking, intoxication, the relationship
of drinking to such problems as marital discord, the legal controls
of production and distribution, drinking and driving, law enforcement, and the impact on jails and mental hospitals. Furthermore,
the epidemiologist studying the frequency and distribution of alcohol problems is quick to observe that alcoholism and other forms
of pathological drinking occur only in individuals who actively

211

participate in a particular form of social custom: the use of alcoholic beverages. None of the usually mentioned considerations about alcohol has as direct an impact on so great a number of individuals in our society as that of deciding whether to participate in the custom of drinking—"to drink or not to drink." At one or another time, this question is faced by nearly everyone in American society; for some, it presents a continuing dilemma.

In historical and cross-cultural perspective, the existence and nature of drinking customs have been influenced by many factors. Climate is clearly one of these, both in the very cold and the very hot areas of the world. The flora determines to a considerable extent the nature of alcoholic beverage. Topography is related to these factors and also has an impact on drinking customs by facilitating or limiting the distribution of alcoholic beverages. War and conquest are well-known in their effects on the transmission of human customs including the use of alcoholic beverages. In many sections of the world, at particular times, the beliefs of one or another society regarding such matters as nutrition, health and disease, and the struggle with the unknown elements of man's environment, are found to be important. Last, but not least, the stage of technological development has much to do not only with the nature of alcoholic beverages but with their consumption. In contemporary American society nearly every form of drinking belief and practice observed in history and in studies of different cultures has some counterpart.

SOCIALIZATION AND REFERENCE GROUPS

An individual's decision to drink or not to drink occurs in the context of his socialization process. It must be made in the face of conflicting values and attitudes in the total society. It is heavily influenced by the practices and sanctions of his reference groups, together with his individual biological and psychological idiosyncrasies. It is important to define what we mean by socialization and reference groups. *Socialization* is the process of acquiring appropriate roles (customary expected behavior) and of learning what to expect of others so that one may get along in society. Although it is of special significance during infancy, childhood, and adolescence, the process of socialization continues throughout the entire life span. *Reference groups* are those groups in society with whom an individual shares role expectations, values, and behavior. These include the family, age peers, neighborhood, church, educational peers, and ethnic, occupational and fraternal associates. The impact of reference groups on individual behavior is well illustrated by E. L. Koos in *The Health of Regionville*. He tells of an "upper-class" mother who calls a physician to see her child who has chicken pox. She calls him not because she thinks that the illness warrants it, but because if she does not, the girls in her bridge club "will think I'm neglecting him." Koos contrasts this with a "lower-class" woman suffering acutely from a chronic and severe backache who will not see a physician because, if she did, "the girls would hoot me out of town."

The relative impact of different reference groups on the decision regarding drinking varies greatly at different life periods. In childhood, the chief impact is made by the parental family, and by ethnic and church reference groups. In early adolescence, we must add to these the neighborhood, peer group and the school fraternal group. In late adolescence are added the college crowd or fraternal group, the neighborhood "gang," dating companions, and job associates. In adulthood, job associates are of great importance, and we must consider also the "social" crowd, the marital family, and the ethnic, church, and neighborhood groups. Lastly, in order to understand individual variations in response to alcoholic beverages, we must also study physiology and biochemistry as well as personality and motivation.

ADOLESCENT DRINKING

Adolescent drinking customs are of the greatest interest today and have received much attention from scientists as well as from the lay press. In the many studies of American children that have been made [cf. McCarthy], it appears that almost half of the childhood population has had some exposure to alcoholic beverages by the age of ten. This may occur either as part of a family custom (ceremonial, nutritional, medicinal), or as an experiment, or even as a joke. By adolescence, many children are more or less familiar with alcoholic beverages, and the percentage and degree of familiarity increase with nearness to adulthood. Riley and Marden, in their studies of the social pattern of drinking, suggested that the age class 18–21 contains the highest percentage of alcohol users. This is despite the fact that the laws of most states prohibit the sale of alcoholic beverages to individuals under twenty-one years of age. Such laws define "drinking" as an adult form of behavior. It is interesting in this context to note that some individuals cease to use alcoholic beverages after they are legally accorded the right to do so, and that the percentage of individuals who do not drink increases somewhat with advancing age.

We must not, however, exaggerate the importance of alcohol in adolescence, since the vast majority of teen-agers who drink do not drink very often nor do they consume very much at a time. However, drinking by teen-agers does involve problems. We consider chiefly, of course, the problem of intoxication both in its physiological and psychological manifestations. The initial psychological reaction of a novice to the effects of alcohol is a sphere often neglected. Drinking also gives rise to many other problems, some of a purely incidental nature but others more fundamental. It is important to consider the problems which arise when drinking involves breaking with family or religious convictions. Also, drinking frequently involves violation of college or community rules or mores. The individual may be seriously confused when drinking evokes feelings of personal conflict or guilt [cf. Straus and Bacon; Skolnick]. Lastly, drinking is sometimes associated with sexual behavior which evokes similar kinds of conflict.

Studies of drinking patterns of college students reveal that colleges having formal prohibitions of drinking, such as the Mormon and the southern fundamentalist sectarian colleges, have relatively fewer students who use alcoholic beverages than colleges with no restrictions or merely token prohibition. However, at "restricted" schools, those students who break the formal code by drinking tend to drink more frequently and more heavily and are more often involved in drinking-related incidental problems than are students of more "liberal" colleges who drink. As one student noted, "If you have to drive fifty miles to get a drink, you don't take just one drink" [Straus and Bacon]. Discussions with young people in many settings leave an impression that a significant number, especially young women, feel that they are forced to drink in order to be accepted, or to be popular, or just in order to get dates.

ADULT RESPONSES

There is no evidence that links patterns of teen-age drinking directly with alcoholism. Although some young people manifest early prodromal signs of alcoholism, these are no more numerous than are alcoholics in the adult population. However, community studies have revealed a high degree of concern on the part of adults with teen-age drinking. Often, adults confuse such drinking with alcohol pathology. We find parents who tend to blame or fix responsibility upon schools and law-enforcement agencies. Equally we find that schools tend to blame or fix responsibility on parents and law-enforcement agencies, while law-enforcement personnel in turn tend to blame parents and schools. Thus a full cycle of recrimination is developed in the community. Moreover, the press reflects a popular tendency to assume that almost any antisocial behavior involving young people is usually due to their drinking; such assumptions are sometimes made in the face of clear evidence to the contrary.

Like many other social problems, then, the question "to drink or not to drink" elicits a wide variety of ineffectual social responses. Among these are exaggeration of the problem and, in contrast, a selective blindness: "If I don't see it, it can't be there." As well, we find denial, fear and anxiety, bravado and humor, projection of blame, and last but not least, rationalization.

When we consider the phenomenon of adolescent drinking, it becomes apparent that adolescence is a particularly crucial socialization period in our culture. It is a period of transition from dependence on a parental family to independence in marital, employment, and community status. In our culture it is a period during which social and psychological maturity frequently lags behind physical maturity. This contrasts sharply with some societies where the transition to adult status is rapid, often marked by clearly defined rites of passage, and where adolescence as we know it does not exist. However, it is with our culture that we must be chiefly concerned.

PROBLEMS OF THE ADOLESCENTS

Adolescents in our society are faced with many discontinuities and inconsistencies. They are expected to assume certain "adult" roles and responsibilities, while many "adult" rights and privileges are withheld. Much adolescent behavior which is culturally sanctioned does little to prepare the adolescent for the roles required of an adult. This is well illustrated in examining the enormous differences between culturally expected behavior with respect to the custom of dating and the expected roles in marriage. Adolescents, in the face of conflict, inconsistency, and confusion, tend to press for symbolic adult status and to reject symbols of repressive authority. Drinking behavior provides an ideal symbol of the achievement of adult status. It is even defined legally as an adult privilege. At the same time, restrictions against teen-age drinking provide the symbolic "red flag" for rejection of authority.

The restrictions of adolescence are such that many young people develop doubts about their own manliness or womanliness. Drinking behavior for some young people provides a symbolic proof of manliness. For others, alcohol helps remove inhibitions to the actual demonstration of sexual prowess or attraction. Many efforts to control or moderate the drinking of young people, although made with good intent, simply serve to enhance the attractiveness and status of drinking.

The pharmacological properties of alcohol are such that many young people for whom the question of drinking involves conflict can find in the act of drinking temporary relief from the very anxiety that their concern about drinking has created. Such "solace" is denied to young people who may be equally anxious about a decision not to drink which is made in the face of social pressure.

The understanding of problems associated with questions of drinking or not drinking by young people requires much further study in the context of a broader consideration of physiological, biochemical, psychological, and social aspects of adolescence as a phenomenon of our culture.

It is essential in order to advance our understanding of this whole question that we should use a holistic approach. The study of human problems has been characterized during the first half of the twentieth century by a high degree of compartmentalization and fragmentation of scientific knowledge, and by the growth of specialization in its applications. During this period, unprecedented inquiry and discovery in the physical and biological sciences have coincided with the introduction of scientific method and rigor to the study of psychological and sociocultural aspects of behavior. However, the advancement of knowledge within traditional disciplines has led to a focusing of attention on more complex phenomena which do not lend themselves to unidisciplinary approaches.

As a result, research today in many fields of endeavor is crossing the lines of individual disciplines. Laboratories are being organized with a multidiscipline team approach, and it is recognized in the training of scientists that breadth and knowledge in related fields is essential to the attainment of depth with competence in a particular field. Indeed, the current half century seems increasingly to be characterized by a holistic or comprehensive approach to the study of human problems. The study of drinking behavior is particularly demanding of a multidisciplinary approach, and the nature of alcohol is such that alcohol problems lend themselves particularly well to consideration within a holistic frame of reference.

The decision to drink or not to drink is not made within narrow frames of reference. Its significance can only be considered in terms which include all the relevant determinants of behavior—social, biological, physical, psychological, and cultural, in which the role of the individual can be considered.

REFERENCES

Koos, E. L., *The Health of Regionville*, New York, Columbia University Press, 1954.

McCarthy, R. G., *Teen-Agers and Alcohol. A Handbook for the Educator*, New Brunswick, N.J., Rutgers Center of Alcohol Studies, 1956.

Riley, J. W., Jr., and Marden, C. F., The Social Pattern of Alcoholic Drinking, *Quart. J. Studies Alc.*, 8:265–273, 1947.

Skolnick, J. H., Religious Affiliation and Drinking Behavior, *Quart. J. Studies Alc.*, 19:452–470, 1958.

Straus, R., and Bacon, S. D., *Drinking in College*, New Haven, Yale University Press, 1953.

Straus, R., and McCarthy, R. G., Nonaddictive Pathological Drinking Patterns of Homeless Men, *Quart. J. Studies Alc.*, 12:601–611, 1951.

Kettil Bruun, Ph.D.

The Finnish Foundation for Alcohol Studies
Helsinki, Finland

DRINKING PRACTICES
AND THEIR
SOCIAL FUNCTION

Editor's Note *When considering the social functions of alcohol,
Dr. Kettil Bruun argues, study by the special techniques of social
science is particularly appropriate—in some respects potentially
more useful than the multidisciplinary approach advocated by
others. Dr. Bruun emphasizes the importance of the study of
drinking practices; until now such objective studies have rarely
been undertaken. Past research, he notes, tended to start from a
biased approach—though the bias may have been unintended.
Chiefly medically oriented, the investigations were directed at
seeking out the harmful effects of alcohol; hence, they dealt
with such topics as alcoholic diseases. Even investigations with a
social-science orientation were similarly biased; thus, studies of the
effects of alcohol on family life assumed that the effects must be
bad—for instance, by causing family disruption. But a proper
scientific study would ask what favorable as well as what
unfavorable effects drinking might have on family life as well as
questions concerning the sort of drinking and the circumstances
under which drinking occurs. In illustration of the advantages
of applying the functional-analytic method to the study of drinking,
Dr. Bruun cites investigations carried out by the Finnish
Foundation for Alcohol Studies among small drinking-groups in
Helsinki. He warns that society has no chance of exercising effective
control, with respect to drinking, before the facts about drinking
practices are established by formal research.*

At the outset, I should like to make it clear that my paper is concerned with a sociological approach to alcohol research. This does
not imply an attempt to rank disciplines according to importance
or to deny the relevance of a multidisciplinary approach to alcohol

problems. I think, however, the relevance of sociology to alcohol research is important enough to motivate a paper without sidelong glances at other disciplines. I am also convinced that there are important areas in alcohol research where a unidisciplinary approach is more promising than a multidisciplinary one. Furthermore, it is crucial to develop theories in alcohol research, and in this, I think, a multidisciplinary approach may prove to be a hindrance.

Sociology as a science is a newcomer in alcohol research. This fact may be surmised from the scattered alcohol researches and works of reference on alcohol problems published before World War II. In reading alcohol research literature from the first three decades of this century, it is apparent that the dominant approach to alcohol problems was a medical one. Traditionally, the main topics were the effects of alcohol on health, on longevity, etc., and occasionally on such nonmedical questions as the effect of alcohol on skills. When the social aspect was touched upon, the problems usually concerned the relationships between alcohol, on the one hand, and poverty and crime, on the other. I say these things not to show what kind of work has been done but rather to point out what kind of work *has not* been done in alcohol research: there has been practically no information about drinking habits, no reference to the use of alcohol either on the individual or the group level.

INFLUENCE OF ATTITUDES ON CHOICE OF RESEARCH PROBLEMS

This has to do not only with the fact that social science abandoned armchair philosophy in favor of empirical observation rather late. It has also to do with the motivation behind the interest in alcohol problems and in alcohol research, and I think this may be the more important reason. Before World War II, alcohol researchers and alcohol policy makers were recruited mainly from the temperance movement—from people adhering to the ideology of abstinence. This is why alcohol research was mainly interested in showing the evil effects of the use of alcohol. This ideological orientation strongly affected the choice of certain areas of inquiry and the conspicuous neglect of others. Among the neglected areas are drinking practices and their social function.

Before proceeding with my remarks on drinking practices, let me underline the importance of systematic investigations in this area. Social control agencies concerned with drinking problems, at least some of them, try to change drinking practices. But without knowing what the drinking practices are, control is not effective and its results cannot be evaluated. Furthermore, there has been an increasing concern with the phenomenon of alcoholism, with accompanying research enterprises in that field. But research on alcoholism is not fruitful as long as we do not clearly know the actual drinking habits of alcoholics themselves and how they compare with those of nonalcoholics. It appears that there is a great deal of confusion as to which drinking habits constitute alcoholism, and it could be that the moralistic stand against drinking is at least partly responsible for this state of affairs.

What do we actually know about drinking practices today? In the first place, there are alcohol production and consumption statistics which give the general consumption level and the type of alcoholic beverages used in a given country, but it is impossible to make specific inferences about drinking from these figures. Secondly, the psychiatric and the anthropological literatures describe, respectively, drinking among deviant individuals and in different cultures. As far as the psychiatric literature is concerned, it is in general limited to individuals with alcohol problems. To be sure, it sometimes tells us something about the social background of the individuals concerned and their drinking careers. But the data from this source are heavily influenced by the therapeutic situation and the orientation of the psychiatrist and are, for this reason, seldom useful in scientific analysis and not conducive to generalizations for larger populations. At best, these data provide valuable sources for the formulation of hypotheses in sociological research.

The anthropological literature gives us scattered descriptions of drinking customs in primitive cultures, usually in connection with religious and other ceremonies. Works like Ruth Bunzel's on Chichicastenango and Chamula, and Chandler Washburne's recent book, *Primitive Drinking*, give us valuable information about the role of drinking within some cultures and the variations in drinking practices and related activities in different cultures. Anthropologists have helped us to see drinking in a cross-cultural perspective and have made important contributions to functional analysis in general, and especially with respect to drinking.

RESEARCH ON DRINKING CUSTOMS

For a description and analysis of drinking customs in modern societies, we must turn to sociological studies. In this connection, I might mention the following: the Gallup poll which has been carried out in various countries, with all its methodological limitations; studies among Italians in Italy and the United States; Maxwell's survey in the state of Washington; a similar work by Mulford and Miller in Iowa; and the survey of drinking in American colleges by Straus and Bacon.

Somewhat ethnocentrically, I might also add studies carried out under the auspices of the Finnish Foundation for Alcohol Studies: Sariola's description of drinking in semiprohibition areas in Finnish Lapland; and Kuusi's report on drinking in Finnish rural areas. This list could probably be extended but, I am certain, not to any great length.

I have deliberately left out two as yet unpublished studies because I think they deserve special attention. They are both cross-cultural in scope and methodologically thorough, though perhaps in a different sense in each case. One is E. M. Jellinek's ambitious study in nine different countries which he has carried out in cooperation with local scientists. In this study each country was divided into diverse cultural regions, and the population in each region was stratified into several social classes. For each social class in every cultural region, a panel of five expert informants was set up who jointly filled out a standardized questionnaire concerning drinking practices. The other study is one of the drinking practices among young men in the capitals of Denmark, Finland, Norway, and Sweden, which was coordinated by the Finnish Foundation for Alcohol Studies. I might say that this represents the unique example of comparative studies of drinking customs where the procedures of data collection and analysis are rigorously standardized. This is not an appropriate occasion for presenting the findings of this study in detail, but it is worth mentioning two points. First, we found that fourteen-year-old boys in all four capitals were similar in their drinking habits, as were the sixteen-year-old and eighteen-year-old boys. Second, there were notable differences between these three age groups within each city.

At this juncture when investigations of drinking practices are growing in number, I should like to point out some methodological problems concerning measurement in this area. Drinking is usually described in terms of quantity and frequency, but there has been no significant attempt to standardize the measurement of these variables, which, among other things, makes it difficult to compare data from different sources. Furthermore, it seems to me that many studies which are supposed to describe drinking practices have ignored important aspects which are essential in establishing that there are what may be reasonably called drinking customs by virtue of regularity in occurrence. There appear to be at least two such aspects of drinking that ought to be taken into consideration. One is what may be called evenness of drinking. We would say drinking is "even in quantity" if the amount consumed remains constant over a given time interval and "even in frequency" if the drinking occasions are separated by the same length of time. And the other may be designated, periodicity. Drinking would be considered "periodic in quantity" if the amounts consumed on different occasions show a regular pattern which repeats itself, and "periodic in frequency" if a group of successive drinking occasions repeats itself in a regular pattern. An even drinking in frequency is periodic by definition, but an uneven drinking could be either periodic or nonperiodic depending on the regularity of drinking occasions. In my view, drinking customs must be established for different populations by using standardized techniques of measuring quantity and frequency of drinking, and especially by taking into consideration the evenness and periodicity aspects of drinking. This means that studies of drinking practices at the initial stage must record every drinking occasion of the individuals in the sample over a given length of time. As far as I know, a study of drinking among Italian-Americans in New Haven [Williams and Straus] is the only one that has attempted this, at least in principle.

From a sociological point of view, drinking practices in themselves are not very interesting, and certainly methodological activities concerning the measurement of different aspects of drinking are only means to further scientific analysis. They are important for relating drinking customs to other sociological variables.

SOCIAL FUNCTIONS OF DRINKING

Drinking is a social custom surrounded by social institutions and social control measures. Information on actual drinking practices, as I pointed out earlier, is important for social control agents because they must know what they are trying to control and change. However, from the point of view of the sociologist, drinking practices are the basis for an analysis of the social function of drinking. Functionalism has in recent years become an increasingly important sociological orientation. There is no reason for me to go into a philosophico-theoretical discussion of functionalism in sociological thinking. I would like only to point out that the functional approach has largely been neglected in alcohol research, although it could be a fruitful frame of reference for research in this area. I am presently going to indicate the kind of problems which I think can be fruitfully tackled along this line, but let me first briefly sum up the basic principles of functionalism. For the purpose at hand, I might single out four traditional tenets of functionalism.

1. Every social system has certain needs for the maintenance of the system.

2. Every social custom is functional in the sense that it fulfills some of the needs of the social system.

3. A social need may be fulfilled by different social customs; or, to put it in another way, different social customs may serve the same social function in different social systems or at different times within a given social system. The social customs which satisfy the same social need are called functional alternatives.

4. Social customs hang together to make up a meaningful whole, so that a change in one social custom entails changes in one or more of the other customs.

In recent years, there have been many important modifications and refinements of these basic principles, notably due to Robert Merton. Here I would like to mention two pairs of concepts which Merton has contributed to functional analysis in sociology. In the first place, he distinguishes the manifest from the latent function. A social custom has a manifest function if its consequences contributory to the fulfillment of social needs are both intended and recognized by the participants in the social system. A social custom, on the other hand, has a latent function if its consequences are neither intended nor recognized as contributory to the fulfillment of social needs by the participants in the social system. Secondly, he introduces the notion of dysfunction as opposed to eufunction. Eufunction is contributory and dysfunction is harmful to the maintenance of a social system. From now on, I shall use the words eufunction and eufunctional whenever I want to emphasize the positive effects of a social custom for a social system.

Let us now ask, from the standpoint of the functionalist, what information do we have concerning the social function of drinking? What do we know about the objective consequences of drinking? The information is scarce. A glance at the activities in the field of alcohol research makes it clear that the dysfunctional aspect of drinking has been heavily emphasized. For instance, at present, reference works on alcohol topics such as alcohol and crime, alcohol and divorce, alcohol and diseases, problems of alcoholism, and so on, predominate. Drinking is often considered dysfunctional with respect to the family institution, because it is thought to cause divorce in some cases. But it may be fruitfully asked whether alcohol could not also have the eufunction of preserving marriages. As far as I know, there is not a single study that asks this question concerning alcohol and the family institution. Without such a study, statements about the relation between alcohol and divorce do not tell the full story about alcohol and the family from the point of view of the functional analyst. I shall come back to this problem later.

The most important study concerning the social function of drinking is Donald Horton's study of primitive societies, published in the *Quarterly Journal of Studies on Alcohol* as early as 1943. Horton's work, despite its early date of publication, represents the most articulately formulated theory on drinking.

Horton proceeds from the empirically demonstrable fact that alcohol retards certain physiological functions and reduces feelings of anxiety, the latter of which can be surmised from experiments with animals, if a little less clearly with human beings. An action which occasions a reduction in feelings of anxiety, such as drinking, is experienced as a reward and tends to be repeated and become a social custom. At the same time, however, drinking tends to encourage forbidden behaviors, that is, transgressions of social norms, such as disapproved expressions of sexual and aggressive impulses, which evoke punishments or social sanctions. Thus alcohol not only reduces feelings of anxiety but can also, through the chain of deviance and social sanction, lead to the emergence of new feelings of anxiety. Horton formulated three theorems on the basis of this reasoning:

1. The drinking of alcohol tends to be accompanied by release of sexual and aggressive impulses.

2. The strength of the drinking response in any society tends to vary directly with level of anxiety in the society.

3. The strength of the drinking response tends to vary inversely with the strength of the counteranxiety elicited by painful experiences during and after drinking.

Horton made an important contribution to the functional study of drinking with this formulation, but his empirical evidence was weak, and his analysis was limited in scope. Since the publication of Horton's study, more data have been gathered on drinking behavior in different cultures, and functional analysis itself has been further refined. Thus, recently, Washburne took issue with Horton on several points. He notes that drinking not only reduces and sometimes produces feelings of anxiety but also may be irrelevant with respect to anxiety. He suggests that drinking could have other functions. In any event, the relationship between anxiety and alcohol remains to be studied from a broader point of view, and other functions of alcohol ought to be investigated.

In trying to discover other social functions that the use of alcohol may serve, there is little explicit guidance in the alcohol research literature. To be sure, a study like Charles Snyder's *Alcohol and the Jews* gives a clear picture of the connection between alcohol and religious ceremonies, from which social functions of drinking may be inferred. However, the interpretation of work of this type from a functional-analytical point of view can easily become speculative.

SMALL-GROUP DRINKING

In this connection, however, the small-group studies that have been carried out by the Finnish Foundation for Alcohol Studies appear to be relevant. The objective of these studies has been to investigate what really goes on in drinking situations in a laboratory setting closely simulating a restaurant milieu where small male groups drink. Drinking sessions of six-hour duration in this setting have been systematically observed in order to study the changes in social structure during each drinking session.

The results of these studies, though valid perhaps only for the working class milieu in the capital of Finland, clearly indicate that the intensity of communication increases after drinking and that the communication becomes more negatively emotional, showing especially an increase in verbal aggression. Drinks appear to change the individual's behavior in a different manner and to a different extent depending on his role in the group.

The effect of the increased aggression upon the social structure and the cohesion of the groups depends on the direction of aggression. Thus, in drinking situations, aggressions of the members directed to one another tend to decrease the cohesion of the group, and aggressions directed toward persons outside the group tend to increase it [Bruun, 1959].

These are selected observations from the small-group experiments we have conducted in Helsinki. Let us now consider what conclusions we might draw from these findings about the social functions of alcohol.

It seems clear that alcohol works as a catalyst in releasing aggressions and tensions in social groups and thus has a definite social function. This was already pointed out by Horton. However, on the basis of our observations, we must add that this tension release may be eufunctional or dysfunctional for the social system, depending on the social situation. It remains for future researches to reveal the conditions under which drinking is eufunctional or dysfunctional.

Here it is interesting to speculate on the real meaning of an increase in communications in a small group because of the use of alcohol. It could be that the increased communication clarifies the social roles of the group members and the social norms of the group. However, it is by no means clear that the same social norms operate in a drinking situation as in other situations. If this is true, then how can the social norms of nondrinking situations be clarified in drinking situations? Moreover, supposing that the norms in drinking and nondrinking situations are identical, intoxication may cause the norms to be violated more often. This would raise the question, how do social sanctions operate in drinking situations as compared with nondrinking situations? These questions could lead to fruitful hypotheses concerning the function of drinking in relation to social norms and social sanctions.

Let me now turn to some speculations concerning the social functions of drinking in the society at large and indicate the kind of investigation that might be carried out in this field.

It seems to me that the use of alcohol has a definite function in creating new social groups. Drinking, among other things, makes the process of getting acquainted with people easier, owing to the free flow of information occasioned by drinking. It might, for instance, have an important bearing on the process of mate selection. This and other possible functional aspects of drinking, however, are still imperfectly understood and must be investigated. It also seems clear that drinking facilitates communication between members of different statuses within the same social system, which in turn strengthens informal norms, relaxes the rigors of bureaucracy, and contributes to the smooth functioning of a social system.

One could extend the list of possible social functions of drinking as a useful guide for sociological research in the field of alcohol. But instead of presenting such a list here, which is not the purpose of this paper, let me confine myself to some remarks concerning drinking vis-à-vis a particular social system, namely the family. Drinking may contribute to the disintegration of the family, as I pointed out earlier, and be dysfunctional in this sense in some cases, but, on the other hand, it may help to hold the family together by facilitating solutions of sexual and other marital problems and hence be eufunctional in other cases. In this connection, we need studies relying on information concerning drinking in families in natural settings, including the kind and extent of interactions among the family members before, during, and after each drinking occasion over a period of time. Needless to say, this type of study has not yet been done. In stressing the importance of studies of this type, I do not intend to imply that there are no functional alternatives; they must be investigated and specified, so that they may be substituted for drinking in the cases where this latter is dysfunctional.

REFERENCES

Bruun, K., "Drinking Behavior in Small Groups" (*Alcohol Research in the Northern Countries*), Helsinki, The Finnish Foundation for Alcohol Studies, 1959.

Bruun, K., and Hauge, R., "Drinking Habits among Northern Youth" (*Alcohol Research in the Northern Countries*), Helsinki, The Finnish Foundation for Alcohol Studies, 1963.

Bunzel, R., The Role of Alcoholism in Two Central American Cultures, *Psychiatry*, 3:361–387, 1940.

Horton, D., The Functions of Alcohol in Primitive Societies: A Cross-cultural Study. *Quart. J. Studies Alc.*, 4:199–320, 1943.

Kuusi, P., "Alcohol Sales Experiment in Rural Finland" (*Alcohol Research in the Northern Countries*), Helsinki, The Finnish Foundation for Alcohol Studies, 1957.

Lolli, G., Serianni, E., Golder, G. M., and Luzzatto-Fegiz, P., *Alcohol in*

Italian Culture. Food and Wine in Relation to Sobriety among Italians and Italian Americans, Glencoe, N.Y., Free Press, and New Brunswick, N.J., Rutgers Center of Alcohol Studies, 1958.

Maxwell, M., Drinking Behavior in the State of Washington, *Quart. J. Studies Alc.*, **13**:219–239, 1952.

Merton, R. K., *Social Theory and Social Structure*, Glencoe, Ill. Free Press, 1957.

Mulford, H. A., and Miller, D. W., Drinking in Iowa. I–V. *Quart. J. Studies Alc.*, **20**:704–726, 1959; **21**:26–39, 267–278, 279–291, 483–499, 1960.

Sariola, S., *Lappi ja Väkijuomat* (Lapland and Liquors), Helsinki, The Finnish Foundation for Alcohol Studies, 1954.

Snyder, C. R., *Alcohol and the Jews. A Cultural Study of Drinking and Sobriety*. New Brunswick, N.J., Rutgers Center of Alcohol Studies, and Glencoe, N.Y., Free Press, 1958.

Straus, R., and Bacon, S. D., *Drinking in College*, New Haven, Yale University Press, 1953.

Washburne, C., *Primitive Drinking*, New Haven, Conn.; College & University Press, 1961.

Williams, P. H., and Straus, R., Drinking Patterns of Italians in New Haven. Utilization of the Personal Diary as a Research Technique, *Quart. J. Studies Alc.*, **11**:51–91, 250–308, 452–483, 586–629, 1950.

The Honorable John M. Murtagh

Chief Justice, Court of Special Sessions
New York City

ALCOHOL AND THE LAW

Editor's Note   In a social problem of restricted scope—the fate of
the "skid row bum"—Judge John M. Murtagh discovers a social
problem of the highest moral significance—the problem of human
justice. He notes that the police throughout the United States make
about a million arrests each year on a charge of public intoxication—
though for technical reasons the offense in various jurisdictions may
be labeled disorderly conduct, breach of the peace, and the like. Who,
he asks, are the people thus jailed—and repeatedly released and re-
arrested? They constitute an embarrassment to society—but is their
treatment at the hands of society morally and legally just?

From the viewpoint of a philosophy of law that would forbid
interfering with behavior that does not injure others, Judge Murtagh
argues that public intoxication should not be classified as a crime unless accompanied by overt harmful behavior. Going further, he asserts
that most men on skid row, though often intoxicated, are not essentially alcoholics. They are the inadequately developed people, psychologically deprived from childhood, who are incapable of meeting the
demands of ordinary life in our society. Rejected by society and with
no other resource, they seek some sort of security in the way of life
known as skid row. There, heavy drinking is a part of the way of life,
though for most of the men it is not the helpless compulsion which
rules the alcohol addict.

In pleading for more adequate justice for these people, Judge
Murtagh emphasizes that as yet there is not enough systematic
knowledge about the cause of their individual and social condition to
allow effective remedial programs to be instituted.

The subject of the law and alcohol is a rather narrow and special
aspect of the total subject of alcoholism. At the outset we must, of
course, give some reflection to the subject of what alcoholism means.
In the various addresses thus far there has been no special effort to

define alcoholism. I realize I am talking to a sophisticated group that in the main knows just as well as I do what the term means and knows that the differences with respect thereto are a matter of semantics; but be that as it may, to the degree that I use the term "alcoholism" in my address, I have reference primarily to a condition that includes a pathological craving for drink. I have in mind the compulsive drinker, the human being who if he takes a single drink on occasion may be completely without will power to curb his further drinking and to avoid going on to oblivion.

One frequently is curious as to why a judge ever got involved in the subject of alcoholism. Mine, I confess, is a completely professional interest, or at least it initially was. In 1950 I was appointed Chief Magistrate in New York City. In New York, of course, everything is a little on the large side. There are fifty-four magistrates and so the Chief Magistrate is not so much a judge as he is a housekeeper. He may or may not preside regularly in court, but in any event his primary responsibility is the effective functioning of the fifty-odd courts that constitute the system. One could hardly assume such a responsibility without adverting to matters of policy, without reflecting on the validity and the nature and the effectiveness of particular aspects of the judicial function. It was in this light that I first viewed the arraignment of people on a so-called "drunk" charge.

DRUNK OR DISORDERLY?

Now in New York it isn't strictly a drunkenness charge. Almost without exception, the charge in New York City is disorderly conduct; the individual found under the influence of alcohol is charged with conduct that tends to breach the peace; this is especially the practice in our Night Court. We have one city-wide court for the arraignment of petty offenders at night. There are groups of ten to twenty individuals regularly arraigned before the bench on such a charge; the charge is read by a court officer rather methodically; the individual is invariably advised in detail as to his rights, right to counsel, and so forth. Almost invariably, after the ritual has been completed, one of the more adequate of the less adequate steps forward and says "guilty," and the rest follow like sheep, and so the entire thing is brought into focus, and the law is empowered to dispose of his liberty for a greater or lesser period.

One could hardly reflect on this drama without having certain questions or without having certain misgivings. Those of us in the law recognize that disorderly conduct is a specific crime, lowly as it is, just as murder, burglary, robbery, or anything else. You are not guilty of disorderly conduct in most any state by merely being obnoxious, by being a minor nuisance, or by being offensive. You must have committed specific acts in order to be guilty of disorderly conduct. I couldn't help reflecting that if these fellows didn't plead guilty, that if they put the police, the State, to a proof, so to speak, it would be difficult for a judge to convict them of disorderly conduct.

My great interest was in trying to help these individuals. That is the instinct, I think, of any decent human being, a feeling of shock at their utter degradation and a desire to improve their lot.

By coincidence, in that year 1950, others in the city government evidenced an interest in such a project, and they took the initiative and created a so-called Rehabilitation Center. Initially it was something of a failure. In my enthusiasm I revised judicial procedures to conform to this program, and by coercing those who might have been jailed into volunteering for a program of rehabilitation, I somehow managed to encourage volunteers. I felt rather proud, and in retrospect I think a few were helped, but only a few. My interest continued on. I spent a good deal of time getting acquainted with the Bowery, trying to learn from those who had spent a great deal of time in studying the skid row derelict, and, of course, I proceeded on the assumption that I was concerned with the problem of alcoholism.

A JUDGE GOES BACK TO SCHOOL

Eventually, in 1953, I went back to school for the first and last time since leaving law school. I went to New Haven and took that thirty-day summer course on alcohol problems. I now boast, incidentally, that I got my law at Harvard and my alcohol at Yale.

Those of you who attended that course—most any group that I address on this subject includes a number of alumni—know that, just as this symposium, it is a well-balanced approach to the problems, with emphasis on learning intelligently how to approach social problems rather than on gaining specific knowledge on the subject of alcohol. But among other things, knowledge of the nature, the cause, and the treatment of alcoholism, which is still very limited, is presented. The primary gain from the systematic study of the subject is greater recognition of the necessity of employing the knowledge of all disciplines and integrating this knowledge with the discipline of philosophy to the end that we approach problems of this kind with as much intellectual honesty and wisdom as is possible.

Since that experience I have continued to a degree to shift my thinking. I remember that shortly after my experience at Yale—of course, immediately after that thirty days I was an expert on the subject—one of my classmates, a Jesuit priest who teaches at a college in Syracuse and who had also become an expert in thirty days, presumed to give a group of lectures on the subject in Syracuse. Of course, he invited me to speak on alcohol and the law—this was back in the beginning of 1954. I had an interesting session for about an hour and then subjected myself to a question-and-answer period. In the course of my remarks I referred to the custom in New York of arresting the alcoholic on a disorderly conduct charge, and I mildly questioned the legality of such an approach. Unfortunately for me there was a lawyer in the house, and he asked a rather sharp question. He said, in effect, "You seem unhappy with charging the individual with disorderly conduct because you feel that his conduct does not make out the crime of disorderly conduct in most instances. Why don't you resolve it by charging him with public intoxication?"

That had me stumped. I resorted to double talk. Indeed, I had never heard, up to that point, of a charge of public intoxication. I was a little amazed that there might be such a statute. I got back to New York. I looked up the law, and I found in the penal law that there was a statute that made it a crime to be drunk in a public place, but the last paragraph applied the statute to the entire state with the exception of the five counties of the City of New York. It is humorous, and it did give me solace for about two years. I thought it explained my ignorance, but actually it didn't.

I was subsequently to find out, some two years later, that the only reason for that exception was that there was then, and there had been previously, a substantially identical statute in the New York City Criminal Courts Act, and the exception was made because the law was already in effect.

Of course I was troubled. Why was I ignorant of the existence of the statute, and why was just about anyone in New York City to whom I talked unaware of the existence of the statute, and above all, why weren't we charging people who apparently were guilty of public intoxication with public intoxication instead of disorderly conduct?

I resorted to a little research, and by good luck I stumbled across a bit of correspondence in the files inherited from one of my predecessors. It seemed that way back in 1936 we had a judge, Magistrate Frank Oliver, who was regarded as a bit of an eccentric. He was very sensitive to police oppression. If he sensed that an arrest was not strictly legal, he would dismiss the charge because the individual's human rights had been invaded.

The series of events that I came across in the files related to such an incident. A man in 1935 in New York City had been arrested for public intoxication. The charge read that he had been found lying on the sidewalk under the influence of liquor, all in violation of the Public Intoxication Statute. Judge Oliver took a look at the complaint and on his own motion dismissed the charge, expressing the opinion that in order to sustain a charge of public intoxication it was incumbent upon the people both to allege and to prove not only that the individual was drunk in public but that his conduct tended to be a breach of the peace. I must say that I thought the worthy jurist was a bit confused, that he had disorderly conduct confused with public intoxication.

I reread the statute. It said nothing about being disorderly, nothing about breaching the peace, so I concluded the man was confused. But be that as it may, because I don't think now that he was confused—I will come back to that—it seemed that four years later the then mayor appointed a Chief Magistrate by the name of Henry Curran, and he, interestingly, was one of the few who shared the opinion of Judge Oliver. Being an administrator and housekeeper, he had a certain greater power perhaps than any of the other judges, and he ordered the court staff to return to headquarters all the forms dealing with charges of public intoxication, and when he got them, he directed that they be burned.

This technique was designed to preclude the police from thereafter charging people with public intoxication, or making a criminal charge against them, unless they were disorderly.

It was a commendable effort. Actually it wasn't particularly effective. The police since that time have uniformly charged the individual with disorderly conduct rather than public intoxication and that does explain the absence of the latter charge in New York City. But that is not of special significance, in that the police make the same arrests that they would have at any other time, except that they charge them with disorderly conduct, whether they are guilty or not, and the individual, as I said before, pleads guilty and thus the issue is avoided. I repeat—I think if they were to plead not guilty (and indeed I sometimes think that we on the bench have an obligation to enter such a plea for them and put the police to their proof—but be that as it may), the result would be almost invariably a dismissal.

Now getting back to Judge Oliver and his decision on public intoxication. Why do I think that the same logic applies to that charge as to disorderly conduct? Why do I think that Judge Oliver was right in saying that we must prove that he is disorderly as well as drunk?

The one little contribution I would like to make is not meant to enlighten you from the standpoint of behavioral science, in which I am not competent, nor to teach you how to cure or treat either alcoholics or skid row derelicts, but rather to emphasize that whether we are dealing with the law, with behavioral science, or with any of the disciplines, whatever knowledge we cull from investigation in the various disciplines, needs integration, if you will, needs to be fused into a mold that is informed by a basic and fundamental philosophy. So certainly is it true of the law: How often do we in the criminal law ever think of a philosophy? Regretfully, I admit, almost never.

There is hardly anything more frustrating for one like myself than to seek even in the learned treatises any wisdom as to what the criminal law is or should be. Notwithstanding the dearth of enlightenment that I have been able to find in the literature, I have gradually evolved over the years a philosophy of the criminal law. It happens to be based in large measure on the wisdom of St. Thomas Aquinas, who, back in the thirteenth century, seems to have seen this matter about as profoundly as it could be seen.

HUMAN LAW VERSUS MORAL LAW

The only regret I have is that more of his teachings did not inspire people in my field. Basically he taught that human law, or in this connection, criminal law, must be based on the moral law, that in effect we must start with the violations of the moral law or, if you prefer, of accepted standards of social behavior. But he went on, and this is what I want to emphasize: it is not the function of human law or criminal law to take over the entire moral law; rather human law should limit itself to implementing the moral law in that narrow sphere of activities where violations thereof have a substantial impact on others. In plain English he taught that criminal law should be dealing with acts of violence against the person and property; that it was not the function of human law to make men saints— that was largely a matter for the individual himself, and for society through the home, the church, and the school, by teaching and encouraging morality. But the law should not avail itself of the organized authority of the state to force a person to become saintly whether he wills it or not. He taught that indeed we, as individuals and as an organized community, have a right and a responsibility to persuade and to educate, but not to coerce.

This, I suspect, lay fundamentally behind the thinking of Frank Oliver when he said in effect that public intoxication would have to affect others before it was a crime. Evidently he was thinking that if the legislature presumed to proscribe drunkenness in public that did not affect others, it was exceeding its legitimate authority; that under elementary rules of statutory construction we should presume that the legislature was confining itself to its proper sphere and, hence, he read in by implication a limiting sphere of the statute, to wit, "affecting others." That, in brief, is why I think he was right, and that is why I become increasingly intolerant, as the years go by, with society's approach to this problem.

You sensed, doubtless, that I became, in the early fifties, a bit restive and a bit critical of New York City's approach to the problem. Yet one of the many things I learned in New Haven was that New York is unique in being about the only large community in the United States that does not err greatly in this direction. Before I went to New Haven, I had the foresight to try to find out roughly how many such arrests were made annually in New York. I ascertained that it was somewhat less than fifteen thousand a year. This meant little to me other than that it did give some support to my thought that we were invading civil rights to an inordinate degree, but when I got to New Haven, eventually that question was posed, and a judge from the local community was asked how many arrests there were in New Haven. I don't remember the exact figure, but I think it was roughly around eight thousand—in a community population of 165,000.

The first thing that occurred to me was the possibility that those who had given me my figures had been in error. When I returned to New York, I found that they were indeed correct. The national average is infinitely greater than that of New York. I have found that, literally, just one out of every two arrests throughout the United States is for drunkenness; one out of every two arrests for all offenses—from murder down to disorderly conduct or spitting on the sidewalk—are arrests for public drunkenness. Specifically the Federal Bureau of Investigation annually lists roughly two million crimes committed throughout the United States; it lists some 850,000 as being for public drunkenness, and an additional number for charges such as disorderly conduct, as in New York; thus roughly one million out of the two million are for being drunk in a public place.

The percentage in New York is not 50 per cent; it is approximately 3 per cent; it is in sharp contrast.

A city like Los Angeles has almost 100,000 arrests. I don't know just what it is currently here in San Francisco. Until recently it was substantially the same as in Los Angeles, despite the fact that it has a population about a third of Los Angeles.

What the explanation is I don't know, but to my mind it is a very intensive violation of civil rights.

THE NEW YORK CITY SYSTEM

Now the New York picture wasn't always so, and I think it is well to advert a little to what the New York picture was and to trace it historically. For one thing, the police arm of government is something we take for granted. Who is there among us who especially feels that we need a philosophy to govern the police, that there are things in the entire police technique that we should reevaluate? This is the kind of thinking that doesn't often go on, and yet when we reflect on it, in modern society we have had a police department for little more than one hundred years.

In New York City, in particular, the police department as a professional regular department has existed only since 1845. An institution as new as that needs constant evaluation as to its validity, its effectiveness, and its direction.

In the first ten years in which the police department existed in New York, from 1845 to 1855, it managed to make just approximately one hundred thousand arrests for drunkenness. That is a pretty good job for a relatively small community that was practically rural. By 1874 the number had risen to over forty thousand annually and, interestingly, of that number approximately one-third were members of the fair sex. It included children as young as eleven years of age.

Now I think these latter facts are of significance because they point up that, at least at that date, the problem was not so much a problem of either alcoholism or drunkenness as it was a problem of human degradation. Who was being arrested so frequently? It was the hapless soul who came from a society that was ill-equipped to support him, to enable him to develop into maturity as a full, whole, human being, and society in New York was unable to cope with the person so deprived. It was society that sought to escape its responsibility by locking up the "bum."

What was true of New York of the 1870s is, I submit, true of the United States in the year 1961. Do we have a moral right to use constituted authority to coerce a person whose main offense is being in a state of degradation? Should not the criminal law be confined to other types of human conduct? Is not human degradation, which at most is a minor nuisance to the rest of us, essentially a responsibility of society, a public health problem rather than a criminal problem? Of course, I think so.

Now back in 1959 this issue came up in Los Angeles. Police Chief William Parker was arguing against a proposed reduction in the annual budget of the Los Angeles department, and finding himself somewhat behind the eight ball in his argument, he said, in effect, that his only alternative, under a reduced budget, was to adopt the New York system, as he put it, of letting the bums lie in the gutter.

Dramatically, graphically, he portrayed the contrast. Now you may well ask, do I favor letting the bums lie in the gutter? Who are the bums?

THE SKID ROW POPULATION

To my mind, broadly speaking—and, of course, you in the scientific disciplines know that we must beware of generalizations, but nevertheless I think I speak with a fair degree of accuracy—in the main they are the derelict population on skid row. They are the main subject of these arrests. They are hapless souls who can be broadly labeled in the language of the sociologists and psychologists as inadequate personalities, inadequate human beings.

In all probability in their early years they were greatly deprived, and I don't mean especially in the economic sense. They are individuals who for one reason or another did not have maternal attention in the degree to which they needed it. They are individuals who from the cradle up, in all probability, did not quite identify either with the mother or with the father, nor, in due course, with their siblings or with other adolescents; they are human beings who are unequal to developing the social relationships that are essential for a normal human being, who are unable to apply themselves regularly to work, and who lack not so much the work skill as the work habit. They are human beings who in the main do not marry, but who, if they do marry, seldom are able to continue the relationship for any length of time with any degree of success [Cf. Pittman and Gordon].

They are lonesome human beings who very often seek an escape, a refuge, a sense of security, in the skid row habitat. And skid row does indeed give them a degree of comfort—at the same time that it drags them down ever so much the more because, inescapably, they must adopt the culture of skid row, which, among other things, involves the excessive use of drink. Inescapably they tend to use drink to excess in order to blot out reality, to soften the impact, if you will, of the degradation in which they live.

THE MINOR ROLE OF ALCOHOLISM

Now this brings up the question of alcoholism. Initially, as I said, my curiosity was to learn more about alcoholism in order to better understand the problem with which these derelicts confronted me professionally. Many of the experts, such as Dr. Robert Straus, have after considerable research revealed that the problem of skid row is not so much a problem of alcoholism as it is a problem of human degradation. In his words, many of the excessive drinkers on the Bowery or on any skid row are plateau drinkers as distinguished from compulsive drinkers. He describes the individual on the Bowery as one who takes his bottle of wine and consumes a portion until he reaches the kind of plateau that crowds out the reality of his degradation, giving him a certain bliss, at which point the bottle is put back in his pocket and is not brought out again for an hour or two or three, until the plateau has receded to a point where reality is crowding in once again. Then the bottle is produced, reality is crowded out again, and our friend puts the bottle back again in his pocket.

Contrast that with the alcoholic whom we all know. That alcoholic tends to seek oblivion. He is one who on occasion cannot touch a single drop without going on to oblivion. In an individual case it may mean a day; in others it may mean weeks, but if he is an alcoholic there is always the danger that if he takes a single drink, he will not thereafter be the master of his own destiny. The fact that it is only on occasion, rather than invariable experience, is one of his greatest difficulties, because being able to drink intelligently and normally on occasion leads him to think he is not an alcoholic.

Now in the nature of things there are alcoholics on skid row too. There are alcoholics among doctors, among lawyers, among bankers, among candlestick makers. Skid row cannot escape, and indeed probably has a much greater percentage of alcoholics than another community. But I want to emphasize the fact that we should not assume, because we have a chronic excessive drinker on skid row, that he is an alcoholic. More than that, I think it should be emphasized that in all probability, whether he be alcoholic or nonalcoholic, whether he be an alcoholic or a chronic excessive drinker, he probably has a much more deep-seated pathology of which the excessive drinking is symptomatic, a pathology that is in all probability greatly different from that of the typical alcoholic, one that is ever more enigmatic, more baffling, than the pathology of the so-called alcoholic.

INADEQUACY OF THE POLICE APPROACH

I mention this because I want in these last moments to direct myself to the issue of the wisdom of a police approach to this problem, as distinguished from its validity. Granted that indulgence in philosophy is a little unreal—I don't think it is; I think it is valid—but granting for the moment that it is, let's consider the American penal approach from the standpoint of sheer wisdom and effectiveness: What is a skid row derelict? I submit that all of the disciplines combined know very little about the nature of the skid row derelict. He is truly an enigma to science. Now granting that, how much have we to contribute to him by way of therapy? How can we presume to know how to treat him when we don't understand him? It is true that in certain diseases we have learned the cure before we learned the nature of the illness, but I submit that this isn't one of them, that we do not really know how to treat the individual skid row derelict.

Many of those who have, like myself, grown critical of these mass criminal arrests of so-called drunks have veered to the position where they deplore them, and they call upon the legislatures in the various states to abolish criminal arrests and to substitute a procedure of civil commitment, if you will, whereby the individual is adjudged an alcoholic and compelled to undergo a program of therapy. Indeed such a law was passed by no less than the United States Congress to apply to the District of Columbia some fifteen or twenty years ago and has almost never since been used.

Do I favor such a law? Manifestly not. If you are to lock me up by civil rather than criminal process, I submit that it is largely a matter of semantics. You still take my liberty away. If you put me in a medical institution as distinguished from a correctional institution, it is a more humane step, but I question your right to do it or the wisdom of doing it when you don't have a therapy. How can we support the compulsory treatment of skid row derelicts when we don't understand them, when we don't know how to help them?

Traditionally, in a place like New York or Los Angeles, where you do have something in the nature of a so-called modern therapeutic program, what it consists of in the main is good housing, good sleeping, a maintenance work program; but what evidence is there that this is other than temporary relief? I don't think there is any evidence that it is anything more. It dries the fellow out; it gives him a chance to live more normally for a period of confinement, but I query whether he is any less adequate when he leaves than when he came there; I query whether we have the right to make this experiment with these human beings merely because they present a pathology.

I submit again that philosophically, realistically, we only have that right when the conduct of an individual, be he a derelict or otherwise, constitutes a substantial interference with the rest of us. That is the only warrant for the use of the sovereign power of the state.

I decry the wholesale arrests that exist in the United States today; I think they are based on ignorance; I think they are being used primarily to show that society is reluctant to correct this situation. To the degree that they show intolerance of vice I commend them; to the degree that they try to prove this intolerance by injustice, I deplore them.

REFERENCES

Pittman, D. J., and Gordon, C. W., *Revolving Door. A Study of the Chronic Police Case Inebriate*, Glencoe, N.Y., Free Press, and New Brunswick, N.J., Rutgers Center of Alcohol Studies, 1958.

Straus, R., Alcohol and the Homeless Man, *Quart. J. Studies Alc.*, 7:360–404, 1946.

Straus, R., and McCarthy, R. G., Nonaddictive Pathological Drinking Patterns of Homeless Men, *Quart. J. Studies Alc.*, 12:601–611, 1951.

THE RESPONSIBILITY
OF THE INDIVIDUAL
AND THE COMMUNITY

Moderator   David G. Mandelbaum
Participants   Kettil Bruun, the Honorable John M. Murtagh, Chauncey D. Leake

Dr. Mandelbaum   There are really three subjects which might be discussed under our topic. First, what is the responsibility of the community, or the state and its police agencies, in regard to the drinking of alcohol? Secondly, what is our responsibility, as scientists, for research in this field? And thirdly, what is the responsibility of the therapist and the community responsibility for therapy, in cases of pathological alcoholism? Obviously, the fact that very nearly one out of every two arrests made in the United States every year is for drunkenness or public intoxication, or something of that sort, lays a most heavy burden on many agencies of government, not only the police. It takes up clearly a large part of every municipal budget and, as Judge Murtagh indicated, the way in which this problem is handled is not altogether satisfactory.

Judge Murtagh, may I call on you first to speak on this matter of community responsibility?

Judge Murtagh   Yes, I would be glad to address myself to the subject. My main point was that, to the degree that we use the penal processes, that is, arrests and jailing, primarily to solve problems of human degradation, to that degree we are diverting our energies; we are reducing the effectiveness of the arm of law enforcement, and we are accomplishing little.

Now I do not want to be understood as playing down community responsibility, community opportunity to help a person with a drinking problem. When I say that police enforcement should not be used, I do not say that the community does not have a responsibility. There remain obligations, rights and duties beyond law enforcement. All of us have an obligation to try to find out why the derelict is in the condition in which he is, why the alcoholic suffers, and why his family suffers, and to attempt to learn more and to help. That is a community responsibility and a very serious one. In the United States today, there are few public health problems more serious than alcoholism.

Dr. Mandelbaum   Dr. Leake, would you like to carry on with this topic?

Dr. Leake   I would. I think that the most important responsibility, both for the individual and for the community, in regard to alcohol is knowledge; and I think it is the prime responsibility, insofar as the state is concerned, or the community and its agencies, to aid in obtaining and then in distributing verifiable knowledge, which we call the truth, about alcohol and its actions on people. Then, the next step is to go forward in the light of that knowledge and to apply it wisely at an individual level or at a community level for the welfare of the individual and the community. This is a big job.

I was once head of a committee of the National Research Council on the problems on alcohol, and we decided that we should focus on this business of getting knowledge, verifiable knowledge, about alcohol and what it does. Well, actually, after about ten years of effort and spending a great deal of money on it, we came to the general conclusion that the long experience of people in regard to the use of alcohol can be verified by scientific investigation; that is, the knowledge is there. Now our problem is to apply it as wisely as we can for individual and social welfare, the point being always that alcohol, like fire or like nuclear energy, is a most sharp and powerful double-edged sword. At one time it can be a solace and at another time a shame, and we have to know for what purposes, then, we wish to apply our knowledge about it.

Dr. Mandelbaum   Dr. Bruun, I wonder if you would tell us something about the community responsibility for alcohol and alcoholism in Finland.

Dr. Bruun   I can start from the point which I think is important, when there were discussions regarding a change in the police technique in Europe. I should like to know what really has happened in Europe, and I don't think anybody can answer this question. We, in the Finnish Foundation, have been very interested in an experimental approach to this sort of change in the policies within society,[1] and we right now face the same problem. In Finland we arrest many people. We have in the capital of Helsinki about thirty thousand arrests a year for drunkenness, and there are about 450,000 inhabitants. Now a few months ago we agreed with the police to change the policy—not to change the policy of arrest, but the process which follows. And then, we try to follow what really happens in a society after such a change.

Judge Murtagh   I quite agree that I should like to know more about the effect of one policy or another, but I think the first thing we should ask ourselves is if organized society has a moral right to make such arrests, and, secondly, whether there is any evidence that such arrests have any therapeutic value. I think the answer to the second question would have to be in the negative.

Dr. Mandelbaum   At any rate, it doesn't seem that New York City has greatly suffered from the policy of not arresting drunken persons who are not injuring anybody.

Judge Murtagh   I often ask those who are critical of such a policy whether, in their particular city, a drunk ever took a bite out of them. Nobody has yet answered in the affirmative.

Dr. Mandelbaum   There is another aspect to this problem which we have not mentioned so far at this conference, and I think we must mention it. There is a great difference between a skid row wino, who is dragged into the drunk tank and detained a few days, and the man who is drunk and is operating a lethal weapon, namely an automobile.

Now this, of course, is an enormous problem for the police, for the community, and for the state, and I wonder if one of you gentlemen would want to comment on how this problem is being handled and how it might be handled.

Judge Murtagh   I shall be glad to venture in those troublesome waters, and troublesome they are. In the first place, I think every community must endorse a penal approach to this problem, because this is an area that peculiarly warrants police action—conduct that seriously threatens the life and the security of the population. This is the area where we should have a vigorous police enforcement.

My misgiving stems primarily from the fact that some in the

[1] P. Kuusi, "Alcohol Sales Experiment in Rural Finland" (*Alcohol Research in the Northern Countries*), Helsinki, The Finnish Foundation for Alcohol Studies, 1957.

learned disciplines, like sociology, have hypothesized that a greater percentage of the offenders may be alcoholics.[2] If they are, very interesting questions come up as to whether a police approach has a tendency to coerce the alcoholic, the compulsive drinker, into modifying his behavior lest he be arrested, and whether incarceration has any effect in curing him. I am afraid these questions would probably be answered in the negative. Notwithstanding my uneasiness in this regard, I do endorse a police approach to the problem of drunken driving, because compassionate though we may be to the true alcoholic, his conduct behind the wheel poses a very serious threat to the community. Meanwhile I also endorse more research, to the end that we may be able to contribute to the individual's welfare as well as affect his confinement.

Dr. Leake   There has been some benefit derived from an attempt to promote responsibility on individuals with regard to driving. In Texas there is a very vigorous campaign with signs on the road in connection with drivers' licenses, tests, and all that sort of thing, about, "If you drink, don't drive, and if you drive, don't drink," and also, "Take a coffee for the stirrup cup." This has been rather significantly effective but it is part of not only the business of promoting responsibility on an individual level, but also, in effect, it helps in rehabilitation.

Dr. Mandelbaum   Dr. Bruun, is there any problem with drunken driving in Finland? You don't have as many cars as we do?

Dr. Bruun   Not as many, but the approach is the same. Police enforcement is needed, but I do think that public opinion is against any drinking before you drive—to a much greater extent than it is here in the United States.

Judge Murtagh   Don't I gather that public opinion is influenced by a grim policy of police enforcement, to the degree that if a person has two or three drinks in him in Finland and he is behind the wheel, he can be found guilty, whereas we have a tradition in the United States of a much more "liberal" policy?

Dr. Bruun   In Finland you can be sentenced for up to half a year without having been involved in any accident.

Dr. Mandelbaum   Judge Murtagh, would you be in favor of a stiffer policy of that kind in this country?

[2] R. E. Popham, Alcoholism and Traffic Accidents. A Preliminary Study, *Quart. J. Studies Alc.*, 17:225–232, 1956.

Judge Murtagh I don't think it has the support of public opinion.

Dr. Leake There is another aspect, and that is the civil suit if an accident occurs with the driver drunk, and that economic factor can be just as powerful as almost any other sort of police action.

Dr. Mandelbaum Is legislation called for?

Dr. Leake I don't think so. The civil suit will do it, and this puts it on an individual responsibility basis.

Dr. Mandelbaum Let's turn now from the grim and horrifying problem of drunken driving and drunken drivers to something which was brought up yesterday and discussed, and it was in the headlines of this morning's paper, namely the cocktail hour and the cocktail party.

This is clearly a part of American middle-class culture, and since all Americans say they are middle class, it is a problem of American culture.

Now, the question which I want to pose to you, gentlemen, is this: We have evidence that the way the ritual of the cocktail hour as now carried on helps defeat its very own purpose. As Doctor Lolli told us, people come in hungry and they're given a great mass of alcohol—in many cases without food—and the party frequently disintegrates.

Now it seems to me that some of the greatest inventors in world civilization have been housewives, and here is an opportunity for the housewives of America to propound a new form, or at least a reformation of, the cocktail party, so that it will serve the function of realization of happiness, of pleasant society, rather than have the sometimes unfortunate results that we have heard about.

Am I exaggerating, Dr. Leake?

Dr. Leake No, I think you're exactly right; you're putting the responsibility where it belongs. The meal should begin within fifteen to twenty minutes after the first drinks have been taken. Then there would be a more satisfactory socialization of the whole effort around relaxation at the dinner table, rather than the smoke and confusion of the crowded front room.

Dr. Mandelbaum People have to stand up when they drink— this seems to be part of the ritual of the cocktail party. Is it necessary?

Dr. Leake No, because the long tradition of humanity has been to obtain the relaxation and healthful influence of alcoholic beverages along with food. I think here the housewives can really help restore the evening dinner to the social function that it deserves to be.

Dr. Mandelbaum   Dr. Bruun, let me ask you what the pattern of small-group drinking is in Finland. I know you have done experimental studies on it. What is it like?

Dr. Bruun   The main type of beverage used is Finnish vodka, vina, and drinking is done mainly on weekends, but then in relatively large quantities. Public bars and that sort of thing do not exist in Finland. We have more regular restaurants, and so on, and about one-fourth of the consumption of alcohol is in the restaurants.

Dr. Leake   You know, you spoke about the average American and our middle class. To this group, the cocktail hour is quite important because it is an economic device to pay off a great many social obligations in the easiest and simplest way without involving the expense and the difficulty of serving dinner to a large number of people. Now we could make some sort of compromise here, and I believe that the good sense of our housewives may work it out. Perhaps the answer would be frequent small dinner parties to fulfill our social obligations to each other.

Dr. Bruun   Do you really know how frequent the American cocktail hour is?

Dr. Mandelbaum   Our knowledge of how frequent cocktail parties are and what goes on there is limited to our own experience, and we social scientists know that this is not always a reliable guide.

Let me turn briefly, while we are still on the subject of the responsibility of the community, to the question of social welfare agencies. Judge Murtagh, you must have had experience with the work of various social welfare agencies who deal with alcoholics and with problems of alcohol and with the effect of alcohol on families. Do you find that special improvements are needed in that sphere of activity?

Judge Murtagh   Yes, I think the best way society can do this job—which I regard as its responsibility for both the socially inadequate and the accepted drinker—is through a department of welfare, or through an agency of government of that type. Specifically, all of these categories are broad, but we have a category of individual, very akin to the skid row derelict—whom I refer to as the inadequate parent.

Employment-wise he is frequently in a marginal class. In social integration, and so forth, he is not among our outstanding citizens. He is married, which indicates a degree of social adequacy in excess of that held by the skid row derelict, but he is not much of a father or not much of a husband. From his family, all too often, develops the delinquent child. The unhappy spouse is, of course, a by-product. In this area I endorse a police approach when the individual is guilty of overt acts. Certainly I commend these inadequate parents strongly to our social agencies and to our governmental agencies, and in New York I am happy to say we have a special court dealing with the problem, and we have tried to integrate the services of various social and religious agencies throughout the city in our work.

Dr. Mandelbaum   There is a special court for alcoholics?

Judge Murtagh   Well, not for alcoholics but it is called the Home Term Court, and it has to do with the typical family court case, usually where a wife brings the police into action to arrest her husband—for having struck her, for example. Of course the focus usually is to a great degree on a continued course of action, and the approach of the court is essentially to defer action on the specific charge and to try to help both husband and wife and children to the degree that the total family structure is affected favorably, and to the degree that it thinks some agency or the court itself may be able to help. I make no pretense as to the adequacy of the services because even in New York—as in most large cities— those services could be more adequate, but we are at least, I think, approaching the problem in the right direction.

Dr. Mandelbaum   Let's now turn to the second of our three topics, that is, the research responsibility. Dr. Bruun told us that although there has been a great deal of research of various kinds on alcohol, we still know comparatively little about the way in which alcohol is actually used in the various societies of the world. Dr. Bruun, I wonder if you would give us some idea of what direction you think research ought to take.

Dr. Bruun   I think that we should follow individuals and see the same individuals on different occasions in order to learn how their drinking habits develop and how they vary in different situations.

Dr. Mandelbaum   I think you also mentioned, and this was a most interesting point to me, that we know very little of the good effects of alcohol, of what you called the "eufunctional" effects. Dr. Leake, in your talk you had something to say on that also.

Dr. Leake I am very interested in the whole research picture. As I indicated before, this was a major problem before our National Research Council committee, but I think that the basic business of research is to find the verifiable truth about what alcohol does on living material; that is what we are basically after. Nevertheless, in this particular problem we have to consider also research from the standpoint of the purpose toward which we are directing our research.

One matter that we need to stress is a new line of approach in connection with biology—that is, to consider the different levels of organization of biological material. Alcohol is a chemical molecule, and it reacts only with other chemical molecules, but chemical molecules can be grouped together to make cells, and they have remarkable properties. We don't know what it is that makes the cell and all the molecules that are in it operate as a unit. We don't know whether alcohol interferes with cellular activity by disturbing the integrating mechanisms within that cell, or by reacting with some molecule in the cell.

Now, cells are organized into the organs and the tissues of our body, and then these are organized into an individual. The integrative factors in that individual are very obscure—we know little about them except that they are of two sorts, that is, chemical and nervous. And after all, the nervous integration comes back to chemical factors, too. But when we come to the next level of organization and bring individuals together into a society, whatever the reference group may be, again there are factors of integration in that reference group with which we are totally unfamiliar.

We do know that the same dose of alcohol acts differently on an individual who is isolated and may drink quite a lot from what it does on that individual or other individuals in a social group. This, I think, is an important area for a new approach in fundamental research on the alcohol problem.

Dr. Mandelbaum Dr. Leake, there is one question on biology which has come up and on which you may be able to cast some light, and that is, to what degree are there individual differences in capacity to handle alcohol?

Dr. Leake Very great indeed. There is just as great a degree in biochemical differentiations between us as individuals as there is between our different faces. We recognize each other by differences in our structural make-up, and we have just as much biochemical individuality as we have a structural or nervous and mental individuality.

Dr. Mandelbaum We now come to our third major topic, and that is therapy. I think we might introduce a question submitted from the audience.

This question is from a teacher. He says that in the California schools it is required by law to teach the effects of alcohol on the human body, and he asks, "Just what are we to teach the child and the teenager? As a teacher in an extremely depressed area," this note says, "where 60 per cent are on welfare much of the year, a great majority of the men are what we believe to be alcoholics. What can we do?" The question then goes on to mention the drastic effects of drinking in that area on the family pattern and on the child. What are we to do by way of therapy? Gentlemen, I turn the question to you.

Dr. Leake I would like to pick that right up, because I am very interested in this matter.

The school is a social reference group, and the discussions in the school can always be at a social level. The individuals are sharp enough to be able to put the shoe on if it fits, and this helps to reduce whatever shame or feeling of disgrace there may be among the students in the school if it does happen that there are parents of the type that are socially unacceptable. We discussed the social agency a moment ago—the social agency acts with regard to individuals. Our program in therapy should be directed toward rehabilitation of the individual so that the individual is socially useful and feels so, and this depends largely on the process of reconditioning, which is a sound psychological process and can be undertaken. But the original conditioning, in my opinion, can be just as importantly developed in the school toward social welfare as it can in the home.

The basic point I would like to come back to is derived from St. Paul, and that is the emphasis on faith, hope, and love—and they are important. It is in the school that faith can be generated in the endeavor that we are working together for our individual and group satisfactions. We can engender in the school the hope that these satisfactions can be obtained individually and socially, and we do it largely, it seems to me, through the process of love and the demonstration of it. I mean the Greek *arete*, not erotic love, but the affection that human beings in a common environment can have for each other by their common understanding of their common problems. School children can get this, and when they do get it, it may help to engender the faith and the hope that is so important for their future.

Judge Murtagh It is difficult to answer that question following Dr. Leake, because if anything I say should seem to contradict anything that he said, it would be unfortunate. It was about as eloquent an expression as can be made.

Basically, we have got to strive through the spiritual and through the educational techniques for the improvement of mankind. Specifically, how to do it in schools on a problem like alcoholism bothers me a bit. Unfortunately, the knowledge on alcoholism is so limited and so overcovered with bias, misunderstanding, and ignorance, that I have some apprehension that if we get down to the specifics in the average school today, the schoolteacher will not be equipped to do other than to confuse the child. But to the degree that the teacher does stress the traditional social and moral values, that is all definitely to the good.

Dr. Mandelbaum Dr. Bruun, would you like to comment on it?

Dr. Bruun Only that this is very much discussed also in Finland, and it is quite clear that most of the education on this topic is based on certain moral ideals which seem to be accepted by the majority of people.

Dr. Mandelbaum We now have some time for questions from the group, if there are any.

Dr. Lucia I should like to ask one, referable to a point you brought out: A person under the influence of alcohol has potentially in his hands a very lethal instrument, an automobile. Judge Murtagh discussed the problem of controlling this, and Dr. Leake touched on the punitive potential of civil suits. Why don't we consider, first, a policy of disenfranchisement with teeth in it, and secondly, financial restitution which would put out of business a person who is so socially immoral as to drive an automobile under the influence of alcohol?

Judge Murtagh Dr. Lucia obviously has a degree of intolerance of the excessive drinker, be he alcoholic or otherwise. I share a degree of that intolerance if the individual is not alcoholic, although only a measure of it. In addition, I point up the realities of the situation. It is commendable to be intolerant of vice, immoral action, or social deviancy, but it is also important to be realistic. You can't be intolerant of something and then call for the cops, so to speak. It just doesn't work that way.

In the first place, laws to be effective must have the support of public opinion. On the American scene there is not a sufficient awareness of the menace of the drunken driver to sanction a strong enforcement program. However, I confess that we in the courts, and the police themselves, have a degree of responsibility to move on, notwithstanding that support. But the degree to which we do move is somewhat limited, and, quite frankly, we have those misgivings that spring from the lack of knowledge. We don't know, and we can't in the nature of things know, whether we are dealing with a nonalcoholic or with an alcoholic. We can't prescribe for the individual the way we should like to.

Not long ago I had before me for sentence, after a plea of guilty, an individual whose background showed him to be a menace to the community. On one occasion, although he was acquitted, he had been involved in an accident which resulted in a death. His violations of the drunken driving law were considerable, although somewhat in the past. In any event, to make a long story short, I gave him a year in the penitentiary. I did it with some degree of uncertainty, because I knew in the nature of things that the penitentiary would in all probability not have the wherewithal to help him. It might have some deterrent effect, and I used it for that reason.

I do know that Alcoholics Anonymous, which is an organization that I warmly endorse, is available in this particular penitentiary. I encouraged this individual to avail himself of it, but the entire approach to his problem had in the nature of things to be less scientific than I would desire. All these factors limit the judge in practice. It is one thing to be intolerant; it is another thing to use governmental authority.

Dr. Mandelbaum   Are there any other questions?

From the Floor   My question is, can we expect the average citizen of the United States to know what the law is when the eminent jurists do not know themselves?

Judge Murtagh   I will respond by saying that all too many jurists would not admit their ignorance. A judge is just as human as the next fellow. If he pretends to be all wise, then it is doubtful that he is a good judge.

Dr. Mandelbaum   We have time for one more question.

From the Floor Judge Murtagh, it is said that 9 per cent of the alcoholic population of 6½ million people reside on skid row. Would you differentiate the problem of the homeless man, the skid row person who drinks, and the true compulsive drinker, the alcoholic? Can such a distinction be made?

Judge Murtagh Without regard to the exactness of your statistics, I think a distinction can be made. We have got to guard against overgeneralization; we have got to guard against the problem of merely dealing in semantics, but I regard alcoholism as a pathology that is characterized primarily by compulsive craving for drink, whereby an individual, if he takes a drink, may become unable to stop.

Now doubtless there is a percentage of the habitués of skid row who are alcoholics. Some people on skid row, incidentally, never drink at all. The bulk of them drink to excess, but for us to assume that all of them are alcoholics is to fall into error. Dr. Robert Straus, who has conducted considerable research in this area,[3] is of the opinion, and this opinion is shared by many, that perhaps the majority of excessive drinkers on skid row are not alcoholics in the sense of having a pathological craving. Their chronic excessive drinking results both from their culture and from their desire to crowd out reality. It does not result from a pathological craving. This is the main distinction.

[3] R. Straus and R. G. McCarthy, Nonaddictive Pathological Drinking Patterns of Homeless Men, *Quart. J. Studies Alc.*, 12:601–611, 1951.

5

SPECIFIC VIEWPOINTS

Dr. Bowman *Do you think we are finding any way of measuring the amount of alcoholism in the community?*

Dr. Lolli *I don't feel that we can measure alcoholism because we cannot define alcoholism.*

Prof. Drew *We should . . . give up trying to do anything but make broad statements about what causes alcoholism, because I don't believe we are within several hundred years of doing that.*

From the Floor *Kids would come to the bar. . . . If you could talk to them, you'd find out that they're taught at home how to brush their teeth, they don't push people under trolleys, and they try to behave. But no one at home takes the time out to teach what can be expressed to a child as good and evil in alcohol. I personally feel that alcohol is a subject for the home and not the school.*

PANEL 1

CLINICAL

Participants   Dr. Leon A. Greenberg, Dr. Chauncey D. Leake, and Dr. Salvatore P. Lucia

Dr. Leake   There are two important phases of alcohol ingestion. Pharmacologically, one deals with the classic physiological effects of alcohol when it is taken as a medicine, and the other is the responsibility that physicians may have in the management of the abuse of alcohol when they're dealing with patients who are suffering from some aspect of its abuse. If we keep our attention on those two problems, we are covering our responsibility for the topic of this panel.

Dr. Lucia   I would remind myself and the audience that the word clinical means "at the bedside." And there would be two facets to this problem: one, the use of alcoholic beverages of one type or another for therapeutic purposes; and two, the restriction and perhaps the use of limited amounts of certain kinds of alcoholic beverage in the treatment of persons who are overtly alcoholics. This latter area I do not wish to discuss because I believe that it is a totally different area. I believe that it deals with another type of discipline entirely. If I were to state in a simple way what I believe, I should say that there is an artful use of alcohol, in the form of wines, spirits, and other fermented beverages, that has about four thousand years of precedent behind it. And this is the area I should prefer to discuss, by personal selection.

CONGENERS IN BEVERAGES

Dr. Warfield   Dr. Greenberg, it was brought out by Dr. Lucia yesterday that you were the authority who stressed the differences between wines and the congeners of rum, gin, brandy, and whiskey, and their effects on the experimental animal. Did you note any physiological differences between red and white wines?

Dr. Greenberg   I heard Dr. Lucia refer to that point, and, of course, in some ways, it is always very gratifying to discover what a

257

great expert you are, especially as you get further away from home. Some years ago, Dr. Howard W. Haggard and I did a series of studies on certain aspects of the differential toxicity of a number of alcoholic beverages.[1] We pointed out in this work, however, that we didn't know why the beverages we studied were different in this respect. We suggested that the differences might be due to the various combinations of materials present in the several beverages which distinguish each one from every other. Contrary to your impression, we never determined that it was specifically due to the different so-called congener materials.

Dr. Leake   That's toxicity you're talking about.

Dr. Greenberg   That's right, toxicity.

Dr. Leake   All right, now, keep it at that level. That's quite different from other aspects.

Dr. Greenberg   Now, as a matter of fact, I should amplify that. What we called toxicity is how much it takes to kill.

Dr. Lucia   The effect was measured upon the respiratory mechanism?

Dr. Greenberg   Yes, how much it took to cause breathing to stop. This, to me, means dying.

Dr. Lucia   But you see, this is a very delicate end point. The effects are measured by the point of reference you use to indicate the cessation of life.

Dr. Greenberg   Yes. However, even though we used that end point, we always had some reservations about the adequacy of this cutoff point as a general measure of toxicity, because most people don't drink to die. They drink to a much lower level of alcohol content.

Dr. Leake   I just want to summarize here—to keep in mind the scientific things we're talking about. This is the intensity of action of a drug, and it is dependent on dosage; that is, mass of the drug per mass of living material in comparison with a ratio between the rate of absorption, which is so important in alcohol, compared to the rate of its destruction or removal from the body. Given a concentration in the body, these two together, at any given moment after administration, determine the ultimate effect. The other factors are the physicochemical characteristics of the drug, and the peculiar

[1] H. W. Haggard, L. A. Greenberg, and L. H. Cohen, The Influence of the Congeners of Distilled Spirits upon the Physiological Action of Alcohol, *Quart. J. Studies Alc.*, 4:3–56, 1943.

characteristics of the living material—every subject being different.

Now focus attention on concentration for a moment. If you plot the concentration of alcohol, or any drug, against time, there are always two types of curves that result. If your purpose in taking alcohol, for example, is to reach a certain degree of relaxation in your mood, this would be called, if you wish, the effect of range. And if you start out with a very high concentration, you can get the desired effect in a relatively short time. Now if you start at any concentration and want to maintain that concentration against the rate of removal, you'd have to continue to administer the drug. If you maintain that concentration, if it is high enough, then there is a finite time at which it will produce death. Now, however, if you have a lower concentration, it may take a much longer time to produce the desired effect, but you may be able to extend the time-duration of the effect indefinitely without death. This is generally true of any drug, and it's directly applicable to the alcohol problem.

Dr. Greenberg   Now, if I may, let me finish answering the question that was asked. Maybe you got the answer in that formula, but just in case you haven't, I shall tell you this. In general, the undesirable toxic effect of drinking an alcoholic beverage is proportional, in one sense, to the rate at which that beverage, after you drink it, gets into the blood stream, because until it gets into the bloodstream, it has no effect; it really isn't inside the body. In a simplified way, one can consider the body to be a sort of cylinder with a tube running down the middle, the alimentary canal. When things are introduced here, as long as they remain only inside the alimentary canal, we may consider them as not inside the body. And so, how toxic or how effective a beverage is, or how intoxicated a person may become from drinking a given amount of a given beverage in a certain time, depends on how rapidly the alcohol is transferred from inside the lumen of this flue, if you will, into the bloodstream, and ultimately into the tissues. So the rate of absorption becomes a very important factor in the speed and the intensity of action, or the toxicity or drunkenness, if it is going to occur, from a given amount of alcohol.

One of the very important factors that influences the rate of absorption is the nutritional state of the stomach. Alcohol doesn't have to be digested. This is one of the unique qualities of alcohol as a foodstuff, and I use the word food here in a physiological sense; namely, that it is burned in the body, and in the process of its burning, it liberates calories; it liberates energy, just like carbohydrate, like fat, like protein. And in this sense, it is a food. If you take too much, it's a bad food, but this is true of anything; if one lives only on sugar, he will die—it's a bad food if you live on it exclusively. Now, alcohol doesn't have to be digested; it is ready for immediate use. All that has to be done is for it to be transported across the membranes of the alimentary canal into the blood stream, and then it becomes utilized and active in the body. This transfer into the blood stream occurs very slowly from the stomach itself, because the stomach is primarily not intended as an absorption mechanism. It is intended to prepare materials so that they can then pass along into the small intestine to be absorbed. If there is food in the stomach, the passage of the alcoholic beverage from the stomach into the intestine is delayed, and therefore its absorption is delayed. This is the reason why different beverages have a different intensity of effect. A beverage such as simple alcohol in water will be absorbed very rapidly because it contains no solid food substances. Other beverages, such as beer or wine, contain some of the solid materials that were present in the original fruit or cereal from which they were made, or contain buffering substances that slow their passage.

If one drinks a beverage such as wine or beer, one would never achieve the same blood alcohol level and therefore never the same level or intensity of effect, as with plain alcohol. This is one very important reason why there are differences between different beverages. And another important reason is that the various beverages contain different combinations of materials other than alcohol that give them the characteristic flavor, taste, odor, bouquet, whatever you want to call it, and these materials themselves in many instances have toxic effects. Now, the possible effects of these other materials, the congeners, have been suggested, but there has been very little research done on this.

Dr. Leake   Yes, but isn't it true that when you speak of congeners, you usually refer to a distilled liquor which involves other types of chemicals that come over in the distillation—that is, the higher alcohols?

Dr. Greenberg   They are also present in the original brew, or ferment. That's where they came from.

Dr. Leake   Yes, but they can also be produced by the heat of distillation.

Dr. Greenberg No, I don't think that there is any evidence that this happens.

Dr. Lucia I don't think you should limit the word congener to the concept that it is an element that comes over in distillation.

Dr. Leake One part of the question interests me and that is the possible difference between white wine and red wine, and I think that question should be explored for a moment.

Dr. Greenberg Well, I had hoped that you wouldn't bring that up, because I don't know the answer to that one.

Dr Leake I don't know the answer either, so I'm going to ask. First, is there a significant amount of tannin in red wine?

Dr. Lucia Yes.

Dr. Leake Okay. Is there much tannin in white wine?

Dr. Lucia No, unless it is a bad white wine.

Dr. Leake Okay, that's my point precisely. Tannin is an extremely important agent with respect to absorption, because it spreads very readily over the mucous membranes of the stomach and the intestines, and it will inhibit absorption. Red wine is, then, by virtue of the amount of tannin that's in it, perhaps absorbed more slowly than white wine. And, in general, I think also that dryness of a wine is associated with its tannin content.

Dr. Lucia Usually. But we're on a very touchy point. Let me clarify this. We were talking about white wine versus red wine and the tannin content of a red wine impeding its absorption. Now, historically and currently, in countries where wine is used as a therapeutic agent, a word of warning is always issued about the effect of white wine on the nervous system. This, I think, is the point you had in mind, and I believe that this is involved in our discussion here.

I should like to correct another thing. Let us not leave this room with the concept that whiskey is alcohol and water, because it is not. There are many substances present in the original ferment that come over in the distillation. These you can call congeners, if you wish. They contain acids, certainly aldehydes, very complicated ethers, and in addition—and this is something most people don't know—the reason why they will put their pennies on the White Horse is because they like what it has to offer to the palate. This concerns the whole matter of cachet. Cachet—specific and often secret flavors—is a matter of something which the manufacturer adds. And I must tell you that within the law you can add a considerable amount of concentrated materials—which can come from any aromatic substance—to a whiskey in order to give it its characteristic cachet, the thing which you are willing to pay for when you buy a spirituous liquor. Now this constitutes one of the important differences between light Scotch, heavy Scotch, bourbon, rum, etc.

Dr. Greenberg   I quite agree with you and I want to add something; namely, people do pay a lot of money for one taste rather than for another taste, but we must now, in exploring that idea, step out of the bounds of the clinical or the physiological, because I think this is a matter of the science of Madison Avenue in our culture. People *do* like certain things, and they don't like other things, and their likes may be precisely the reverse of what people in another culture like and don't like. This is now no longer a matter of physiological, or nutritional, or clinical consideration.

Dr. Lucia   I've held myself back, because I agree with you that the physiological side is one thing, and if you can measure it physiologically, you have end points of very discrete discrimination. On the clinical side, it is another matter entirely. It may be more difficult to control a clinical experiment, but you cannot tell me that you can get the same effect on lobar pneumonia from Scotch whiskey that you can from bourbon, because that isn't true.

Dr. Greenberg   Which effect are you referring to?

Dr. Lucia   That's clinical experience, and this is what I am talking about now. I will admit that when you transcend something which can be worked into a laboratory experiment, it doesn't mean that the other thing is invalid. It means that you have to use a totally different set of criteria in order to evaluate what you're dealing with in its special setting. I want to come back to just one pertinent point. In the experiments of Dr. Greenberg and Dr. Haggard, they corrected for the concentration of alcohol, and they used beverages which ranged from gin—the least toxic, as measured by arresting respiration in the mouse—to cognac. Dr. Leake, you are correct, the data hold for the rat. Among the more complicated beverages were Scotch whiskey, bourbon, cognac, and vermouth. The point of the experiment is that the alcohol content was rendered constant as to percentage, yet the toxicity of cognac and vermouth, in terms of arresting respiration in the animal, was twice as great as that of gin. I think that an experiment such as this is a significant experiment in that it tells you that one must investigate the physiological reactions of the other ingredients, which produce the aroma, the flavor, and the specific qualities of the beverage.

Dr. Greenberg Nobody has done that. I want to emphasize that I don't know whether or not the difference in toxicity was due to the differences in congeners. All the beverages we tested, incidentally, were distilled beverages. We did not test any wines.

Dr. Lucia I thought you included vermouth in your list.

Dr. Greenberg No, just distilled beverages. And we could not know whether the differences might be due to the presence of materials that were either inherent in the original distillate or that may have come into the beverage in the process of aging in oak barrels. We could not answer that question, though in fact we tested the same beverage at different periods of aging. We did obtain some data that were very intriguing but did not continue to try to discover what the differences in toxicity were really due to. Nobody else has answered it since then.

Dr. Lucia One thing you do know is that the differences in toxicity were not due to differences in alcohol content, since the latter was kept constant. They were therefore due to the X substances.

Dr. Greenberg Yes. Now on the question of tannins, as between red and white wine, I am not aware of any controlled study that may have been made of the possible difference in effects from this material.

Dr. Lucia I think, in the manufacture of a white wine, if it is a very high-class product, they are trying to keep tannin out of it, and they do it in a variety of ways. One way is, of course, not to allow the wine—pardon me this poetic license—to rot in wood. The object is to get it out of wood as soon as possible.

Dr. Greenberg Do you know why they want to keep the tannins out, other than taste?

Dr. Lucia Well, what one likes to have in a white wine is lightness, freshness, crispness, flower, and the specific bloom of the grape.

Dr. Greenberg Well, none of these are things that we measured.

Dr. Lucia I know that. Nevertheless, these are the qualities which make such wines particularly palatable. Now, an expert can tell whether a fine white wine is made of the riesling, sylvaner, pinot chardonnay or pinot blanc grapes, and many other varieties too. I might like pinot chardonnay, and that makes a difference in my selection of a white wine. So you see that there are many problems brought out in this question, i. e., alcohol content, white versus red wine, aromatic substances, and a myriad of other technical features.

Dr. Greenberg   I think we should not make this a panel discussion on wine. Let's get to some other topic.

From the Floor   In alcohol intoxication, we're interested in the concentration of alcohol in the blood stream, not the rate of its absorption. When the alcohol content in the blood stream rises to a certain percentage, say 0.3 per cent, is there any difference in the intoxication of the individual with regard to whether he took wine or whiskey or what he took?

Dr. Greenberg   To the best of our knowledge today, there is no difference.

Dr. Leake   Well, except this, that if alcoholic beverages are to be used medicinally, it is necessary to take into account the preferences of the patient. This makes it much more palatable to the patient, and it makes it much easier to use alcohol medicinally if some regard is given to the experience, background, preference, or what else the patient has. He's more at home with what he likes.

From the Floor   Yes, but regardless of what beverage you give, is the intoxication going to be any different? I mean if a man takes 2 qt of a very light white wine, instead of 2 tablespoons, he's going to get intoxicated—whether he took that much alcohol in wine or in gin. What I'm asking is, what difference does the congener make in the abuse or the effects of alcohol? We're not talking about using it as a beverage. Now, this beverage talk is fine for the outsider, but we're here on a different purpose—to understand more about alcohol, and what alcohol does to the body, and the use of alcohol by society.

Dr. Lucia   You bring in a very important question. You talk about just the alcohol moiety of what a person may drink. I disagree with you heartily. Purely on a scientific basis, what's in an alcoholic beverage is added to or alters the activity of the alcohol itself, and this you must not forget. If you do not believe me, then try the same concentration of alcohol as a light white wine and as a very heavy unpurified vinous product.

ANTI-ALCOHOL VIEWPOINT

From the Floor   The very best authority I know, Dr. Andrew Ivy, says that there is not one place in medicine where you need alcohol. He says that you have wonder drugs. Now you used it in the Civil War and thousands and hundreds of thousands died. In Korea, what did we have? We had penicillin and sulfa, of course. They're losing their potency because of the way doctors use them, and we're getting almost immune to them, because they're used for colds and all that. But we're in the age of wonder drugs, and we've got to go back to the Civil War to have alcohol talked about so much as it is here. It's not necessary, according to Dr. Andrew Ivy, and he's tops. And if it isn't necessary—why do we spend so much time? Now I have a question to ask, and this is it. Where did yellow fever go? We didn't say, we'll have more stagnant water; we'll have more mosquitoes and more yellow fever. Where did trichinosis go? We cooked our meat. Where did typhoid go? We cleaned up our wells and our water supplies. Where did polio go? Why, today, we're pulling in money from polio for the children who are born defective, one out of sixteen is the estimate, in our civilized America. And where are these civilized countries we are talking about? Where is Greece today? They keep talking about the civilizations on down through time. Where are the Romans today? We don't need wine, and we don't need alcohol, but why haven't we stopped alcoholism? Thousands of dollars have been spent for polio, and many more than thousands, millions, to take care of alcoholics.

Dr. Leake There are many ways of answering this very important point, and they should be considered. Every drug that has been used to eradicate the diseases of which you speak, or to prevent them, is a dangerous agent in itself.

From the Floor But it doesn't drive people insane.

Dr. Leake It may. It may kill people, even as penicillin may.

From the Floor But we're stopping the use of it.

Dr. Leake No, we're not. On the other hand, the point of a discussion of this character is to try to find out what those values in the drug, alcohol, are that do have and have had an influence on civilization over the course of history, and in what way the useful aspects of that drug can continue to be used to promote our civilizing effort. Now, you mentioned someone who is well known for his fanatical position in all sorts of scientific aspects of medicine. It's not a particularly helpful contribution from him.

From the Floor Pardon me. I think he's had three gold medals from the American Medical Association.

Dr. Leake   Yes, he's done lots of good work, but only on certain things—he's not a pharmacologist, actually.

ALCOHOLISM

From the Floor   There is always a sociological problem before the clinical problem. Tuberculosis is a social problem before it gets to the doctor and becomes a clinical problem, and it's the same way with alcoholism; the heavy use of alcohol is a social problem before it comes to be a clinical problem. One of the things that interests me is whether any research has been done on the congeners? Has there been any work done that might show them to be the causative factors that may render some people biochemically addicted?

Dr. Greenberg   I can give you a delightfully brief answer. No.

From the Floor   I'm going to ask why.

Dr. Greenberg   Well, I think the major reason that there hasn't been is that the relationship is entirely evident. We're talking about alcoholism, the inability to refrain from the excessive use of ethyl alcohol. And there happens to be no reason for thinking that the congeneric materials in beverages can cause addiction to ethyl alcohol. For the rest, the alcoholic's troubles are multiplied by the excessive use of ethyl alcohol, and there is no question—and I think you will like this—that ethyl alcohol in sufficient amounts is a destructive agent.

Dr. Leake   Right. Here's a point, I think, of very great importance. You indicated that these are sociological problems. I take issue a little bit on that point. They are individual problems first; they become social problems when the number of individuals who are concerned constitute in some way a disturbance of the social setup. So the sociological aspects of these matters come after the individual difficulty occurs. Now alcoholism, in which there is an enormous amount of interest and study, has many factors. One, certainly, is the conditioning that an individual learns in the way that alcohol will give relief or escape from an intolerable environment, or something of that sort. It can become conditioned. There is, however, good evidence to show that a craving for alcohol may be associated with certain types of biochemical deficiencies: biochemical, and not necessarily nutritional. It may involve the thyroid, for example. Dr. Curt Richter of Baltimore has shown very definitely that there may be something there.[2] If you have a series of animals and give them free choice of plain drinking water, or water with alcohol, or different concentrations of alcohol, for example, and subject them to certain deficiencies or biochemical changes, they will exercise their choice of an alcoholic beverage, and they'll stop it when the deficiency is relieved. So there may be a factor of this sort that occurs in alcoholism. It's an extremely complicated matter, and it involves, further, psychological factors. When the alcoholic becomes ashamed of himself, he suffers from guilt feelings; then he knows he can get relief by drinking alcohol, so he does it. There are many things that lead him to take alcohol, and when he takes it in excess, then not only does he do harm to himself as an individual, but usually it is reflected in a social problem.

Dr. Greenberg I think that there is no particular alcoholic beverage that has a monopoly on alcoholism. It occurs, in those people in whom it is going to occur, no matter what alcoholic beverage is taken, notwithstanding the fact that we have so-called winos, and so-called beer alcoholics, and so-called rum alcoholics—they all suffer from an excessive use of alcohol.

Dr. Leake An economic factor comes in. They usually select the one that is cheapest, that will give the effect they want quickest. To return just a moment to the medicinal use of different types of alcoholic beverages, one of the characteristics of the development of medical management in the eighteenth century and part of the nineteenth century refers to the use of alcohol to help produce sleep, which is a well-known phenomenon. Now, as part of the amenities of the social setup in England, for example, there was usually the custom of drinking port wine at night to induce sleep, and I think of all the alcoholic beverages, probably port wine, in proportion to the amount of alcohol it contains, will be the most effective in inducing sleep. I don't know why, and I don't think anybody knows why, but after long experience in using different kinds of alcoholic beverages to induce sleep, they come back to port.

Dr. Greenberg Well, I think that ought to be tested experimentally.

[2] C. P. Richter, Loss of Appetite for Alcohol and Alcoholic Beverages Produced in Rats by Treatment with Thyroid Preparations, *Endocrinology*, 59:472–478, 1956.

ALCOHOL AND EFFICIENCY

From the Floor May I ask Dr. Greenberg a clinical question now? Dr. Greenberg, you tested some numbers of rats. You took the blood level of rats up to the point below intoxication, at 0.05, and then higher to see how they would react under stress. Now on this stress, did you take your rats up to 0.08 over any specific length of time?

Dr. Greenberg This was the audiogenic seizure experiment that I spoke about,[3] where they have convulsions as an expression of emotional excitement. The animals were taken to several intermediate levels. One group was between 0.02 and 0.04 per cent alcohol in the blood. Another group, 0.04 to 0.06, and then 0.06 to 0.08. There were these three groups of animals.

From the Floor On the level between 0.04 and 0.06, if these rats were kept on this level for any long duration, what deterioration, if any, did you note?

Dr. Greenberg In these animals? This was one acute experiment. There's an animal given a certain amount of alcohol and he reaches, let's say, 0.06 per cent alcohol in the blood. They weren't kept that way for any long period of time. This was done for the purpose of this experiment, a period of a couple of hours.

From the Floor Does stress, handled by what you termed a sedated state, result in an individual who might be termed normal, if he is sedated over a long period of time to avoid stress?

Dr. Greenberg If he were kept on sedation all the time?

From the Floor Yes, with the use of alcohol.

Dr. Greenberg I don't think it would be very advisable. I did point out, I'm sure, that any concentration of alcohol—or of any drug that is a central nervous system depressant—which alcohol is, even at this level, and that's why it does what it does—that this effect in blocking the response to any stress experience is accompanied by other effects. This individual will have an impaired reaction time; he will have some impairment in his judgment and in his discrimination. This was mentioned by a number of people who have spoken at this symposium. Now it was also mentioned that some of these functions, although they are impaired at this level, may not necessarily result in an impairment of efficiency of total behavior in a given situation. There are some people who are anx-

[3] L. A. Greenberg and D. Lester, The Effect of Alcohol on Audiogenic Seizures of Rats, *Quart. J. Studies Alc.*, 14:385–389, 1953.

ious, who have inhibitions, who feel restrained, and they never express the full extent of their talents. They are reserved. They don't do the job 100 per cent because of certain personality characteristics they may have. One of them may be inhibition, may be restraint, may be anxiety. Such a person may take an amount of alcohol insufficient to seriously impair his reaction time or his coordination, but sufficient to remove that restraint, that inhibition, that anxiety, and he may do a better job under that condition.

A classic hypothetical example, cited by Dr. E. M. Jellinek, I think, in illustration of this paradox, is that of a target shooter.[4] This man, when practicing and not in competition, could score, let us say, ninety-seven bull's-eyes out of a hundred tries. The exact figures are not essential. But in competition he was tense, anxious, nervous, and instead of scoring ninety-seven, he scored only eighty-three. But then, if he had a few drinks, his score in competition came up to ninety-one. Now, what shall we say about that amount of alcohol? Was it bad for him? Was it good for him? Did it improve his functioning? Was it a sedative or a stimulant? You might be wise to avoid these words and try, rather, to describe what it actually does. And we know what it did here. We know that the alcohol in this case removed certain restraints to maximum performance, even while it impaired other functions essential to maximum performance. And so again I would say, in relation to man, you can't answer the question whether a dose of alcohol will lower his efficiency or increase it unless you specify efficiency for what. What kind of a task? If I were going to go home and wanted to sit down and feel relaxed and comfortable with some friends in the living room after I'd been at my job all day, hiring and firing, making decisions, and if I were very tense—if I wanted to get away from all this, and to relax, *this* would be good. On the other hand, if I were going to take an examination in higher mathematics, *this* would be bad. Or if I were going to drive an automobile, I think *this* would be bad.

From the Floor   I'd like to ask a question. The man's score is ninety-seven with no anxiety, and he goes down to eighty-three. Then he's given alcohol to achieve an 0.04 per cent blood alcohol level, which shoots him back to ninety-one. If he is kept at the 0.04 level until the next day, then what is his score?

[4] How Alcohol Affects Psychological Behavior, *Quart. J. Studies Alc.* (*Lay Suppl.* 11), 1944.

Dr. Greenberg He'll be very tired the next day, because to keep at that level, he'd have to stay up drinking all that time—about an ounce of whiskey an hour. But you are quite right, and I was glad that you are keeping us on a good bookkeeping system. We'll stick to ninety-seven. His score goes down to eighty-three, and with a couple of drinks he shoots at ninety-one. He isn't ninety-seven again, because this alcohol does have some effect, but there are differential levels of effect. The effect at that level of alcohol on one component was so much more important toward the total performance than the depreciating effect on the other component, that the net result was an improvement. But you are absolutely right; it will not make this man better. If he were ninety-seven and completely relaxed, uninhibited, unanxious, you would be wasting the drinks giving them to him. They might deteriorate his performance.

From the Floor The relaxation was improved, but the perfection of his performance was lowered.

Dr. Greenberg I think it's fair to assume that a different balance was achieved.

Dr. Lucia Why don't we come to some reasonable understanding about this and say that whatever has happened to bring the performance to the level of ninety-one is an improvement over the basic performance which is used as the point of reference.

Dr. Greenberg If the score of eighty-three is the point of reference, then it is improvement.

Dr. Lucia It is an improvement. Now the next question I was thinking of, as you were being forced to commit yourself to something, is this: If you continue a stimulus, I don't care to what level you go, ultimately you are going to exhaust the reactive power, so that if you continue the use of alcohol with the target shooter, you must give it for twenty-four hours, or forty-eight hours. What do you think this fellow is, a perpetual-motion machine?

Dr. Greenberg Well, either you exhaust the animal or you exhaust your supply.

Dr. Lucia You exhaust your reaction, of course.

From the Floor It's not a stimulant reaction.

Dr. Lucia I'm not talking about a stimulant reaction. I'm talking about the fact that if this is maintained, will the subject be the same twenty-four hours later? Of course not. The point I'm making is basic common sense and physiology.

Dr. Greenberg This is a rather academic question.

Dr. Lucia   No, it's not an academic question. It's a basic question of fundamental biology.

Dr. Greenberg   You mean the question, should people stay in the state of euphoria at all times? I think I answered that in the negative way for a very real reason—that life isn't just one level of uniform challenge. There are situations of all kinds that we're called upon to meet. Some of them require a much greater degree of alertness, and some of them require certain kinds of judgments, for which you don't want anything at all that will impair the capacities demanded by that particular situation. But there are other situations to meet and other kinds of tasks that you're called upon to do where it's perhaps advantageous to relieve some of the anxiety, some of the tension.

From the Floor   At the 0.04 per cent level, would anybody have a state of euphoria? Would they stay on the level of 0.04?

Dr. Greenberg   Would they stay on it?

From the Floor   I mean, this is unrealistic also, because one can't stay on it; it's too low. Would anybody who stays on the level, drinking all the time, stay on that plateau of 0.05?

Dr. Greenberg   It depends on how much they drink steadily. Let's take some figures. In a man of average size, alcohol is dissipated from the body at the rate of about an ounce of whiskey, or its equivalent in some other beverage, per hour. So if a man took enough alcohol, let's say one ounce of whiskey, he would reach 0.02 per cent alcohol in the blood; or let's say he took 2 oz; then he would reach a level of 0.04 per cent. Now, if he wanted to maintain the 0.04 per cent level all the time, he would have to drink 1 oz of whiskey every hour. If he went to sleep and stopped, it would go down again. If he tried to build up a reserve in advance, he could no longer be at 0.04 per cent; he would be in another stage of euphoria altogether, if you want to call it that. So he's got to drink 1 oz every hour, and it has no reality when you talk about maintaining somebody at 0.04 per cent. You could do it only in an experimental situation.

ATHLETICS

Dr. Seymour   I can give you some information in relation to athletics because I've been on several Olympic teams. If you have an athlete who runs, let's say, a 9.6 in a 100-yard dash in practice, and this athlete begins to suffer from anxiety because he is not a champion and hasn't yet developed concentrated abilities, and he takes a drink or two, it's very possible that because of his anxiety he may turn out a 9.6 performance in national competition. Or, he might turn out 9.5. But in becoming a champion, what happens usually is that your sprinter who runs 10.0 flat in a would-be championship match would go to pieces. He won't run around 10.5 or 11.0 because he cannot control the anxiety that your sharpshooters experience. But after he becomes a champion, he turns all this power of the autonomic nervous system into directed and coordinated energy, of which you spoke, and then he turns it into a 9.3 or a 9.4. I know what I'm speaking about. I have known athletes to become so ill that they throw up after a race. This is "championitis."

I remember when I was competing, earlier, that I used to hold on to the equipment, the javelin, so hard it would be breaking in half before the performance. If I had taken a drink, it would have relaxed me. But later, working with Dean Cromwell, he said that the equipment should be held so lightly, the athlete should learn to handle it so well, that if you just touched the equipment, it fell out of your hand. This was learned, but alcohol would destroy this balance and performance. So, if this man were shooting ninety-seven in practice and he wants to hit a bull's-eye, he'd better not drink, because the competition in a champion will sharpen his reflexes. His only possibility is to sharpen his reflexes and go from ninety-seven to one hundred without any alcohol. But if he's not a champion and he's untrained, he may fall to pieces.

Dr. Greenberg So there will be no misunderstanding, I didn't bring this up as a recommendation that athletes should drink; I brought it up as an example of a principle and a physiological operation that actually occurs, in order to explain what these people have all been talking about when they said that small amounts of alcohol in certain kinds of activities, in certain situations, improve performance.

From the Floor The mature person who is really coordinated will be well disciplined and mature; that is the sense of the word, isn't it?

Dr. Greenberg Unfortunately, this doesn't describe most of us.

From the Floor That's right. But the person with complete coordination, attention, average resources, and capabilities does not need alcohol.

Dr. Greenberg I think it's wonderful if you can overcome these tensions without it.

From the Floor The greatest difference between beginners in athletics and the champions is that at the greatest moment of stress, with 100,000 people watching them, they are for a split second so relaxed they go far. At this split second of relaxation, they say, "Now we turn on our automatic nervous system."

Dr. Greenberg I think nobody is suggesting that a championship 50-yard dash be run after the cocktail hour.

Dr. Leake No. I'll say this, Dr. Seymour. You put your finger on something of very great importance when you said it is learned. And people can learn, but their capacity for learning varies enormously. It is amazing how the capacity for learning about alcohol varies so greatly with different individuals.

EFFECTS OF FOOD AND BLOOD SUGAR

From the Floor You mentioned earlier about the alcohol level in the blood, and it was my understanding that although the subject may have the same level of blood alcohol, he will not experience the same effects if he takes it *with* food or *without* food. Is this correct?

Dr. Leake There's a little bit of misunderstanding or lack of clarity. Food in the stomach will inhibit the rate of absorption of alcohol.

From the Floor I thought the speaker said equal levels in the blood with food would not give you the same effect as if you took it without food.

Dr. Leake No, I think that there is a misunderstanding at that point.

Dr. Greenberg May I correct that, Dr. Leake? I think the reference is to Dr. Lolli's statement. Is that right? I have spoken with Dr. Lolli privately about this, and he has told me that with the same concentration of alcohol in the blood achieved with a meal and without a meal, there are significant and striking differences in performance. Now I would point out that this observation has not yet appeared in the literature, so it is not possible to evaluate it on the basis of the exact data.

Dr. Leake Well, it would be perfectly logical to expect that there might be a difference in the effects of a certain concentration of alcohol in the blood, from the standpoint of the state of metabolism of the individual, which would depend on whether he had just eaten a meal or was in a starved state, because after all, there are very complex mechanisms in the blood itself. Furthermore, there are factors in the blood that under certain conditions will bind alcohol and will keep alcohol from the cells, so that in a way, the concentration in the blood is only a rough index. You're getting into a very fine point now on the activity of alcohol, but it is important. For example, high blood sugar after a meal is a different situation from starvation. This has an influence on the whole enzyme mechanism all along the line which is of importance in the destruction or removal of alcohol itself, because alcohol is a competitor for enzyme systems along with other molecules. At this point of discussion, you're getting at a very fine point of biological activity.

From the Floor It was pointed out that alcohol actually depresses the blood sugar level, so when you have a low or fasting blood sugar level, it would be conceivable that the alcohol would have a stronger effect.

Dr. Greenberg The whole relationship of blood sugar levels and alcohol is really very simple. If you have an animal or a person who is in a starved state, has no sugar, no glycogen in his liver, and you give that animal alcohol, nothing happens to the blood sugar. If you have an animal that is well fed so that he has a large store of sugar in his liver—not in the blood stream—and you give that animal alcohol, then the sugar level of the blood goes up. So you can get one effect or another effect, depending on the nutritional state of the animal. Again I would point out that if the blood sugar level makes any difference in what effect X concentration of alcohol in the blood has on a person's performance, the scientific literature as of today has no information on that point.

Dr. Leake But the point of interest here is that alcohol, being a drug, is in competition with the usual or ordinary metabolic enzyme system which ordinarily keeps us in equilibrium. Alcohol coming in from the outside will compete with various components of that system and in that way it can disturb the whole equilibrium.

ALCOHOLISM AND KIND OF BEVERAGE

Dr. Greenberg Dr. Leake, I should like to say just a few words, because one question hasn't been answered entirely, and that is the relationship of alcoholism to the kind of beverage. In the first place, I think that all of the evidence would indicate that the major commodity with which we are dealing, in alcoholism, is alcohol. However, when one is an alcoholic and is seen by the clinician as an alcoholic, part of the picture of his being an alcoholic is not only that he is now in some way addicted to the use of alcohol, but also that he is a sick man; he has possibly a bad liver, a polyneuropathy, or any of a variety of pathologies characteristic of the alcoholic. We now know that most of these disorders are caused by the excessive use of alcohol in combination with such conditions as malnutrition, and possibly with pathologies occurring as the result of the toxic action of other materials in the beverages. Clinically, one may find that the alcoholic whose major consumption has been one kind of beverage will have certain characteristic pathologies which will not be found in the alcoholic whose major consumption has been another kind of beverage. To this extent one can say, yes, the kind of beverage used is a contributing factor to the overall picture of alcoholism as we see it. However, alcohol is the predominant factor.

MEDICINAL USE OF ALCOHOL

Dr. Lucia May I add a point here? We have been discussing alcohol as a pharmacological agent and as a drug. We have taken perhaps a prejudiced point of view, as I have heard it. Let us spend just a minute on an area that is not so precise. It is quite nebulous in a way, but it won't be nebulous if you can recall a situation wherein alcohol in a clinical area has given a person a psychological response. It is more important than perhaps anything else he gets from his experience of being sick. This to me is not very easily quantitated, but certainly we have inferred it, Dr. Greenberg and Dr. Leake. We inferred that we are changing the reaction pattern of the individual and of his needs for something, regardless of what it is. If his need is for something which produces a beneficial effect, we mustn't invoke all the potentially bad reactions of excessive dosage any more for alcohol than we do for any other medicinal agent, so that we can change the atmosphere of a relatively dour and sour discussion into something that has some element of hope in it. Physicians, you know, have been working with this problem for quite a few thousand years, if four thousand means anything, and you can't cancel it out, unless you are going to do what the little boy in Mark Twain did. He said, "Listen, I need a case knife to dig this grave." His friend said, "You don't dig a grave with a case knife, you need a spade." "Okay, whatever you call it, but for me it's a case knife." This is a matter of pressing a prejudice. Well, I like my prejudices, and I would preserve the right of everyone in this audience to indulge his prejudices.

From the Floor There's only one thing wrong with that. If you get an alcoholic, and you tell him a little is good for him as medicine, and he doesn't tell you he has a problem—then you're stuck.

Dr. Lucia But as a clinician you know when not to use alcohol.

From the Floor You don't. You don't know when you have an alcoholic as a patient.

From the Floor I treat alcoholics every day, and I would like to ask, even though alcohol has been in use for thousands of years, have we made any progress on other drugs that will do this equally well?

Dr. Greenberg Yes, if you pick out certain particular things, there are other drugs that will do it.

Dr. Leake Yes, but it always becomes complicated when you compare one drug with another for various effects that it will produce. Sure, for any single one of the activities of alcohol that could be used medicinally, we have other drugs that can do the job, but in the overall picture there are very few if any drugs that have as wide a possible beneficial use in medicine as alcohol. But there's one other point in this, and that is the cost point. Now, cost of alcohol is going up all the time, but most of the drugs that will do any better than alcohol for the particular thing that you want done, will cost more. I don't know whether that's a very serious point or not. Now there's another point that I'd like to make and that is, there is scarcely any drug that has an overall beneficial effect equal to that of alcoholic beverages in old age. There's the psychological factor, where they may be allowed the use of something they have hitherto long been denied, and there's always a great joy in that sort of thing. Then there's the relaxation it produces, the relief from ordinary annoyances and irritations, the protection from exertion, the tendency to promote sleep, and the comforts that it gives—for all these alcohol is highly effective for old people, and this has been well documented for a long time.

PANEL 2

ALCOHOL INTOXICATION:
THE ACUTE EPISODE

Participants Dr. Franz Alexander, Dr. Olof A. Forsander, Dr. Leonard Goldberg

Dr. Goldberg Shall we start with "the acute episode," which is in our title? How would you define the acute attack?

Dr. Alexander Well, we wouldn't speak of an "acute attack" if somebody took a Scotch and soda and felt perfectly well afterwards. The word "attack" implies that we speak of a pathological condition, so I would propose to define our topic as the immediate physiological and psychological sequelae of the excessive ingestion of alcohol.

Dr. Goldberg Then we have already in this definition the word excessive, and by immediate we may mean within a limited time —a few hours; that is, as long as alcohol is in the body, what happens to medical functions, or physiological functions.

Dr. Alexander I should say to the person as a whole.

Dr. Goldberg Yes, the integration of it, the person as a whole.

From the Floor I should like an interpretation of what happens biochemically. Does isolated drinking have a different effect on a person than drinking socially?

Dr. Forsander This is not a very difficult question; biochemically, there would not be any difference at all. We are considering the two effects of alcohol: the pharmacological effect and the biochemical effect. By biochemical, I mean the oxidation of the alcohol molecule, and that is mostly not metabolism of alcohol but the metabolized products of alcohol. The pharmacological effect is what produces intoxication and produces the abnormal situation. I think this discussion should pertain mostly to the pharmacological effects of alcohol.

SUBSTANCES THAT MODIFY EFFECTS OF ALCOHOL

Dr. Goldberg We know that blood alcohol is just one factor in this whole picture of the acute effects of alcohol, but there are many thresholds for the different functions which are affected and these different thresholds vary from subject to subject. This is what makes the picture so complicated. And that brings us up to the point which I think is so very difficult to ascertain from an experimental point of view—the difference in immediate effects between different beverages even if the same blood alcohol level is attained. Someone conducted experiments of this type and found that a solution of 12 per cent alcohol and water gave a different effect than the same amount of wine.[1] Dr. Forsander, your colleagues have conducted experiments of this kind in Helsinki, where you gave beer on one side and hard liquor on the other.[2] You found that even with the same amount of alcohol in their blood, the subjects would react differently: they were more aggressive on the whiskey than they were on beer.

Dr. Forsander Yes, that is right.

Dr. Goldberg So this brings the experimenter to the point of asking, Why? What do these other substances do?

Dr. Forsander We have studied a group of rats under the influence of intoxication, and we have measured the effects of glucose on intoxication. If the rats are given glucose simultaneously with alcohol, the degree of intoxication is much lower than with alcohol alone. But if insulin is substituted for the glucose, the animals are much more intoxicated. If you give glucose and insulin at the same time, the effect is the same as that obtained with alcohol alone. So we have some methods by which we try to study the influence of a specific substance on the degree of intoxication, even when the blood alcohol is quite similar.

Dr. Goldberg One factor which has to be studied to see if it works with men also is the effect of carbohydrates, in this case, glucose. All the agents which clinicians use for helping an intoxicated patient should be studied. If a patient comes in heavily intoxicated, which is what we clinically think of as the acute episode, what do you do for him, Dr. Alexander?

[1] L. A. Greenberg and J. A. Carpenter, The Effect of Alcoholic Beverages on Skin Conductance and Emotional Tension. I. Wine, Whisky and Alcohol, *Quart. J. Studies Alc.*, 18:190–204, 1957.

[2] M. Takala, T. A. Pinkanen, and T. Markkanen, *The Effects of Distilled and Brewed Beverages. A Physiological, Neurological and Psychological Study*, Helsinki, The Finnish Foundation for Alcohol Studies, 1957.

EFFECTS OF DRINKER'S MOOD AND ENVIRONMENT

Dr. Alexander Before I answer this question, I should like to recall what Dr. Bowman has called to our attention—that the difficulty with this sort of study is that the human being's threshold is not a constant figure because it is influenced by the emotional state of the person. Dr. Bowman mentioned the man who reacted to alcohol in a very gay, extremely boisterous manner. He was gay, not offensive, but boisterous and delightful. Everybody knew that if he took one drink, he was like a different person and was very amusing. After his wife, to whom he was very devoted, died, he continued to use alcohol in the hope of again regaining this fine feeling. But the effect was just the opposite; he did not become gay and boisterous, but, as he told Dr. Bowman, "I became more depressed than ever, so I gave up alcohol."

You see, it's very nice and interesting with rats, who can't talk, and you can get some very nice statistics; but human beings, who can talk, are more complicated, and their interpersonal relationships can be so complex! How one reacts to alcohol depends very much on the emotional state when ingesting the alcohol. In the presence of an attractive girl, you may become very active and, let us say, daring; with boring company, the depressive phase might be predominant. The behavioral curve does not parallel the curve of alcohol concentration but is influenced by many other factors, for example, the environment. If you are in boring company, the alcohol may make you sleepy; if you are in a stimulating company, something else happens. That's no miracle, because obviously the states correspond to different equilibria in the different recesses of the brain. So if, let us say, the cortex is already stimulated, then probably the early stimulating effect of the alcohol is different than when you are asleep. When we move from rats to human beings, other parameters enter in and complicate the picture. When you measure the blood sugar and then try to correlate it with behavior, you must introduce some extremely complicated patterns.

Dr. Goldberg This, of course, is a challenging point. There are many examples of the same drug acting differently on different occasions. I think what you pointed out is extremely important—that so much depends on the state of the body. So what we experimenters do, of course, is to try to reproduce a few of these situations.

EFFECT OF STRESS

Dr. Forsander At the Finnish Foundation we have done studies on how a stress situation influences intoxication.[3] We are using rats because humans are too complicated.

There are two groups of rats. One group was just resting, the other group was swimming in cold water (they don't like to swim). The degree of intoxication, the blood alcohol, was the same in both groups, but there was a big difference in effect.

From the Floor Was it the animals that were swimming which had the more severe effects, or the animals that were resting?

Dr. Forsander The animals swimming showed less intoxication.

From the Floor But they had the same alcohol levels?

Dr. Forsander Yes, that's right. It's just a stress situation. A stress situation acts variously; you can have an output of ACTH, or of epinephrine or norepinephrine, which would block part of the effect of alcohol at the same level.

From the Floor Could this be explained by the output of sugar by the liver?

Dr. Goldberg Yes, the emptying of the glycogen, and glucose, and so on. There are all kinds of explanations.

From the Floor Is it because glucose stimulates the whole carbohydrate cycle and the alcohol is metabolized faster?

Dr. Forsander We don't know in which way alcohol influences the central nervous system—the point of metabolic effect. I don't think we can answer this, but there is no indication that the alcohol was metabolized faster.[4]

EFFECT OF PERSONALITY TYPE

Dr Alexander May I just introduce that other interesting complication, that is, the fate of the psychologist, of the human psychologist—not the animal psychologist—as he deals with complications. I should like to refer to an observation which I made. You can divide the reaction of human beings to alcohol into two groups: (1) The people who are normal in behavior in their everyday life. Let us say they are somewhat inhibited, subdued, with-

[3] A. Leikola, Influence of Stress on Alcohol Intoxication in Rats, *Quart. J. Studies Alc.*, **23**:369–375, 1962.
[4] Reference is made also to the discussion in another panel: See pp. 351–352.

drawn persons—people who are retiring types. Many of those react to alcohol by getting an unexpected change in character. The fellow who before drinking was quiet, sitting in a corner quietly conversing; after alcohol becomes more and more aggressive; sometimes even dangerous. (2) The people who, in their everyday life, are slightly hypomanic, direct, outspoken, friendly. After alcohol many of them become just the opposite; they become sentimental, weepy.

I first observed this in Germany where I was an honorary member (being a foreign student I could not be a real member) of one of those fencing groups, *Burschenschaft*, and I noticed that many of those students, who appeared to be real bullies, after drinking a few beers became very sentimental. They hugged each other, almost kissed each other; they became good fellows, you know, but fearful, talking about their souls, and so on. But the timid ones became aggressive. The psychologists, and particularly the psychoanalysts, are interested in finding out why—why does alcohol reverse the natural or usual conduct, and feelings too. I came to the conclusion that when the inhibited person drinks, he gets rid of these excess inhibitions. The alcohol has a stimulating effect probably because those very high centers which are responsible for the cortical inhibitory effect are removed. The superimposed self which is very often retiring—most likely a compensating measure—is displaced by uncovering his basic aggressiveness. They are aggressive, but they learn so thoroughly how to control their natural impulses, that they become, so to say, overly domesticated animals. Those people get a relieving effect from the alcohol. The other ones, who become soft and sentimental, many of them are latent homosexuals. These people are really intimidated human beings who have a great many inhibitions. They overcompensate for their feminine or homosexual drives and hide their basic character by this defense mechanism of aggressiveness. Now the alcohol knocks out the superimposed defense mechanism—the aggressiveness—from the basically "soft" person, and the softness from the basically aggressive ones.

These are clinical examples of how different people react because the *original* state is different. The pendulum of the basic equilibrium between inhibitory and exhibitory processes determines how a person will react to alcohol. The blood sugar has a great deal to do with this, but it is not in a 1 to 1 relation. We simply can't predict on the basis of the blood sugar whether the person will become aggressive or retiring.

Now, to go back to rats. Are there differences in the strains of rats?

Dr. Forsander   Yes. We have two groups of rats; one active type, and one very inactive.

GENETIC DIFFERENCES

Dr. Goldberg   A quantitative genetic difference has been found by a research group at Berkeley.[5] Out of seven strains of mice, they picked out two. One showed a high tolerance to alcohol with very little evidence of intoxication; the other showed the reverse situation. If you gave the two strains the same amount of alcohol, one strain was in every single case less intoxicated than the other one. And they found that these two strains differed in the amount of enzyme in their liver. But the moment they go one step further, this finding doesn't check any more. This is a finding not correlated with anything else, so they have guessed that there must be a genetic difference.

From the Floor   Mardones in Chile has also shown you can breed rat strains that prefer more alcohol.[6]

From the Floor   I have been trying to account for Dr. Alexander's point. It sounds like the alcohol removed fear and tension, in his two types of people: one is afraid to show himself sentimental, and the other is afraid to be more aggressive. The question might be, what then is the basis for the difference between these people—psychological or physiological?

From the Floor   I was wondering if this might also have something to do with the acute episode.

Dr. Goldberg   Very definitely so. Consider, for example, the difference of taking a cocktail in the home of your parents-in-law-to-be the first time you are in their house, and the same cocktail and

[5] G. E. McClearn and D. A. Rodgers, Differences in Alcohol Preference among Inbred Strains of Mice, *Quart. J. Studies Alc.*, 20:691–695, 1959.

[6] R. J. Mardones, M. N. Segovia, and D. A. Hederra, Herencía del alcoholismo en ratas. I. Comportamiento de la primera generacion de ratas bebedoras, colocadas en dieta carenciada en factor N_1 (Inheritance of Alcoholism in Rats. I. Behavior of the First Generation of Alcoholic Rats Placed on Diets Lacking Factor N_1), *Rev. med. aliment.*, 9:61–62, 1950.

R. J. Mardones, M. N. Segovia, and D. A. Hederra, Heredity of Experimental Alcohol Preference in Rats. II. Coefficient of Heredity, *Quart. J. Studies Alc.*, 14:1–2, 1953.

how it acts when you are together with your own friends. I mean, of course, the state of mind does make a difference.

Dr. Alexander Another example is the use of Thorazine and chlorpromazine. Chlorpromazine has a tranquilizing effect on hypomanics and manics, and agitates the depressed, but in a different sense. It makes the depressed person more depressed. So you have the same drug tranquilizing one person and depressing another.

Yesterday we had an argument with Dr. Lucia. He said that alcohol is a depressant of cellular activity and therefore we should call it a depressant. But we must consider not only the isolated cell but a complex cell structure arranged in certain histological units, and if the central nervous system is affected, it will inhibit the function of other units. If you knock out the inhibitory cells, you get stimulation in spite of the fact that the basic effect of alcohol is depressant.

Dr. Forsander We have done some work on the stimulating effect of alcohol in the patient in hangover.

DEVELOPMENT OF ALCOHOLISM

From the Floor Does this character change, which we talked about, occur in the three general groups of drinkers we are discussing: the moderate, the middle, and the alcoholic group? Do you notice a change from quiet to aggressor? And does this character change also occur when the drinker goes from one state into the next?

Dr. Alexander I have a number of cases in my files on this; for example, there is the person who is a moderate drinker for years and then, in one period of his life, he becomes a problem. And yet it's the same person, the same central nervous system, the same liver, and so on. As his marriage began to become shaky, he started to drink more and more. Now, what has happened? Is it an accident that he was a moderate drinker, and then suddenly he becomes a problem drinker? These people always experience tension, worry, pressures, and so on, and they can't figure out what happened—and alcohol helps. According to the principle of conditioning, if these persons experience again and again that stress is relieved by ingestion of alcohol, even if it is only temporary, then in a continuous, very difficult stress situation, the motivation increases, because the motivation is now reinforced through this conditioning of past experience.

In some more favorable cases, they might go to Alcoholics Anonymous, develop new rules, and institute them in their lives, and the need for this type of escape diminishes. So the human being is an animal who is difficult to deal with, and the clinicians see these complications.

There are certain general criteria one can use for predicting the development of an alcoholic. First, we see that the person's tolerance for frustration is extremely low. That is often a culturally determined factor because some social groups and certain sects are trained to endure the vicissitudes of life from early childhood on—pain met with stoicism—which can become part of their ego structure. These latter are people whose tolerance against frustrations in life is very good, and if you could test them psychologically, you could measure at least this ego strength—the capacity to tolerate frustration, to postpone immediate action. You can predict that people with this kind of great ego strength probably will not become alcoholics even in the extremest stress situations.

The others belong to the first group—Knight[7] describes them very beautifully——people who from childhood on had a very indulgent mother, who never could tolerate any frustrations in their childhood, who were overprotected. And, let us say, their father was just the opposite, a very inconsistent human being, sometimes punishing and strict, and sometimes very forgiving. Such inconsistent parental influence is apt to make the child less able to tolerate frustration, and these people as they grow up might constitute the group of serious alcoholics whom we call "essential alcoholics." Is it possible that there may be a metabolic reason why all of us are not always drinking alcohol?

Dr. Forsander I believe there is a metabolic reason. Alcohol is not very good for most people.

If you study how rats like alcohol, in free-choice experiments where they are given a choice between water and a 10 per cent solution of alcohol, you will find that they usually drink water—so they like water more than alcohol. Guinea pigs don't like alcohol at all, the hamster, on the other hand, likes alcohol.[8] Now, you can

[7] R. P. Knight, The Psychodynamics of Chronic Alcoholism, *J. Nervous Mental Disease*, 86:538–548, 1937.

[8] A. Arvola and O. Forsander, Comparison between Water and Alcohol Consumption in Six Animal Species in Free Choice Experiments, *Nature*, London, 191:819–820, 1961.

change this attitude toward alcohol in different ways—usually it involves a change in metabolism. For example, if the hamster is pregnant, she will start to drink water, but postpartum she returns to her former liking for alcohol. If you give rats insulin, which changes their carbohydrate metabolism, they will start to drink more alcohol. But it is only the hamster who seems to have a true liking for alcohol; he prefers drinking alcohol; whereas rats normally prefer water. In fact, most animals prefer water; there are very few animals who really like alcohol. And I think that children too have an inborn preference for water—which might lead us to believe that there is a metabolic factor involved.

Moderator   Dr. Karl M. Bowman
Participants   Dr. J. Anthony Deutsch, Prof. George C. Drew,
                 Dr. Giorgio Lolli

Dr. Bowman   Let us start off by asking the several members of
the panel to talk for about ten minutes each, to give us their own
spontaneous observations on the subject of this particular panel—the
psychological aspects of alcohol in civilization. Now we will start
off by asking Dr. Deutsch if he will say a few words.

MOTIVATION FOR DRINKING

Dr. Deutsch   It seems to me there are roughly three types of
questions that psychologists might ask about the ingestion of alcohol.

The first question is: What leads to its ingestion in the first
place? I myself have been interested in the ingestion of various
types of fluid besides alcohol and in trying to work out some kind of
connection between the taste of a liquid and the amount that is
drunk to satiation. That is, supposing you have a thirsty man, the
amount that he will drink is, to a large extent, dependent upon his
psychological deficits, how hungry and thirsty he is at the time.
Also, the taste of the fluid is a factor.

It is possible to show that with certain types of fluid there is
an overdrinking which takes place when the animal is thirsty, merely
because of its particular taste. That is, the man or the animal will
tend to overdrink a fluid because it does not provide the correct
kind of stimulus which he needs to satiate his thirst, and so he will
drink it for much longer than he would if he were given, say, water.
This is one of the things that I have tried to go into in my own research. I am trying to see whether alcohol is a kind of fluid which
is overdrunk when a man is thirsty because it plays tricks on the
sensory input. This is one of the topics that might be considered. It
might acount for excessive drinking of alcohol, after an absence
of drinking, before any type of addictive factor has occurred.

Secondly, I think the type of question that a psychologist might ask is about the effects of alcohol in small doses. There has been a lot of discussion about alcoholism, but it seems to me that, for instance, the type of research that Professor Drew has done has pointed out the dangers of the ingestion of alcohol even in very small doses in the type of civilization that we live in, that is, a highly mechanized civilization, where speed of reaction time and judgment is of very great importance in safety and survival.

The third type of question that I think psychologists might ask is about the nature of the effect of alcohol on the central nervous system. It seems that the assumption is made that the effects are, to a large extent, of a depressing nature, acting on the so-called higher nerve center of the cortex, and this therefore reduces fear and liberates some kind of libido or something like that. This appears to be the general assumption that is made.

It seems to me, at least, that such assumptions ought to be questioned. I don't think they are particularly in line with what one might expect from present day knowledge of the mediation of fear, and it would be worthwhile to inquire into the effects of alcohol on the central nervous system with a view of explaining specific effects in producing an addiction.

Dr. Bowman Thank you, Dr. Deutsch. Professor Drew, would you care to say a few words?

ALCOHOL AND SKILL

Prof. Drew My interests in alcohol are really twofold. I was not primarily interested in alcohol but in the analysis of skill. I originally used alcohol simply because I felt that in the way in which psychologists had been working on skills, we had been getting very little information, and I used alcohol as a way of breaking a skill. There is some evidence that we can get information on these rather complex processes in man by breaking them down that we can't get by studying the working mechanism—rather like the neurologist who gets information from brain functions in studying damaged cases, whereas he can't get much information by watching the operating brain, except nowadays with more elaborate electric recording techniques.

Starting from this general point of view, I found the effects of alcohol proved to be quite different from what I expected. Hence, I have become interested in alcohol itself. There seemed to me to be a very large number of problems which need to be studied from this more basic point of view about alcohol, and they are relevant to the second interest that I have, which is the effect of drinking on traffic accidents and the practical application in a road traffic situation.

I feel, for example, that a great deal more needs to be done on the interaction between the personal characteristics of the individual and the effects of alcohol.

The two things I am quite sure of are: one, that there is a relationship of this kind; two, that the one I previously described as extroversion and introversion is the wrong one. It is not just that; it is much more complicated than that, but we don't know what it is yet, and I think we need to work on this a great deal more.

ALCOHOL AND TENSION

We have also heard a good deal about the tension-reducing qualities of small doses of alcohol, and this is a very popular statement. It relieves any guilt feelings we have, for one thing, but it is also a very popular defense of drinking.

I am not preaching one way or the other because I myself drink moderately, but it is used very often as a statement of justification for drinking when individuals are driving, on the grounds that the conditions in modern traffic are such as to produce tension, and that alcohol will reduce tension and will in fact produce an improvement in their performance. This is a very popular alibi.

Now the interesting thing to me—and this is where a great deal more work needs to be done—is the interaction between these kinds of situations, the kind of situation in which alcohol has been shown to be tension producing, the kind of situation that Dr. Greenberg mentioned yesterday, and the conditions where there is a good deal of social direction between members of a group. On the other hand, according to one study by Vogel, which is very difficult to explain indeed, there is no evidence in the literature that alcohol, in however small doses one likes to talk about, has any effect on skilled performance through tension reduction. It has not been demonstrated so far. I am not saying that it doesn't exist but it has not been demonstrated, and hence I think this is an area where a good deal of work needs to be done.

It is quite clear that alcohol does have a tranquilizing effect under some conditions. This sort of tranquilizing effect is not discernible in the error scores which people make in any kind of skill situation. It seems to me that this is an anomaly. If it acts as a tranquilizer in one situation, it ought to be discernible as such in a situation of skill if one can get the motivation of people high enough.

This seems to me to be an area I should like to know a great deal more about. There seem to be discrepancies of information, and I think a good deal more work needs to be done in this area so that we may know how the two kinds of measures fit in with one another. They can't be contradictory; this is obvious. There must be some kind of limitation, some parameter of action, which we don't know at the present moment.

I think it is most important, therefore, that we should avoid making any general statements about effects of small doses in terms of tranquilizing effects or deteriorating effects, except by qualifying them, by defining the situation which we're talking about at the present stage, because there apparently are discrepant situations here, but we don't know why they are discrepant. This is the point of information I should like to get.

PERSONALITY AND EFFECT OF DRINKING

Dr. Bowman You think we could say that perhaps alcohol affects different persons in different ways because of their own personalities, and secondly, that the same dosage of alcohol may affect the same person in different ways depending upon his state of fatigue or emotion or something like that?

Prof. Drew I am quite sure that if one's measures are sensitive enough, one will be able to find differences with various personalities and also differences with his subject's present condition—whether he is fatigued or not.

On the other hand, the thing which bothers me a good deal is that although one has sufficiently sensitive measures and can pick out these differences, they don't produce a situation, in a complicated skilled task, in which the alcohol is a sufficient tension reducer in any individual with any performances that we have measured so far, or in any varying condition of the same individual such as to produce the improvement of performance which one would expect if the individual is under tension. If his performance on a skilled task is less good than it would be if he were not under tension, then the effect of alcohol in reducing the tension should be to improve the performance of a skilled task. You can show that there is a difference in the behavior of various individuals; they get bad in different ways, but this is the point that I find very puzzling.

PERSONALITY, DRIVING, AND ALCOHOL

Dr. Bowman The police in a number of our states—I have talked with many of them—tell me that oftentimes they spot the drunken driver because here is an individual driving quite slowly, and obviously with great care, way over on the right side of the road. He realizes his condition and he is really trying to correct for it, but it only results in his getting himself caught. Secondly, the idea that the indecisive person, the so-called obsessive neurotic who can never make up his mind to do this or that—and there are so many women here I don't dare use the man-made phrase that the so-called woman driver makes up her mind to do one thing and then does the other—that type of driver at least under the effect of alcohol sometimes shows great improvement in driving, because there is the lessening of the indecisiveness and tension and inability to make decisions.

Would you think that could occur in such cases?

Prof. Drew In the first place, I think it is perfectly true that you get a slow, careful driver after alcohol; and they are—I think we're able to show this—slow and careful only as long as they are in a completely controlled situation. When the situation takes control of them, then they become incompetent, very grossly incompetent. They certainly do get picked up, and it is a traditional belief in London that if one walks the edge of a road at eleven o'clock on Saturday night, one can see the stream of traffic quite clearly, and of course they are not all under the influence of alcohol, but one can sort the different personality types out according to speed.

How frequently these people get picked up in the United States by the police I wouldn't know. The evidence in England is that they don't get picked up by the police unless they have very, very high blood alcohols indeed.

The situation at the present moment is that two surveys have been carried out, one in the southwest of England and the other in the northeast of England. Those who are caught and on whom tests are made, who are involved in accidents, have an average alcohol level of about 0.25 per cent. Those who are picked up by the police for being drunk, who are not involved in accidents, have a mean average blood alcohol of around something over 0.30 per cent. This is quite a fantastic figure, and it doesn't suggest that it is the individual with low doses who is driving carefully and getting picked up, not in England anyway.

In England, it is very difficult to make a drunken driving charge stick; therefore, the police don't prefer a charge of driving under the influence unless they are pretty sure they can make it stick. One reason is that clinical, medical testimony is given, and the defense can always call his own doctor; and one's own doctor, if he is a reasonable chap, produces a conflict of expert testimony in the court, and the individual gets dismissed.

Dr. Bowman Now to the question of the indecisive driver.

Prof. Drew Yes, this is constantly being said, and all I can say is that I have never come across an actual example of this sort of case, and I have looked for it. The only sort of case where I have seen any evidence of this appearing is where the neurotic indecision is such that the individual has been a patient in a mental hospital. Now these people, in my view, would not be driving anyhow. I get the feeling that before alcohol will have very significant effects on changing the driving behavior of people of that nature, their indecision has to be of such an order that they ought not to be driving without alcohol. I expect the people that need alcohol to drive ought not to be driving at all—but I am beginning to sound rather like a temperance preacher. I don't mean to be.

I think it is a problem that needs a good deal more research.

Dr. Bowman Dr. Lolli, would you care to make a few remarks?

Dr. Lolli From what Dr. Deutsch and Professor Drew have already said, it's obvious psychology represents one of the main keys for the understanding of the issues, so to speak, of alcohol, and I am sure that this is becoming even more clear during the discussion of this panel.

PUBLIC HEALTH PROBLEM

I would only like to add to what they have said that I think psychology can contribute also to the definition of the role of alcohol in our society as seen from the public health issue. Let's forget the words, "public health problem." I think there are public health issues, and alcohol represents definitely an issue in the field of public health. One of the troubles which have preyed on us who have worked in this field so far is the difficulty of finding yardsticks for measuring drinking behavior and drinking attitudes, and unquestionably psychology together with biochemistry can contribute immensely by translating into the precise language of numbers what so far has been stated in rather vague terms.

From the angle of the public health person, the alcohol problems so far have been more or less polarized to two issues, either to drink or not to drink; on one side total abstention, on the other the extreme difficulties of alcohol excesses, "alcoholism." Frankly, I think it is impossible to give a definition of alcoholism. I think we are wasting a good deal of our time if we follow that direction.

On the other hand, from the angle of the public health problem, if we polarize our attention to the work that Professor Drew has been doing—alcohol-induced inefficiencies or alcohol-induced efficiencies——and measure those efficiencies, we have a chance of working more within the area of real public health. One of the main problems in public health is the definition of goals. Unless we are able to define goals it will be rather difficult to get results and understanding of public health problems. Again, when we deal with alcoholism, we do not define goals—witness the great uncertainties about statistics regarding the incidence of alcoholism in any given country.

You all know what formulas are applied today, correlations which attempt to establish a relationship between the death rate from cirrhosis of the liver and alcoholism without complications, and from these correlations, which are all based on very simple data, one reaches the conclusion that San Francisco has a very high rate of alcoholism and other cities don't. Data that are not objective are not scientific data.

On the other hand, if we polarize our attention to the facts of alcohol and try to establish how many people drink, how much they drink, how frequently they drink or how many hours a day they drink, and try to carry out surveys in determining our blood alcohol concentrations in random or selected samples of individuals, sooner or later we shall have a body of evidence which will be along the lines that we have in many other fields, and which at this stage we do not have in the field of alcohol and also alcohol problems.

It is very strange that we should have forgotten that before reaching the extreme excesses of alcohol, people get plainly inebriated, and this should be the focus and target of all of our effort. Here again, from the standpoint of public health, we have an ideal situation. In public health we are taught that a problem has a chance of being solved when the distance between cause and effect is not too great. In the field of alcohol it is postulated that the causes are very, very remote from the so-called effects. In the field of inebriety, there is the cause and effect, no doubt about that. Again, here we have the most promising field, and again Professor Drew's research has opened quite a few new vistas.[1] There is some initial evidence, which has to be corroborated, about some types of individuals who are, so to say, more sensitive to alcohol-induced inefficiencies, and other types who are not.

INCIDENCE OF ALCOHOLISM

Dr. Bowman I should like to bring up this question of the incidence of alcoholism. Do you think we are finding any other way of measuring the amount of alcoholism in the community? Since the Jellinek formula has been not too satisfactory, I just wondered if you know of any other measure that is taking its place?

Dr. Lolli Dr. Bowman, I don't feel that we can measure alcoholism because we cannot define alcoholism. We can define inebriated behavior, but I don't think that at this stage of the game anyone has given a satisfactory definition of alcoholism which would withstand a critical examination by the tools of logic.

I think if you were to submit some of the definitions to a logician—Professor Drew comes from England and they have some rather competent students of logic—these men would laugh at us. Would you agree, Professor Drew?

Prof. Drew Yes, I think they would.

Dr. Bowman Well, it is of interest that Stanford University has a course in logic which has been given to the medical students for a number of years with the idea that most doctors are not very good logicians. If they were, a lot of medical articles announcing various results would never have been produced. Perhaps most of us

[1] G. C. Drew, W. P. Colquhoun, and H. A. Long, Effect of Small Doses of Alcohol on a Skill Resembling Driving, *Brit. Med. J.*, 2:993–999, 1958.

would agree that we should like better logic here, but I don't know of any logician who has come in and offered to help us out with a new definition of alcoholism.

Dr. Lolli   It seems to me that we have approached the whole problem from a completely pure viewpoint: broad surveys in the community of who drinks, why he drinks, and how much, trying to convey to the community just some of this information that men like Professor Drew gather about specific measurable effects of specific doses of alcohol on specific individuals. With this information we might be able to prevent a good deal of excessive drinking and therefore prevent alcoholism. Anyhow I hope so.

Dr. Bowman   There is one attempt being made here in San Francisco to make a public health survey on the incidence of drinking in certain communities.

Dr. Deutsch, you spoke of your interest in the nature and effect of alcohol on the central nervous system. I don't know what strictly belongs under psychology and what doesn't, but it seems to me this should belong under it. I wonder if you would care to elaborate a little bit about the problem as you see it and the possible ways of trying to check on this?

ALCOHOL AND THE CENTRAL NERVOUS SYSTEM

Dr. Deutsch   Well, I should like to say in my own defense before I start that this is an interest which is just developing. It really arose as the result of some things that the people said at the conference here, so I am not going to speak as being particularly informed about this. However, it struck me that the assumptions that were made about the effect of alcohol are based on a kind of psychology which is being inherited from Plato. That is, the idea seems to be that your highest function is the reason and that this is then enforced by some kind of guardian or some kind of police force; that at the bottom you have your passions or emotions; and that when you get drunk, the reason and the police force, as it were, are asleep, and the passions then have a very good time. This has become a sort of link with some kind of anatomical observations about the cortex and subcortical centers, and it seems to be believed that when you drink, the cortex goes to sleep and the subcortical centers, which are places where the drives, emotions, or things like that reside, have a good time. This, of course, is also very much the type of thing, the kind of Freudian picture of the soul which also was inherited from Plato, and Plato's own explanation seems very much like a Freudian one. He says that when the reason goes to sleep, then the passions during sleep make you do things or imagine things which you wouldn't do when you are awake. For instance, he mentioned that you sometimes dream of sleeping with your mother, and this shows, of course that the lower centers or the lower parts of the soul have become released. This seems to be the kind of picture of the action of alcohol also.

It seems to me that this is likely to be a very wrong picture. I think it has been very amply demonstrated that fear, disgust, aggression, and the various things which alcohol is said to affect—not aggression, perhaps, but certainly fear—are the types of things which very probably are tied up with functions of subcortical centers, but you can, in fact, produce fear in animals with all their cortex missing.

You can produce fear in animals by stimulation of various parts of the central nervous system which are not cortical. For instance, you will all be aware of the recent work on intracranial self-stimulation where a rat is given a small shock to the central nervous system. It would seem to me much more likely that there is probably a specific selective effect of alcohol on certain subcortical centers apart from this effect on the cortex. I think one can show that there are effects on things like reaction time and threshold, but I think these are likely to be different and apart from the specific effects on certain drive systems, such as those underlying fear, because there does seem to be a consensus of opinion about a specific fear or guilt-removing function of alcohol. I don't know what Professor Drew will have to say about this, but I should like to know what his thoughts on this particular subject are.

Prof. Drew Well, I agree that the action of alcohol on such a nervous system is a problem which could very well be studied. I don't believe there is any point whatsoever in trying to speculate on the effects on the nervous system by talking about effects on behavior. We know far too little about the relation of the central nervous system and such complicated things as drive, emotions, crises, and so on. I should say the statement that alcohol is a central nervous system depressant is a fairly well-based statement in the sense that if you take the actual cell, the central nervous system cell, and measure the metabolism rate, the breathing rate of the cell in vitro, and then place it in a solution of exceedingly minute quantities of alcohol, you will find that alcohol has an effect on the metabolism of the cell. If the quantity is very minute, for a very short period of time, a matter of about a few minutes, the alcohol increases the rate of metabolism, but immediately after that it decreases the rate of metabolism.

If the concentration is stronger, well below that which one considers in evaluating any kind of behavior change, at that concentration the effect is, right from the beginning, to produce a depression in the rate of metabolism of the nerve cell. Now I think this is the sort of evidence on which the statement that alcohol is a depressant is based, not in terms of the behavior effects.

If I might just say one more thing, I think it would be exceedingly useful and worthwhile for people to work on specific effects of alcohol on the central nervous system.

Bradley has shown a good deal of information on the side direction of various tranquilizers and has found that quite a number of them act on the activation system, so what we are getting, in fact, is a breakdown of some mechanism, and the individual is not getting stimulated; but if you then bang him with a harder stimulus, you get the same response as you would otherwise. Alcohol, I suspect, may act in this sort of way.

I think you have to be very careful indeed about discussing behavior. First of all, I don't think we know enough about the relationship between behavior and central nervous system activity. Concerning the visual threshold effects, there is a good deal of evidence that so far as the absolute thresholds are concerned, this is a peripheral effect; the alcohol is having a peripheral effect; it changes the chemical constitution of the hydroxyl fluids, and this, in fact, does change, particularly, the adaptation. During the war the RAF discovered this. They used to fed the men carrots and that produced dark adaptation. This, of course, I have always understood was a peripheral effect.

Dr. Deutsch Well, I wasn't suggesting that we speculate on the basis of behavior as to where the action of alcohol might be; I was suggesting that we actually investigate the possible site of action by a mixture of behavioral and physiological tests.

The business of the threshold reminds me that I myself, upon trying to do what Professor Drew has so ably himself accomplished, also tried to impair a skill by the ingestion of alcohol. I think any of you that might have heard a junkie singing would be convinced there is an effect of large doses of alcohol on the skill of holding a note or singing a tune. As alcohol is a very popular tool, there is no shortage of volunteer subjects when you use it. We thought we might try to use its disruptive effect on the skills of singing, which we were then studying. We were studying the nature of the feedback mechanism which governs your ability to hold a steady note.

Instead of developing an interest in alcohol from this, we rather threw it up in despair, because we found that the effects of alcohol were measurable in many different ways—that is, we couldn't get a clear or clean differentiation of the various factors. Anything which we measured which might have been relevant to the skills seems to have been impaired by the administration of alcohol. We found that the threshold for detecting the change in a note was impaired; we found that the reaction time to when one strayed from a note was also impaired, so, unfortunately, we did not go on with the experiment, though it was a very amusing one.

CAUSES OF ALCOHOLISM

Dr. Bowman I wonder if perhaps we can get over to a more general question. The first one I should like to ask any member of the panel who would volunteer is: To what extent do you think we should explain alcoholism—meaning by that what you would all agree was alcoholism—as being due essentially to psychological causes as opposed to physiological causes. For example, there is the idea of Roger Williams[2] that it is a metabolic defect which produces the craving for alcohol, and so forth, which does not seem to have been substantiated but which is very interesting. Do you think that we can find an adequate explanation in psychological factors as to why a man becomes an alcoholic, or are you all completely dissatisfied with any such attempts, or do you know of some better way?

Dr. Lolli, would you care to start?

Dr. Lolli I am a kind of a rebel, Doctor. I don't know whether I feel that at this stage of the game we can explain the physiological and psychological causes. It seems to me that we are talking of one world which for the time being has to be described in two languages, so to speak, the physiological, because we cannot find anything better,

[2] R. J. Williams, The Etiology of Alcoholism: A Working Hypothesis Involving the Interplay of Hereditary and Environmental Factors, *Quart. J. Studies Alc.*, 7:567–587, 1947.

and the psychological, also because we cannot find anything better.

As far as tangible chemical determinable causes of troubles with alcohol, we have really absolutely no evidence of any. Frankly, the biochemical viewpoint of some vitamin lack as the cause of trouble does not seem too plausible.

I was sold on the psychological or psychiatric cause of trouble for ten or fifteen years, having run several programs for the prevention and treatment of alcoholism. Of course, we find a lot of psychopathology in the extreme excesses of alcohol addiction, but at the time we see them, we reconstruct their past lives from the point of troubles and where they occurred. We still don't know how much of the dependency or independence or what fixations and regressions were present before the trouble, nor how many members of the citizenry will never turn to drinking to such excesses as to deserve a label of addicted drinkers, even if they have the same characteristics.

In other words, it seems to me our reconstructions might be very correct, but still we don't have any validation to prove their relevance in persons who drink alcohol to excess.

Prof. Drew   I agree very much indeed with Dr. Lolli on this one. It seems to me that when one talks about the causes of alcoholism, what one gets into is a statement that alcoholics are people who have failed to adjust, and they have this or that psychopathology, and we have no way of knowing how many individuals who have a similar psychopathology don't take to alcoholism.

I think it is altogether too complicated from this angle, because I suspect that one could draw a very general picture, but then in each case one would have to have an individual case history, and there will be factors in any given case which are different from any other case. I suspect that in this respect alcoholism will have exactly the same kind of history as, for example, the investigation of juvenile delinquency.

We have a program going on in my department on what we call in England "young offenders," sixteen to twenty-one-year-olds, and we find it is very much worthwhile. In fact, we can now do quite a bit by taking the population who are delinquent and studying this population. We can now produce fairly accurate predictions as to which of these individuals are going to yield to treatment and which are not, which will be recidivists and which will not. There are some indications that we may be able to go further than this and pick out the kind of individuals who will benefit most by which kind of treatment—there are a variety of forms of treatment, from prison to detention, and so on. But we get exactly the same as everybody else gets—that is, you have a very high proportion of people from broken homes. You start from the other end and take children from broken homes, and you find the great majority don't have to become delinquent, and these factors which are important for differentiating within the delinquent population are not sufficient to define, from the general population, which population will become delinquent. Thus we become completely frustrated, and we get absolutely nowhere, aside from very broad generalizations. I suspect it is exactly the same case with alcoholism.

We should be very much better off to study the psychopathology and background history of alcoholics to see whether we can use diagnostic and predictive techniques for discovering the treatability of the individual and give up trying to do anything but make broad statements about what causes alcoholism, because I don't believe we are within several hundred years of doing that.

Dr. Bowman There is an interesting report I should like to mention to you and see what you may think of it. MacKay[3] of the Peter Bent Brigham Hospital in Boston, at the Alcoholism Clinic, studied seventeen adolescents, boys and girls, who drank excessively and who showed a great deal of hostility, depression, compulsiveness, and sexual confusion. The fathers of most were alcoholics and in some cases the mothers were also alcoholics. The weakness of the alcoholic parent was thought to be one reason for the adolescents' drinking, and the reason given here, which seemed to me rather unusual, was that by proving their own ability to drink successfully and contrast it to the way their parents drink, the youths were asserting their independence and superiority over the parents.

This seemed to me a rather new, you might say psychological, explanation of alcoholism, obviously not applying to the vast majority of cases, but does this seem, if we're looking for psychological factors, that an explanation like that is a reasonable thing to keep in mind, or does this seem awfully forced?

Dr. Deutsch It would seem to me that obviously in homes like that there would be a very large number of possible factors, anything

[3] J. R. MacKay, Clinical Observations on Adolescent Problem Drinkers, *Quart. J. Studies Alc.*, 22:124–134, 1961.

from hereditary influence to almost any fanciful explanation one can devise, and this seems to be one among them. As long as one doesn't devise critical tests or run surveys to distinguish between these various possibilities, it seems to me that one can only say that it should be kept in mind.

Prof. Drew I think it is possible that under those conditions it may apply to that specific group. One can find an equal number of cases where the children, the adolescents who are drinking heavily, come from homes where the parents are very rigid abstainers, and there the argument is that they are reacting against the parents, the same as they're doing in the opposite way here. This may be true, but I think this kind of explanation is too glib. It is the sort of explanation which I was talking about just now, and one can make statements, but I don't believe they help at all.

In London there is a particularly tough area where there are gangs of adolescent youths who have been causing trouble since the war. It is less difficult now, but they have been causing trouble. I knew the man who opened a youth club in that area to look after those particular boys that we call "teddy boys" because they were a roughneck lot. Here the explanation was that they were such a rough and badly behaved group because the parents in this particular area all spent their evenings in the local pubs, and that since the parents liked to do their drinking quietly, they had instructed the licensees of the pubs not to allow their children into the pubs to drink, otherwise the parents wouldn't drink there. As the parents drink more than the children do, there was an economic pressure on the licensee to keep these children out of the pubs. That was the reason given, that they were not allowed in the pubs, and therefore supposedly they entertained themselves by taking the train from London to Brighton, beating up the teddy boys in Brighton, and then on the way back slashing up the upholstery in the carriages and on the train. The explanation, in other words, was that this was a revolt against their parents' excluding them from the pubs.

This kind of explanation may be true, but there is no possible way, it seems to me, of doing more than describing them in very broad terms. I don't think they have any diagnostic or useful significance at all. At the very best, they are just convenient ways of describing a situation. I don't think they have any more value than that.

Dr. Deutsch It strikes me that they are rather inconvenient ways to describe the situation.

GROUP THERAPY IN ALCOHOLISM

Dr. Bowman If you are trying to go as far as possible along psychological lines, I should like to raise another question. We have spoken a great deal of psychological factors in the production of alcoholism and in its treatment. We know that a large percentage of treatment is what we would call essentially psychological, but there is one factor which seems to be universally agreed upon, that alcoholics as a group do unusually well under group psychotherapy. This is becoming generally used, as far as I know, throughout the world and seems to have, if anything, a degree of success greater than group psychotherapy in other conditions.

I wonder if any of you have had experience in this area. Perhaps we can get some comments on the mechanisms, or perhaps even disagree with this formula.

Dr. Lolli Again, Doctor, we face this problem of measuring results, which is a very serious problem. I have had group sessions with alcoholics and maybe it was due to my inability, but certainly I did not feel that my group did unusually well. I have kept referring and I still refer and I shall keep referring patients to Alcoholics Anonymous, and I am aware of the results that Alcoholics Anonymous have achieved. However, I dare say very openly that I am not convinced that the results of Alcoholics Anonymous are as good as they are claimed. Again, from the public health angle, we have to see how many times they get drunk between group sessions, between attendance at meetings, and so on and so forth. Certain results have been achieved, but I don't think they belong in the category of the measurable results which we consider as physicians, or, if you want to say, as scientists.

Dr. Bowman I think what has been noted and commented on time and time again is that Alcoholics Anonymous have had particular success with the cases which the psychiatrists generally have regarded as the poorest risks and with which they have had their poorest results. These are the cases which the psychiatrists generally explain on the ground that this man is not yet ready for treatment: he has not dropped down enough yet; he has not hit bottom, as the phrase goes. In Alcoholics Anonymous we see a type of group psychotherapy in which a whole group of therapists is available to one patient. We have the special situation there of a patient who does not ordinarily feel on the defensive, the way he does in almost any other situation, because here are a group of individuals who have been just as far down as he has and who tell him so and encourage him that he can come back. Then, their social meetings and the fact that they are available for a call at any moment are some of the very special points of Alcoholics Anonymous.

You have not been convinced of what I think is a fairly commonly expressed idea that alcoholics generally do better in group psychotherapy?

Dr. Lolli No. Frankly I am convinced that we do not have any evidence for such a statement.

I should like only to pick up one remark dealing with the Alcoholics Anonymous philosophy and also dealing with the philosophy of some of us therapists. The alcoholic has, it is said, to hit bottom. Well, I frankly am very much against this concept of letting a person go to ruin before saving him, pulling him out of trouble. Again I am very much more in favor of taking steps the very first time that boy came home intoxicated after having been out with that girl. At that time, I think we can do a great amount of psychiatric, social, medical and psychological preventive and educational work. It seems to me that the key to all of our problems that concern alcohol is just this. If we want to deal with the cancer problem or the polio problem we can disseminate information on cancer or on paralytic polio, and we wouldn't wait. I don't know if these are valid comparisons, but still I think there is a grain of truth in it, and I speak from personal experience, because there is evidence that you can really achieve results, especially in youngsters—not bring them back to total abstention but educate them as to how they can drink and to what limit they can drink and not go beyond. In other words, avoid any possible form of inebriety.

I think the condoning of inebriety, of which we see so much in our society, is the very first step to alcoholism.

Dr. Bowman Professor Drew, do you have anything to add to the topic of group psychotherapy?

Prof. Drew No, I have not, and there is very, very little alcoholism as such in England. This may very well be a question of definition, as Dr. Lolli indicated earlier, but in terms of people who are being treated, there is a very low incidence indeed. In the past ten years, something like three-quarters of the treatment facilities have been closed down because they didn't get enough patients. In looking for people with alcoholic psychoses, particularly Korsakoff cases, we had to search all over the country, and I think only two were found in Scotland. The reason is that England is predominantly a beer-drinking country. Our beer is very weak—only 2½ per cent alcohol—and you run out of volume long before you get inebriated.

Dr. Bowman This point you make is true also within the Scandinavian countries. Denmark is the beer-drinking country in Scandinavia, and Denmark has a very much lower incidence of alcoholism than any of the other Scandinavian countries where they have primarily alcohol spirits.

Dr. Lolli And aside from the lower alcohol, they obtain carbohydrates and have the protective effect of the food, which is very important.

Prof. Drew The result is that there are alcoholics, certainly, but there are very few treatment places. I know they do use group psychotherapy quite a bit for it, and I understand that it is regarded as being a very successful technique in England, but I have had no personal experience along these lines.

ALCOHOLISM AND PREVENTION OF INEBRIETY

Dr. Bowman As to the low incidence in England, I think we are all very much interested in that point, because reports from other countries indicate that there is a tremendous increase in alcoholism. There is a recent report from Germany that there are now 7 million excessive drinkers in West Germany of whom 300,000 are regarded as true alcohol addicts. The statement from Czechoslovakia indicates a tremendous increase there. Russia now admits that their alcoholism problem is equal to that of other countries. France, a wine-drinking country, has been tremendously disturbed by the large amount of alcoholism they have been having in the last two or three years, and the way it has been increasing. It almost seems as if Great Britain is unique with its decreasing amount of alcoholism because I don't think anybody feels that it is decreasing in the United States, and one sees it increasing in the Orient.

Prof. Drew There is, if I may say so, just one difference here which may be relevant in this respect, and that is that it does vary. There is the highest incidence per capita in London. The situation in England, generally, is that the great bulk of individuals who drink, drink in public houses. You will agree with that?

Dr. Deutsch Yes.

Prof. Drew The owner, the licensee, or whoever is in charge of a public house, is responsible by law that he does not serve anybody with alcohol if that individual looks as though he is going to become inebriated, and the tradition varies from different towns. The town I know best in this respect is Bristol, where I spent the last two years. There every public house in the town could expect to have the police visit about twice a week, and they don't know when the police are going to come. If the police see anyone inebriated in there, then the publican may well be charged, and if he is charged and found guilty, he loses his license, and he may never again obtain a license to sell liquor, so that his livelihood is gone. Hence, there are very strong compulsions on the part of the licensee to prevent his customers from drinking to a point where the police are likely to become interested in the amount they had to drink. Obviously, this system operates to varying degrees of success in different places.

In the center of London it virtually does not operate at all, and the figures for central London show that alcoholism in central London is very much higher than prosecutions for drunkenness. The police are supposed to take into custody and to charge any individuals in the streets who are inebriated. They don't always do it, and they don't do it in the center of London anywhere nearly as much as they do in the provincial towns, but the combination of these two factors does tend to hold the drinking down below the levels where they're actually inebriated. I think Dr. Lolli is very right. If you stop people at the point of becoming inebriated, you stop them from becoming alcoholics. I think the emphasis in England is on the responsibility of the individual who sells the liquor, and the fact that if he is found guilty of selling liquor to the point where the individual may become inebriated, he may lose his license and hence his livelihood. This may be one of the factors that keeps alcoholism down.

We have exactly the same problem everybody else has. There is an increase in drinking rate in the adolescents. But again, the licensee is not supposed to sell liquor to anyone under the age of eighteen, and it has been an offense only for people who supply the liquor. It is now an offense for people under eighteen years to accept liquor, and in my own home town just outside of London, about three weeks ago, a licensee was prosecuted and fined 1,000 pounds for selling liquor to two girls who were sixteen and who told him that they were eighteen. There is now in our town a law that every adolescent has to bring in his birth certificate, because the penalty is on the licensee if he makes a mistake.

Dr. Deutsch There are also economic differences in the sense that the earning power of the individual, as compared with the price of hard liquor, may be an important factor in England as opposed to the United States.

Prof. Drew There is a very potent point in that comparison. The price of hard liquor in England and here is roughly the same, while the earning power of the individual here is considerably higher than the average in England. The fact that beer is so very much cheaper in England than hard liquor makes people drink beer rather than hard liquor.

Dr. Bowman I should like at this time now to throw the meeting open to questions from the audience.

From the Floor Dr. Lolli, I am a public health person, and I am interested in your statement about trying to salvage the beginning drinker, so to speak, and meaning the young people primarily. I am interested in how you would go about this; how do we get help to the early drinker?

Dr. Lolli I don't think I can answer this question in just a few words, as I am probably supposed to do. It seems to me you need teams of workers, medical, psychiatric, social, and some such others.

I can mention only one little episode. For several years during the two or three weeks preceding the Yale prom, a biology teacher in New Haven asked me to give a talk to the girls of a fancy prep school who were supposedly invited to the prom. I think you can do a lot by individual work, by talks, by education with the group—and they are very keen, very eager to learn, and very eager to drink and not to get drunk, unquestionably so.

Dr. Bowman Are there any other questions?

From the Floor Dr. Lolli, isn't the best therapy the example of the parents themselves, in setting an example of sobriety to the teen-ager?

Dr. Lolli I agree 100 per cent on that. I should also add that unfortunately in some groups, at least, inebriety carries no social stigma and therefore the example is not set; in other words, inebriety is tolerated. When inebriety is not tolerated, I think it makes a difference.

Dr. Bowman I think one might very well raise the question what we mean by sobriety: whether by that was meant use of alcohol in moderation or no alcohol at all?

From the Floor I meant, Dr. Bowman, the use in moderation, because I don't think prohibition would solve any problem.

Dr. Bowman The answer is that use in moderation is meant, and I raised that question because there has been a recent popular article claiming that the best way to prevent alcoholism is not to keep alcohol away from the children but to have alcohol served in the home and used with moderation by the parents; the children from a fairly early age are allowed to indulge moderately. In favor of this it is pointed out what many claim is the reason that we have so little alcoholism among the Jews as compared with other groups—the Jewish children see alcohol served in the home; it is linked with religious ceremonials, and they partake of it at an early age; there is a great taboo against drunkenness, and they have the lowest percentage of alcoholism of any group.

There is a recent article, in the *Quarterly Journal of Studies on Alcohol*,[4] on a study of various religious groups. It shows that when the individuals of a very puritanical religious group opposed completely to alcohol drink, these drinkers exhibit a high rate of inebriety, whereas the Jews have a very high percentage of persons who drink but have very few alcoholics. The statistics are based particularly on the Mormons who, of course, have the strongest taboos possible against alcohol. The idea is that when they do start to drink, they have already broken many of their barriers and contacts and are breaking away from other things, and therefore they are liable to go to excess, whereas the claim is that this does not apply to the Jews, and that was one of the explanations.

RESEARCH GOALS

From the Floor We heard briefly from Dr. Deutsch. I should like to hear from Dr. Lolli and Professor Drew, if I might, what they would like to learn next in the further understanding of alcoholism?

[4] J. H. Skolnick, Religious Affiliation and Drinking Behavior, *Quart. J. Studies Alc.*, 19:452–470, 1958.

Prof. Drew. In very bold terms, there are two lines that I am currently working on, and they are, first, the question of defining much more carefully what a person's variables are which are relevant, and just how these variables interact with alcohol and skill—that is one thing.

The second thing I want to know very much is, where in the kind of skill chain, starting with the perception of the stimulus to the actual movement which is made as the result of this, where in this chain the alcohol acts. I want to know if it is, in fact, primarily a perceptual effect or primarily a muscle effect, or whether it is primarily in some central analyzing capacity. I suspect from the evidence we have gotten so far that it looks as though alcohol in small doses acts first on the central analyzing capacity, the black box, the single general black box. And it looks as though what alcohol does is to reduce the capacity of this central analytical mechanism, so things have to queue up longer before they can get in and get analyzed. After large doses the perceptual side seems to be affected, and quite obviously in intoxication the muscular responses are gone, too, but what I should like to do is to plot more carefully exactly how it happens.

Dr. Lolli Well, I should like to study more of the protective effects of food and of specific food items. We—and I say "we" to include the people who work with me in cooperation with researchers at the National Institute of Psychology of the Italian National Research Council—we are working on different types of foods and different quantities of alcoholic beverages to see the interplay of these two factors and to try to find out which is the optimum amount of food that produces a reasonable and measurable amount of protection against untoward effects of all the different alcoholic beverages.

Next is a wish—to go with a team of fellow workers into saloons, taverns, private homes, at five or six o'clock, with machines for measuring blood alcohol, to interview people to find out what really happens when people drink. This sound ridiculous, but I do feel it can be done provided it is done gently and diplomatically, and it can yield a good deal of very interesting information.

Prof. Drew One of the brewers in England has a sociological department which is starting that type of work in the public houses: a sociological group plotting how much the individuals are drinking, and getting information whether they are driving; what they are doing; and their general behavior. They have been in contact with me simply because I have some machines, one of the few in England at present, to test the blood alcohol, so it is related to what you are saying.

Dr. Lolli   I am happy to hear that.

HANGOVER

From the Floor   In one of the lectures the statement was made that to do away with the hangover is to do away with alcoholism. I wonder whether perhaps Dr. Deutsch would like to comment on that and see if this is really true. This would indicate that were it not for the hangover, the state of inebriation would not be sought.

Dr. Deutsch   Presuming what was meant is that the reason why alcohol is taken on subsequent occasions is because it produced a discomfort on a previous occasion—well, as somebody who has tried to study some of the problems of motivation, I find this somewhat difficult to swallow. The only instance in which I could imagine this to be the case would be where alcohol was taken in order to abolish the evil aftereffects of previous drinking. But I should think that, if some period were allowed to elapse, if anything, it should discourage any further drinking, except for some kind of addictive effect of the alcohol which would not then of itself necessarily be linked to the state of a hangover, but it could lead to some kind of permanent craving for the drug itself. Still I hate to discuss this. I am sure the speaker who said this had much greater experience in this sort of thing than I.

From the Floor   That was Dr. Goldberg, I believe.

Prof. Drew   Perhaps it was a specifically Scandinavian statement.

Dr. Deutsch   If you got nothing from drinking except the hangover, I should think that most people wouldn't drink any more than they would drink some similar unpleasant liquid.

ANTABUSE

From the Floor   Would you talk a little bit about the implications of control on the alcoholic, specifically the possibility of taking Antabuse and what this means to an alcoholic?

Dr. Lolli   Well, the idea of creating a kind of disgust for alcoholic beverages is a very old one. The Romans put eels in wine in order to discourage their drunkards.

In recent years the Antabuse drug came out. Frankly, I am very much against it. I am against it on ethical grounds, first. I think we as doctors are supposed never to place people in jeopardy. In some way Antabuse is something that places an individual in a difficult situation, and especially an individual who almost by definition is not entirely endowed at the time we use this treatment with so-called free will. In other words, he is not as free to make a decision as a person who has not been using alcohol so much.

I never used it on patients, but I did let some of my younger and more enthusiastic associates use it. Nothing serious and dramatic ever happened, however, and again, I am not at all convinced that it serves any purpose whatsoever. I am convinced that it mostly distracts the patient from the basic issue, which is how to achieve total and permanent sobriety by means of a reorientation of his personal life, by means of establishing controls which are not established by means of a pill, and by means of trying to avoid, so to speak, metaphors. What pleases immensely—and wrongfully so, unfortunately—is that an addictive drinker is to be considered as sick, as diseased. The pill given to him places him immediately in the category of the diseased person and temporarily removes from him the responsibility for his drinking or his not drinking, which is exactly the opposite of what we want to do as a therapeutic goal. In other words, in my mind, Antabuse adds confusion. The guilt connected with excessive drinking, which is still and always present in these patients, cannot be ruled out by legislative action or by statements coming from doctors that too much drinking can be considered a disease.

ADDICTION

From the Floor I wonder if there is any relationship between becoming addicted to alcohol and other kinds of addiction?

Prof. Drew The only thing I would say in answer to that is that I visited an alcoholism clinic in Sweden last summer, and they were using tranquilizers as a method of treating the alcoholics. The doctor in charge of the clinic told me that he was having very considerable trouble because he found that the individual, if he were dished out tranquilizers X number of times a day, would store them up and then go on a real tranquilizer binge, or jag, whatever the phrase is, and that he would cease to be an alcoholic but would become addicted to whatever he was being treated with.

The general position, as I understand it, is that the alcohol addict is a chap who is very liable to becoming addicted, and alcohol is the substance he becomes addicted to because it is the easiest one for him to get hold of, but if that becomes difficult, he will become addicted very rapidly to other drugs.

Dr. Bowman I think this is all we have time for. I should like to thank the participants for their aid in this discussion and the audience for their attention and help in the latter part.

PANEL 4

SOCIOLOGICAL

Participants   Dr. Claudia Balboni, Dr. David G. Mandelbaum and
Mr. Berton Roueché

Dr. Mandelbaum   Ladies and Gentlemen, this session is labeled
"Sociological." Since our directives did not state what we were to
cover, I propose that we talk about whatever we want to talk about,
ask whatever questions we want to ask, and when we come to a
stopping point, we'll stop. Some of us have been talking, and some
of you have been bursting, I know, with things to say.

We have with us Christian Bay, who is a member of the faculty
of Stanford University, and who just entered the field of studies in
alcoholism recently. Christian, why don't you start us off?

EDUCATION ABOUT ALCOHOL

Dr. Bay   I thought that some of the questions in the earlier panels
were very inadequately answered, and, in particular, the question
that the school teacher asked, "Just what should we teach the
children about alcohol?"

Dr. Mandelbaum   Yes, this is a problem. I didn't know that it
was required by law in this state to teach about alcohol in the junior
high schools. I have three children who've been to junior high, two
of them are there now. I think they get some information on this
subject in their science course.

Dr. Bay   Isn't this supposed to be taught from kindergarten?

Dr. Mandelbaum   What does the law say?

From the Floor   It says, in mentioning alcohol, that more or
less spiritual values, and so on, will be taught, and that this will be
part of the curriculum. They're not required to teach that alcohol is
good or bad. And every school board, or school administration, is
allowed to interpret that and place the teaching of the subject
where they think it is most favorable.

Dr. Mandelbaum   Well, now we have several questions, at
least. What is actually taught? Do we have any people who have
information on this?

311

From the Floor   I have seen a syllabus put out by the [California] State Department of Education, and this can be used in any way the teacher wants.

Dr. Mandelbaum   At any particular level or at all levels?

From the Floor   At varying levels. The one I saw is high school level, but I'm sure there are others for the lower grades. I'd like to make a categorical statement, though, on a matter that is frequently ignored. I think there are too many other things to occupy the school program.

Dr. Mandelbaum   So that as far as any practical results are concerned, or effects, it doesn't mean anything, but there is such a law on the statute books.

Now we come to the next question. Suppose this is a real problem, as it clearly is. This teacher said that 60 per cent of her children had fathers or mothers who are alcoholics. Then, by golly, it seems to me that the school ought to say something. Not that it will necessarily be very effective, but something ought to be said by way of putting this in some other perspective than the one they get at home.

From the Floor   There is a Division of Alcoholic Rehabilitation in the State Department of Public Health, and the State Department of Education has asked this Division for modern information, modern knowledge about alcohol, with the idea that such information should be incorporated into the teaching materials. This kind of advice has been given, and there have been indications that a little progress is being made in schools throughout the state. For instance, there have been teaching institutes—one at the state college in Sacramento and another in Los Angeles—where teachers and school administrators were asked or invited to attend. One purpose of these sessions was to get away from the sort of moralistic orientation towards alcoholism that has been incorporated in the past.

Dr. Bay   May I restate my initial question? I really am less interested in knowing what is being done than in thinking about what ought to be done from our knowledge of alcoholism. Is it to be treated in a moralistic fashion, or is it to be deemphasized, or what?

Dr. Mandelbaum   What ought to be done? You don't mean only in the schools?

Dr. Bay   I mean, now, particularly in the high schools, for teen-agers.

Dr. Mandelbaum   Well, it may be even more important at the elementary level than at the junior high school level. Dr. Balboni, would you care to comment on that?

Dr. Balboni Well, all this is new to me, as far as these United States laws are concerned. As you know, I come from Italy, where the problem is quite different, and I wouldn't say it's comparable at all. In our schools we never mention alcohol except in higher schooling, as a chemical compound. But I can say this, there is an attitude toward alcohol in general and, I should say, one in particular which is peculiar and special to that country. As you know, it's a wine-growing country and the main beverage is wine. I should say that this exposure to alcohol and to wine starts from the very early years. The child sips wine at the family table, and the general age of the first drink is between two and five. It's just a sip from his father's glass. Then, after this, starts a custom which is quite widespread—of drinking a little wine, a few drops, in the water, and drinking with the meal. And so the child grows up with this sort of custom.

As far as drinking habits are concerned, as far as the attitude of the parents toward alcohol in relation to the children,—from many inquiries made—there is mainly indifference.[1] If you ask them what they think of the dangers, or what they think of alcohol in relation to their children, they don't think that there is a problem. They don't feel the existence of a problem, and as I said, the attitude is one of indifference. Also, the attitude is one of indifference in relation to the other members of the family. It's taken for granted that you drink a little, and moderately, of course. I'm talking of normal drinking patterns. As you know, alcoholism is relatively much lower in Italy than in many other countries. So we do not have a school program for teaching the use of alcohol, or the dangers of alcohol, or the ways to protect oneself from alcohol, because in a way it's done through a different means—through the family.

Dr. Mandelbaum We obviously can't reconstruct our family circles very easily, but something can be done. There are a number of social, or perhaps religious, patterns that make the situation different. For instance, the Italian population is relatively static; ours is relatively mobile. Our people have very, very short roots, or no roots at all, any place that they may live—nobody lives where he was born— whereas the Italians have deep roots. And the family unit in Italy

[1] P. Luzzatto-Fegiz, and G. Lolli, The Use of Milk and Wine in Italy, *Quart. J. Studies Alc.*, **18**:355–381, 1957.

is very strong, while in this country it is on the verge of disintegration. Italians have virtually one religious background, whereas Americans have a great mixture, if any at all.

Dr. Balboni That's why I began by saying that it's not comparable.

Dr. Mandelbaum I was wondering if everybody else was following this line of thinking and realizing the tremendous factors that make this a very explosive issue for us.

Now, how do we handle it, if at all?

Mr. Harris My name is Andy Harris. I'm Director of Education for the California Council on Alcohol Problems. My main work is either with teachers and teachers' institutes and seminars, or occasionally speaking in schools. Would this be a workable premise—that as teachers our aim should be to supplement or to strengthen the best teaching that the kids get at home; that there be no crusades; that we not be passing out pledge cards; that we help the kids who come from the homes where the parents are total abstainers to understand that this is a perfectly legitimate choice to make, and that they can feel respect for their parents. Kids who come from homes where there is moderate drinking should understand that this, too, is respectable, but that there are some problems: that there are times and places when no one should drink. When the doctor operates on me, I don't want him to have just had a slug of Old Scarecrow, or anything else; nor do I want the bus driver who drives my kids to school to drink on the job.

The kids who come from problem-drinking homes need in some way to be pulled out of themselves so that they can look at the problem of alcoholism for what it is, instead of feeling shame and remorse, such as this teacher indicated in her statement that 60 per cent of the kids in that area come from problem families. This is a tragedy, and the teacher perhaps holds the key to helping these children to understand alcoholism, and perhaps that in turn could trigger eventual help for the whole family.

Dr. Mandelbaum How would you present that in those areas, or schools, where 60 per cent of the families have an alcohol problem? What would you tell the kids?

Mr. Harris There are one or two people here who have heard the kind of presentation that I give. I use magic, humor, etc., and get the kids to laugh and look at the problem as something rather of an objective analysis of a very tragic thing. I identify myself with them, I hope, by admitting that my own grandfather died of cirrhosis of the liver; he died an alcoholic. And I help them understand that this can happen in perfectly normal families—just because I had a grandfather who was an alcoholic doesn't mean that I couldn't grow up to be a useful member of society. I think that there are ways of presenting the material objectively, and I wouldn't talk about alcohol being a narcotic; I'd talk about it being an anesthetic, because every kid in the class will understand that. Last Wednesday night on "Wagon Train," didn't they see a guy who had his arm shot off? They had to finish taking it off, and they didn't have any ether. What did they do? They gave him a bottle of brandy.

   Dr. Mandelbaum   Is this medically correct? Does it work?

   Dr. Balboni   I don't think it works as ether does.

   Mr. Harris   No, but it has some anesthetic effects.

   Mr. Roueché   I should be interested in the school district where 60 per cent of the families are alcoholic. It seems to me this is fantastic.

   Dr. Mandelbaum   This was the question: She said, "As a teacher in an extremely depressed area, where 60 per cent are on welfare much of the year, and a great majority of the men are what we believe to be alcoholics, what can we do?" So she says that the great majority of the men are alcoholics.

   Mr. Roueché   Well, I think it's an economic problem, as much as anything else. There must be a relationship between the drinking and the environment and the general depression of the area.

   Mr. Plier   I'm Hal Plier, from Christian Brothers Distributors. My question is: How does she know that they are alcoholics, when after three days of these sessions we haven't been able to arrive at a definition of what an alcoholic is? So there are two premises: One, the general area is one of 60 per cent depression, but we have no validation for the figure; and two, what is an alcoholic? By what standard does she measure these qualities?

   Dr. Balboni   There is no such thing as a clear-cut definition of an alcoholic, up to now, at any rate.

   Mr. Roueché   I realize that, and I'm not in any position to give a real definition. But just as a rule of thumb, would this do? Drinking to such excess that it makes it impossible to lead a normal life, and to be too drunk, most of the time, to work.

   Dr. Balboni   That's it, that's right; that would be chronic impairment of efficiency. It means you are unable to face your social and occupational activities, and family responsibilities, and so on, not for a short period or for one or two episodes, but over a prolonged period of time.

Mr. Jameson My name is Harold Jameson. I'm with the Division of Alcoholic Rehabilitation of the State Department of Public Health. We have a program of research and treatment and we're interested in education also. On this matter of the 60 per cent of the families where there is indication of an alcohol problem, stress was put on the fact that this was a very economically depressed area. Well, it would seem likely that the problems of this community are much broader than just alcohol—it's unemployment; it's lack of economic resources; and when you have such conditions, you often have recourse to the use of alcohol. I was wondering, getting back to Dr. Bay's question, maybe, on this business of education, it's sort of an anachronism that we are even trying to teach something about alcohol in the schools. It's a heritage of this moralistic day when there was a right and a wrong, and there was a strong temperance influence throughout our society. Maybe it's just a throwback to that, and it would be better if education on alcohol were handled at a higher level, or through some different kind of facility.

Mr. Roueché I quite agree with you. I think there's not much point in discussing the peculiar case that we were offered; it was so exceptional. My opinion would be that it is certainly wrong to teach at any lower school level anything about alcohol. The tendency, the past custom, of teaching that alcohol is a poison, starting at a grade school level, I think, is a mistake. In the high school level, in general science classes, it might be discussed objectively as one of a number of drugs, but without any pro or con feelings.

Dr. Mandelbaum I think I disagree on several scores. One is this. We've heard the term moralistic used as a term of opprobrium, and it isn't. You know, there's a certain kind of moralistic preaching which I think we all realize is obsolete. But we are moral creatures, let's face it; and alcohol, in our culture, inevitably poses a moral problem. For example, when kids get to high school and they go out on dates—they all try to swipe cans of beer. This, I understand from my son, who's fifteen, is a big thing to do, to swipe cans of beer and to drink them. There's some kind of moral problem involved for the teen-ager. My son doesn't want to keep out of it, because then he'll be a "square," though he really doesn't like the idea of swiping beer, and he doesn't like the taste of it very much.

From the Floor Excuse me, I'm a housewife. You don't really expect the schools to solve this for you, do you? Or handle it for you in any way?

Dr. Mandelbaum Well, for the sake of argument, let me put this possibility before you. This is a matter of choice, or moral choice, and a matter on which adolescents are ambivalent. And because so few families are equipped to give guidance on this—they either say, "Don't do it" or "You go to hell" or "Get out of here," or something—I think the schools might well take a book like *Drinking in College*,[2] or some version thereof, and have it in their social science classes.

From the Floor I'm an elementary school teacher. Now, we're bound to teach a subject I love, in the fifth grade, namely, the history of the United States. You can't get through the business of the settlement of the country, or crossing the plains, or when Dad left Mom to go out west. Now, it seems to me that what I've heard in the last three days is the most encouraging explanation that I can imagine of alcohol. We've had so many ramifications. It seems to me, also, that when we get to this business of the economic medium of exchange in the New England states being rum, I can make a very meaningful message out of this for ten-year-olds. I want to remind everybody, also, and you all know this, it's only a reminder, that television draws us nearer and nearer, ever nearer, to the bottle. Kids spend a lot of their time watching drinking on television.

Mr. Van Patten Now, it seems to me that these kids should have some redirected entertainment, carefully taught, and that the school board, the colleges, and all the rest, should make their evaluation of it before we put it in the schools. This has to be done.

Let's get as objective as we can about this highly subjective matter, and I think we really can profitably teach this subject, starting in the second grade. It's like learning a language when you're five years old—we don't stumble over the conjugations of verbs; we just learn the language and speak.

Mr. Roueché Is it the function of the school to offer information on every aspect of life? Is alcohol, or the use or abuse of al-

[2] R. Straus and S. D. Bacon, *Drinking in College*, New Haven, Yale University Press, 1953.

cohol, a proper subject for education at an elementary grade level? Do we teach about smoking, or speeding, or other things outside of what is taken to be the standard academic?

From the Floor Mr. Roueché, the elementary school teacher in California by state law is charged with fifteen subjects. And if you can get some of this off my back, you'll be my friend forever.

Dr. Mandelbaum Well, one problem concerning smoking and drinking is that they become status symbols of rebellion, of growing independence, and I think it would be much better to have "wearing torn jeans" as a status symbol than swiping beer, or smoking.

From the Floor I wonder if any instruction at an early level, in effect an objective portrayal of alcohol in its desirable quantities, might not introduce quite a conflict in a child who comes from a strictly religious teetotaling family. This would seem, at that early age, to challenge the authority and wisdom of his parents.

From the Floor I think that we need to go back to one of the charges of the public schools—keeping moral and spiritual values. We're sidestepping it; we're staying away from it all we can. I'm not sure I understand why.

It seems to me that if we really took the bull by the horns, we would gradually be able to speak from information available, things that all of us have to accept. For example, alcohol is intoxicating —all of us will accept this as a fact. Now it seems to me that we are sidestepping two basic issues here: one, examination of moral and spiritual values at a public school level, then relating this to alcohol; and two, letting alcohol be taught in the schools in relation to the subject matter, such as history or other fifth grade work, as where alcohol was really a medium of exchange, and as a part of our movement westward.

Dr. Bay I want to go back to the definition of alcoholism again, which I think for most people is related to inefficiency in work. In that case, by definition, people who are chronically unemployed cannot possibly be alcoholics. The real point I want to make is that if you are chronically unemployed, I think it is mean to take alcohol away from you: children should understand some things— let's say causes and good as well as bad effects. And here I think we can learn something from the Italians. Children grow up with alcohol as they do with sex, and it's so much less trouble. It seems that in our puritanical culture, perhaps the root of the evil here is that parents are so prone, in effect, to tell their children to do as I say, not as I do, and you get all this hypocrisy, all this refusal to see the social causes and the real evils of which alcoholism is mostly the symptom. So, I think that the school should have as its primary task, in this field, to try to teach something about the social inter-relatedness of these problems, the lack of moral stigma, of a real moral stigma, in alcoholism; and perhaps also, in a careful way, in some way, to see through the double talk of the parents.

Dr. Mandelbaum Ah, but wait a minute. This has to be taught by teachers, and the teachers are a part of the same culture. If the parents double talk, the teachers are also double talking on this, so you have to start pretty far back, and pretty soon you have to change the basis of our whole culture, and then what will happen?

Let's move slowly as we face this problem, even though this problem must be faced.

From the Floor I think that probably one of the reasons why they don't have the problem in Italy that we have here is that the family is disciplined, society is disciplined—they know something about discipline in the old country. My father, my grandfather, when he came to this country, knew something about discipline, but discipline is a bad word now.

ALCOHOLISM IN FRANCE AND ITALY

Miss Engle I just want to put in one point. In France, where there are similar backgrounds to Italy, like wine culture and so on, there is, and has been for some years, a serious problem of alcoholism among children, not to speak of adults.

Dr. Mandelbaum Yes, but the fact is we really don't know why two cultures as similar as those of Italy and France should be quite so different in so many ways, including alcoholism; nor do we know why certain groups use alcohol quite freely and have no prob-lem, or very few problems of alcoholism, and those using it quite in-frequently have quite a high incidence of alcoholism.

From the Floor Maybe it's due to our value system.

Dr. Mandelbaum Well, that's sort of a blanket term, which, you know, means everything.

Dr. Balboni It's very vague.

From the Floor In regard to the French-Italian problems that were mentioned here, I think Dr. Jellinek pointed out[3] that there are definite reasons for this: one, that there is almost exactly twice as much wine drunk in France as in Italy; and two, it's drunk outside of meals, whereas in Italy, it's drunk with meals. There's another thing. I don't think there's any problem either of teaching about alcohol in school or in defining alcoholism, nor is there a problem of how to present it. To me, there are two problems, and maybe the teachers can solve these: one, to get the teachers prepared to teach this subject; and two, to decide where to put it in the curriculum. That's a really practical problem in California. I don't know whether anyone has any suggestions.

From the Floor Let me ask you what your personal bias is about alcohol?

From the Floor Well, obviously I have none. I should favor a moderate drinker, since that's what I consider myself, I suppose. Nevertheless, I think that the idea of teaching the physical properties of alcohol is no problem, nor is teaching that some people in our society choose to drink and others choose not to drink. You don't have to say that one is good and one is bad. Those who decide not to drink—that's perfectly within their prerogative. And among those who do choose to drink, there are those who do have problems.

DEFINITION OF ALCOHOLISM

From the Floor Are you going to give us a definition of alcoholism?

From the Floor Well, there are many definitions. I think they are all pretty close to Marty Mann's definition.[4] It's when a drinking problem is sufficient to interfere continually with any major area of one's life. That was Marty Mann's definition, and it sums up a lot of the others, and I think it's a workable one.

Mr. Roueché Wouldn't you add the element of compulsion, or the inability to change, even though you recognize that your life is being upset?

Dr. Balboni In other words, the element of drug addiction.

From the Floor Addiction? As Jellinek points out, there are the alpha and the gamma effects of alcoholism. The alpha is just as

[3] E. M. Jellinek, *The Disease Concept of Alcoholism*, New Brunswick, N.J., Hillhouse Press, 1960.
[4] M. Mann, *New Primer on Alcoholism*, New York, Rinehart, 1958.

much of a problem as the gamma, and you still call it alcoholism, and you still can't decide which is the larger in number in the United States. Those are the two that make up 60 per cent of the alcoholics in the United States. And the alphas are not addicted; the gammas are. Yet, the central problem is the same up to the point at which they withdraw from alcohol. They look the same; they talk the same; they drink approximately the same, evidently. So I'm talking about a workable definition for teaching, and I'm not talking about a scientific definition satisfying every condition and type.

It amazes me—when people speak of alcohol, you always hear the word alcoholism. Now we sell, in this country, hundreds of millions of gallons of spiritous beverages, and millions of people drink them. But only a small fraction of these people are alcoholics. The thing that is so ingrained, when we talk about alcohol, is alcoholics and alcoholism. I think that the problem is not with the alcoholic—that is a professional problem. I think it's with the remainder of those who consume alcohol, and their children. This is where the problem lies. Your son, for instance, who is forced to do things that are against his better judgment is an example.

For years, in New York City, I was a bartender. The most difficult time of the year for me was prom night. Kids would come to the bar—the limit is eighteen years old, in New York—they'd come to the bar for a drink, and they'd sit down and order a martini, and I'd say, Why? If you could talk to them, you'd find out that they're taught at home how to brush their teeth, they don't push people under trolleys, and they try to behave. But no one at home takes the time out to teach what can be expressed to a child as good and evil in alcohol. I personally feel that alcohol is a subject for home and not the school. I feel that teachers have more than enough to teach, and that if we can disseminate the information to the parents, perhaps it will reach the children. I occasionally address women's groups, and when I mention this, it's like a light—they're afraid of talking to their children about alcohol. The child is lucky if the parent might be willing to discuss sex, but alcohol—never. I think this is the crux of the problem.

From the Floor Can't we have it at both ends, at home and in school?

Dr. Mandelbaum At what age?

Mr. Van Patten I should think that alcohol literature should be available for third-grade reading level, or first-grade reading level, because I have many twelve-year-olds who read at that level.

I'm fascinated with the presentation here in the last three days, for which I was not prepared. I was prepared to go away having my guilt feelings stirred. In fact, I think that they are not quite so strong. I think this is where we can become more objective about this business of alcohol—the panic sort of disappears.

TEEN-AGE DRINKING

Dr. Mandelbaum   Before we go on, in justice to my son, who is fifteen, I must say that I don't know if he really swiped any beer; he just told me about it.

From the Floor   I am a psychiatric social worker and also the mother of two teen-agers, and I should just like to make a comment about behavior. Mine are in the second semester in their sixteenth year. That's the time when a lot takes place. That's the time when most of the youngsters get their drivers' licenses. And that's the time beer and sex and drivers' licenses all combine with the spring of the year—you can feel it.

Now I'm going to go off the subject a little. Of the many youngsters in the high school classes—there are about thirty or thirty-five in a class—there may be just one or two that come from families where the cocktail is not served before supper. For most of these kids, it's just natural. There may not be verbal education in the home, but there is performance education in the home, and when they're sixteen, they make their decision. This is exactly opposite of what goes on in school.

From the Floor   They make their decision as to whether they're going to what, drink?

From the Floor   Whether this is the time, and how they're going to do it. And the parents are very much interested in how they fall into different patterns. The legal age limit here is twenty-one. You talk to parents who think, "Oh well, it's fun." They don't want their kids to go out and drink, so they rationalize by having a cocktail party for kids under twenty-one in their homes. I think most upper middle-class homes with recreation facilities will do this. I don't know why I'm bringing this up, except for just the observation of what is common in a nice upper middle-class home.

Dr. Mandelbaum   I was thinking it would be particularly strategic to have education on drinking and the use of alcohol taught in connection with driver education.

We've been talking about schools and education, but perhaps there may be some other problems, some other aspects of drinking, that we shouldn't miss. Do we have another topic to go to?

THE SKID ROW PROBLEM

From the Floor As long as you're looking for another topic, we had a very spirited discussion over the noon hour in regard to some of Judge Murtagh's remarks. It had to do with, to what extent you are going to ignore the downtown situation of people staggering on the sidewalks or filling the gutters. Some of the people from New York mentioned that, over there, if these people got a little bit too far out of their skid row area, the paddy wagon would come along and pick them up and take them back into their area.

Dr. Mandelbaum Is that what actually happens?

From the Floor Yes. I understand it's something like you do with the bears in Yosemite—take them back. This brought up the question, Do we need such an area in our cities where you can do what you can't do in the rest of the city?

Dr. Mandelbaum I think that's a most interesting suggestion. It may be that there are, in a large city, enough aberrant personalities so that it's for the civic good and for their own good to be concentrated in the Bowery, or whatever it is.

There's another aspect to it. I read the Question Man in the morning *Chronicle*. He asked: "What do you think of the beatniks?" Several of the respondents said, "We miss them because they were a good tourist attraction."

Mr. Roueché, what, in your opinion, is the parallel or relation between a young Bohemian—beatniks are young Bohemians—and the bums, the skid row bum?

Mr. Roueché Well, I think that the Bohemians, or the beatniks, are in every generation simply the rebels who are opposing conventional life. The bum, skid row bum, is mostly a person who is disturbed mentally. He's an adult, man or woman, of all ages, who is just unable to cope with life.

From the Floor Why have the beatniks disappeared from San Francisco?

Mr. Roueché Well, it may be simply that they've shaved.

Dr. Balboni In other words, it's an attitude, not a real mental disorder.

From the Floor I think it's a mistake to compare alcoholics, or beatniks, or anything else. I would simply ask what's the difference between an alcoholic and a drunk?

From the Floor You know, I have a feeling about this business of skid row. It seems to me that many people are at least as uncomfortable as the guys I found in the Bowery. I think it's a matter of preference where one will be miserable, really.

Mrs. French I'm Mrs. French. I work as a psychiatric social worker. It bothers me to hear these comments about where people prefer to be miserable, because what we try to do in our work is to find out what problem the alcoholic is trying to settle for himself by his excessive drinking. In working to discover this problem—which is very difficult and sometimes not possible—and to help towards finding another solution, we feel that we can do something constructive. But if you set up a moral judgment on the problem to begin with, you can't even look at it.

When you think of educating the children in the schools, I think that there are many ways you can educate them to have some concepts of mental health. And, I think, if you're going to educate them to understand alcoholism, you have to give them some understanding of the mental health aspect.

Mr. Van Patten I'm pretty sure that I made myself clear on this a while ago. I should prefer that we teach the story of alcohol. They willfully kept alcoholism at a low level of the total topics introduced in this symposium, and the title of our symposium here is *Alcohol* and Civilization, not *Alcoholism* and Civilization. I feel that there is a significant difference. If we go back to the original point of view, if we talk about alcohol and civilization, we're talking about a great percentage of the American public. If we talk about alcoholism, as it has to do with our own value judgments, we're talking about so few, really, that the rest of us can't find this of too much value, personally, perhaps.

Mrs. French But alcohol in moderation doesn't pose any problem at all, does it? Has anybody said that it has?

Mr. Van Patten I think an issue was brought up to which I would subscribe. Is it wise to teach alcoholism, value judgments about alcoholism, in the schools? I would say, No. It's just like teaching whether sex is good or bad. This isn't the issue. We must stay out of this department, and we'll probably stay out of alcohol for a long while to come, too. As mentioned by Dr. Mandelbaum, our inability as the teachers to be as objective as we might about both these matters is an important point.

From the Floor I'm practicing psychiatry in Los Angeles, and I deal with a lot of alcoholics. Once in my career, I was at Bellevue Hospital, where I dealt with a great number of the skid row alcoholics. I wonder whether I'm saying something so obvious that I'll have to apologize for it, but when we talk about skid row and the denizens of skid row, are we not now talking about medical and psychiatric problems as such? If we talk about how to prevent skid rows, then, of course, we may be in something sociological. But in answer to the question, should we just take them back in the paddy wagon to skid row, whence they came, or shall we throw them in jail, it seems to me that it may be that they are not a medical problem but they certainly are a psychiatric problem in any event—in which case we might say we want to do something further about it, although they're not very willing to have anything done about it. But I should think that jail would be the very last place that one would want to take them.

From the Floor I wonder if the group here is aware of the work that's being done at the Men's Social Service Center here in San Francisco, and the film that was produced on their work. One of the significant things that came out of their research was that a great share of these men, who most people think are alcoholic bums, are men who are temporarily in some kind of family difficulty, or economic difficulty, and have rather drifted into this area as a place of least resistance, a place where they would be accepted. They were losing respect for themselves and their own ability to cope with situations in life, and they wandered into the soup kitchen. This Men's Social Service Center is a rather nice place, very lovely furniture, and not at all a flophouse. They're having a marvelous record of rehabilitation. The significant thing is that these are not what people think of as skid row derelicts when they look at them on the street. These are men, from nice middle-class homes, who because of some set of circumstances have deteriorated. Somebody reaches them and helps them. They can come back; the home can be salvaged, and some may again become contributing elements in society.

While I agree with the essential premise of Judge Murtagh's

talk, still I'm concerned about these people that we look at and think are skid row derelicts. Maybe they don't choose to be there; maybe if somebody reaches them, they could be helped.

From the Floor In our discussing skid row, there's been quite a bit of stress on the inadequate personality, at least inadequate is a frequent term that is used. Now I think more stress might be put on the social condition, the social circumstances which perhaps are responsible for such a great amount of unemployment in this country—the fact that technologically we have a large portion of our population which is not very useful, or it's only useful for a few years, five or ten years. There are things that can be done right now to improve the situation on skid row. There's nothing there but bars and depraved sorts of situations. Any city in the country could do something right now to make skid row a better place and to cut down on a certain amount of this unhealthful or harmful use of alcohol.

Dr. Mandelbaum Well, I'm wondering about what was said before—in our society, perhaps every city must have a slum, a skid row. And as one is cleaned up and ameliorated, another will just come up someplace else because there are enough people in our society who need that kind of existence. What would you say to that?

From the Floor Yes, that's just the point. I don't think it's that the people are this way to begin with. It's the type of society in which they live and the duties that are required of them which tend to drive them into becoming inadequate.

Dr. Bay This is a very positive contribution. I was thinking much along the same lines, that it is society that is inadequate to the expression of human worth and cooperation much of the time —a society in which it is taboo to criticize free enterprise and which assumes competitiveness and phoney commercial values. I think it becomes so barren in personal relationships when sober, that you've got to have alcohol. In Italy, I think that it's traditionally a cooperative culture.

Dr. Balboni It's based on a family nucleus, essentially. A very few people drink alone. Drinking is done at the table, and they have a feeling of warmth about all this. There is a family mutual moral control, if you could say that, and somehow the environment is different.

From the Floor Wait till free enterprise takes over in Europe and alcohol becomes alcoholism in Italy, too.

Dr. Balboni That's the danger, I know.

From the Floor I'd like to challenge the suggestion by Dr. Bay, which seems to be agreed to by Dr. Balboni and the last speaker from the floor, that our free-enterprise system, and the competitiveness that goes with it, is responsible for alcoholism. This is pretty naïve sociology, it seems to me. In the Soviet Union they don't have any free enterprise—haven't had it for about a couple of generations—and they are just beginning to admit they have a whopping alcoholism problem.

From the Floor I made a study, from February to April 1961, on the background of 927 of the handicapped people we deal with day in and day out on skid row. Most of them have had only about two or three years of primary school education; very few of them had any high school education. I don't think there were more than one or two who had been to college. Most of them, 99 per cent, were not born in San Francisco. So what you have is mostly an untrained, uneducated group of men. Most of them have never married; most of them have tremendously horrible records in the Army—dishonorable discharge or medical discharge for psychiatric reasons. Some have a record of prison, and the problem is that they have no interpersonal relationships. When I ask them, Are you in contact with your family back East, or South, they say, No, They have had no contact with their relatives for many years. Their problem is also being really physically bad off; I mean with cirrhosis of the liver, peripheral neuritis, eye trouble, and many of them are psychos. Actually the problem you have in San Francisco, as in other cities, is a large group of people that could never make it, will never make it, and they themselves will be the first to admit that they want a place where they can just stay for the rest of their life.

You don't really need more research. All you need is a lot more money for each county and just give them a farm. They're very happy down in Los Angeles; they're happy in New York City. They don't want to get rehabilitated. They can't compete with the average high school or college graduate. They can't do it; they have nothing to offer. They don't go to church, they don't marry, they love drinking, and there's nothing to look forward to every day except their bottle.

Dr. Mandelbaum May I ask a question here? How many of the 927 are of Chinese descent? There is presumably very little alcoholism among Chinese. Is this still true?

From the Floor   That's right.

We no longer need a skid row. I think that at one time we did. It was a volatile, dynamic society made up of migratory workers who used this as their winter home. There's only a few of those left—in Sacramento and Stockton. But the kind we're talking about, I think could be easily done away with tomorrow. We wouldn't have any skid row; we wouldn't need any skid row. Many of those who live down there are older people. If a good place was built for them, their skid row would disappear, because we don't have this dynamic society anymore.

I think that perhaps the so-called middle class is the group who currently shoulder the responsibility for the liquor problem.

DRINKING AND CULTURE

Dr. Mandelbaum   Or who *feel* the responsibility?

No, I think we're the ones involved in this business of a few cocktails at home and letting the children understand what this might mean. I wish a high school counselor were here. We have some real problems in the high schools. Not long ago, two boys came into the office inebriated, and it was detected because they couldn't even hold the pen to take their English examination. It turned out that one was a Mexican and one came from a very fine home. The Mexican boy had been invited to the home of the other boy who was used to having a cocktail every afternoon with his folks, and they decided to mix up a batch at noon. Unfortunately, they got caught. So I think that the people with enough money to purchase this stuff are the ones we've got to talk about.

Mr. Roueché   Well, I think the point is made very clear that alcohol is the least of our problems. It's used as a relief, a solution.

Dr. Mandelbaum   At this point we might bring up another topic which perhaps some of you were going to talk about. It looks as though in our culture there is going to be a lot more leisure than there is even now. The work week is going to be reduced even further, and this already is a great problem. I understand that in the Soviet Union, where the work week has been reduced to our own levels, alcohol has become, in this very puritanical society of communism, a major problem, partly because people have more time and more money to use for drinking. Now, the utilization of leisure time is one that is not disconnected from the utilization of alcohol, and I simply pose it as an increasingly important matter for the future. Whether it's going to be a problem in capital letters or not is another question; it may not be at all.

I think the one thing that every culture has in common that seems to be impervious to the so-called alcohol problem is that culture's acceptance of adequate sanctions of the home, the church, the government. The situation in the Chinese culture, where the sanctions are functioning, and in the Jewish culture, which has the highest acceptance of moderate drinking of any culture in the world —with no alcoholism noticeable at all—indicates that these factors are more important than leisure time.

The matter of public drinking or semiprivate drinking is also most interesting because, if I may just briefly invoke some antiquarian archeological material, it has been mentioned that in ancient Babylonia, in the code of Hammurabi, there are regulations about saloon keepers, who were mainly women. They prescribed the price of beer and the quality of beer, and also, who could frequent a tavern. Certain people who were dedicated to religion were not allowed in the tavern.

Mr. Roueché I wonder if the closing hour is of any significance. San Francisco apparently has a greater alcohol problem than New York City, and in New York the bars stay open until 4 A.M. every day except Saturdays, when they close at 3 A.M. But more bars are going out of business in New York City than they are here in San Francisco. I think you have to look at the overall population of a city. In New York, we used to sell 60 per cent of our beverages at bars and 40 per cent in package stores. Since the advent of television, it's the reverse. We're selling more in stores and less in bars, forcing bars out of business. I was amazed to find a different situation in San Francisco. Here, the bars are a meeting place for the young people. This is a transitory city with tremendous rooming houses but no accommodations for people to entertain each other. I find that the bars in this city supplement the living room at home.

Miss Engle I'd like to ask Mr. Roueché, in that comprehensive study you made about alcohol,[5] did you take any notice of substitutes?

Mr. Roueché Substitutes for alcohol? Do you mean, as solutions to emotional problems?

[5] B. Roueché, *The Neutral Spirit: A Portrait of Alcohol*, Boston, Little, Brown, 1960.

Miss Engle Well, not necessarily solutions, but attempts at solutions—overeating, gambling or drugs. I was thinking specifically of other drugs because, for example, I've often speculated on what people did, besides chewing, before tobacco was invented, and I can find practically nothing except that they chewed. Now when you went into the very early history of alcohol, were other substances used?

Mr. Roueché I didn't go into that. I don't know.

Alcohol has been used in religion since very ancient times, and there is no substitute for it. That is to say, drugs are almost never used in this way, even when they're available for religious purposes by way of libations to the gods, for communion, or anything like that. The drug peyote is used in American Indian rituals; and in certain exotic rituals in Asia, hashish is used, but these are very rare and are sort of counter to the ordinary use. That is, these are like the "black mask"; they are specifically against something else. There's a very interesting paper by an English psychiatrist[6] on the use of hashish and of daru, the Indian term for a liquor made from mahuda flowers—an alcoholic liquor, made in the town of Rajputana. The Rajputs like to drink and are a little bit ambivalent about it because drink in India is polluting to the gods. Lots of people drink, but not the most learned and not the priestly classes. Farmers will not take the drug because they say, "If I take the drug I'm useless," but they will drink the liquor. On the other hand, the Brahmans, who may not touch liquor, may not use it for religious reasons, will take the drug, because it gives them the feeling of detachment, dissociation, meditation, and so on.

Dr. Mandelbaum Just one remark on the importance of sanctions. The word "sanctions" is ambiguous—it's both rewards and punishments. I think it is good psychology that punishment does very little good. What does some good, and has done good among the Chinese and among the Jews, is the sense of reward of a life of sobriety. That is, the sense of being acceptable no matter how much or how little you earn, no matter what your status is in larger societies. This sort of reward is the only type of sanction that works.

I think that our particular culture is shot through with certain kinds of values. That is, we're children of our culture, and we

[6] G. M. Carstairs, Daru and Bhang. Cultural Factors in the Choice of Intoxicant, *Quart. J. Studies Alc.*, 15:220–237, 1954.

have to adhere to these values no matter how broadminded we are, and so on. There are societies in the world today where part of the religion is drunkenness; everybody has to get drunk, and in that society we wouldn't hear this kind of discussion. Now we don't live in that society; we live in our own society. We have discussions such as this, and it so happens that it's on a topic which is all too little discussed in this kind of open, informed, and intelligent way.

6

INTERDISCIPLINARY VIEWPOINTS

Dr. Greenberg *I don't think a year has gone by when there have not come to our laboratory, from all over, at least two or three sure-fire cures for alcoholism and for drunkenness. None of them has panned out.*

Dr. Goldberg *We should apply new scientific methods to see how alcoholism spreads in society . . . because if we know something about how it spreads, we will know where to begin prevention and teaching.*

Dr. Leake *We are much more willing to put our money and effort and our learning into an understanding of our physical environment . . . we're a little bit afraid as yet of looking hard at ourselves.*

PANEL A

PSYCHOLOGY, PHYSIOLOGY, AND ANTHROPOLOGY

Participants Dr. J. Anthony Deutsch, Dr. Olof A. Forsander, Dr. David G. Mandelbaum

Dr. Deutsch I think probably the best way to open this meeting would be for us to try to answer any questions you may have, with the proviso that we can say they're not within our competence to answer.

From the Floor We have heard described the communities where drinking is part of the social custom. I was wondering whether that type of community and social structure has gone through a period when it was a dysfunction, which then became modified.

ETHICAL-CULTURAL ASPECTS OF DRINKING PRACTICES

Dr. Mandelbaum Yes, I think so, in certain cases. The classic examples of cultures where alcohol is freely used, but alcoholism is exceedingly rare, are the Chinese, Italians, and Jews. Now, I happen to know more about Jews, so I'll talk about them. In the Old Testament, insofar as we can take that as giving evidence of culture and society, evidently the earliest reference to wine and alcoholic beverage of any kind mentions them as dangerous things. This I have not on my own knowledge, but from Biblical scholars of recent years who feel that the references in the Bible pertaining to wine as a good thing, as relieving anxiety, and so on, are of a later date, and that the earlier mentions are of Noah—Noah who came to disgrace and shame—and of Lot, whose daughters got him drunk so that he could commit incest with them. Alcohol was on that level in the Old Testament. It was apparently something to worry about and to keep away from.

Later as we know, wine became part of the ritual idiom of the Jews, became part of the temple ceremony, the central ceremony, just as Communion is in Christianity. But this came much later.

Other references to the use of alcohol in temple ceremonies in the Old Testament are sort of tacked onto something else. To make a very long story short, what seems to have happened is that the people of the Old Testament at first, in the earliest times, felt very diffident about wine, felt it was dangerous. Then they became comfortable enough with alcohol so that they could adopt it into the liturgy of the temple, although not in a central place. Then, still later, it became central, as a ritual symbol. Now, of course, in Rome, or Italy, there is quite a different story. In regard to the Chinese, I don't know that this story has ever been clearly analyzed.

From the Floor Does that bring the story of alcoholism in the Jewish people up to the present?

Dr. Mandelbaum Well, the present situation is that alcohol is used by Jews in most countries in fairly liberal amounts, but alcoholism is extremely rare. One of the best monographs I know on this subject is the one which came out of the Yale center, by Snyder, *Alcohol and the Jews*.[1] He indicates that the degree of orthodoxy is important, that is, the more orthodox Jews have fewer alcoholics. By and large, Jews drink in fair amounts, though not as much as Italians; and what Italian Jews do I don't know. Although alcoholism is very rare among the Jews, other types of neuroses and psychoses are very common. That doesn't mean that they are necessarily in better mental health; they simply don't choose to use alcohol.

From the Floor The Italians drink a lot more than the Jews. They use wine at every meal, as Dr. Lolli explained yesterday, but there is a buffer in the type of food they use; that is, they use so much carbohydrate in their diet that it prevents the blood alcohol from rising. Italians use 30 gal of wine per year per capita.

Dr. Mandelbaum Also, we mustn't forget that there are societies in the world where our attitudes on alcohol are not observed at all—it's part of their religion to get drunk, and to get dead drunk. So getting drunk is not something that is horrible for them—it's part of man's duty. They aren't drunk every day, or the society couldn't go on, but they are, perhaps, once a month, or something of that order.

From the Floor Studies of drinking habits made on South

---

[1] C. R. Snyder, *Alcohol and the Jews. A Cultural Study of Drinking and Sobriety*, New Brunswick, N.J., Rutgers Center of Alcohol Studies, and Glencoe, N.Y., Free Press, 1958.

Americans, and Americans here in the United States, show that most drinking is done on festive occasions, weekends, paydays, etc. They don't drink other times except to get drunk. Now for the definition of a social drinker. What is a social drinker? One who drinks according to the society he's in, and so in those countries, social drinking means getting drunk. If you don't get drunk, you're not a social drinker. In our groups, if you get drunk, you're out.

From the Floor Is there any period of culture that had no alcoholic beverage whatsoever?

Dr. Mandelbaum Yes. Practically all American Indian societies north of Mexico, in aboriginal times, did not have alcohol. The Plains Indians didn't have very much agriculture; some had no agriculture; and also, some didn't have much pottery. Until you have pots, you can't very well have alcohol. It's possible to have skins and so on, but it really isn't very feasible, so pottery probably antedates alcohol to some degree. But the Pueblo Indians in Mexico and Arizona were agriculturalists; they were in general contact with peoples who used alcohol, but they presumably rejected alcohol. It just didn't fit in with their way of life.

From the Floor What about the Polynesians? They had every means to make alcohol; they had cocoanut and kava.

Dr. Mandelbaum I'm not sure but that kava may be mildly intoxicating. I've read that it is mildly intoxicating. But it's true that the Polynesians did not really have alcohol.

From the Floor Didn't they have other forms of intoxicating liquors?

Dr. Mandelbaum No, not as far as I know, except this kava. Of course, different civilizations have very different ways of handling alcohol. In India, it's compartmentalized. Certain classes, certain castes, may not use alcohol, and everybody else can have it. Or, on certain occasions it can be used. The Babylonians had a pattern very similar to our modern pattern; they regulated taverns, regulated drinking, and prescribed punishment not only for excess drinking but, as I said earlier, for tavern keepers who charged too high prices or served too low a quality of beer. So this was the earliest civilization, and still they were very modern in that sense.

From the Floor Have we become more concerned about alcoholism because of the problems of driving? Or was that trend beginning anyway?

Dr. Mandelbaum I can only guess, because I don't know. Perhaps Dr. Deutsch could answer this better than I. It seems to me that all the things you mention are converging on the subject of alcohol. It's not only driving; it's also increased use of alcohol along with increased availability, more money, more leisure, and so on. Also, I think the increasing loss of the old moralistic basis, whatever it was, either for or against, makes us look for something new, for some new attitude, some new way of dealing with alcohol.

From the Floor   In the early eighteenth century, there were studies on alcoholism. The temperance unions started then, and they were very powerful. In fact, in 1848, about three or four million people signed the temperance pledge, and at that time we had a population of only 13 million. So, are we more concerned with alcoholism now than we were in those days?

Dr. Mandelbaum   But all signers were not teetotalers!

From the Floor   I won't argue that; that's not the point. It's the concern, at the time; that's what we're talking about. They had kids ten years old signing the pledge.

Dr. Mandelbaum   Yes.

From the Floor   They had really powerful programs, in those days, on temperance. Today we're having state and other programs on alcoholism which they didn't have then. It was the concern of private society then—I think that is the big difference.

PHYSIOLOGICAL BASES OF ALCOHOL PREFERENCE IN ANIMALS

From the Floor   Let's ask Dr. Forsander to tell us something about his work on physiological effects of alcohol.

Dr. Forsander   Yes, I have some ideas on drinking habits. I am a biochemist, and I have done most of my experimental work with rats. Now it's very curious that the various animal species have different drinking habits in the free-choice experiments.[2] It's a good idea to do the preliminary work with animals because you can exclude all the sociological aspects. In experiments on rats, giving them free choice between more or less than 10 per cent alcohol, you'll find they are very consistent in making a choice. It takes about

[2] A. Arvola and O. Forsander, Comparison between Water and Alcohol Consumption in Six Animal Species in Free Choice Experiments, *Nature*, London, 191:819–820, 1961.

one week for them to recognize the differences. You find the average rat drinks about 20 per cent of the total solution as alcohol.

Dr. Deutsch You mean that they're drinking 20 per cent alcohol solutions?

Dr. Forsander No, they're drinking 10 per cent alcohol solutions. But of their total liquid consumption, 20 per cent is the alcohol solution.

Dr. Deutsch They're drinking water, too; you have two bottles, one is water, the other is alcohol.

Dr. Forsander That's right.

Dr. Deutsch You find that their intake of alcohol solution is 20 per cent of their total intake, so they're not drinking 20 per cent alcohol.

Dr. Forsander If you use some other species, such as guinea pigs, you will find that they don't like alcohol at all. They're drinking about 5 per cent of their total fluid intake as alcohol. But hamsters like alcohol very much. They drink about 90 per cent. So you have these different attitudes toward alcohol, but the reason for this is very vague. This animal has a preference for water, and this one for alcohol—this would be the same as if you drink 50 per cent alcohol and 50 per cent water, just as the rabbits usually drink. Some days they drink more water, some days just equal amounts of water and alcohol.

From the Floor What's the figure for the humans?

Dr. Forsander You can't investigate the human this way, because here you also have a moralistic point of view.

From the Floor In your experiments, you give the animals a choice between water, and a mixture of water and alcohol. Did you use other substances such as sugar, saccharin, or anything else?

Dr. Forsander So far I have compared only how they like water or water and alcohol.

Dr. Deutsch But that's a very important point! The problem becomes much complicated as soon as you start using other substances.

From the Floor But the choice might be related to calories, taste, or it might be experience.

Dr. Deutsch There are some complications which I'd like to mention. The first is that you get different figures depending on what dilution of alcohol you use.

Dr. Forsander That's right. But with the hamster you can even give him 40 per cent.

Dr. Deutsch Yes, the percentage will shift quite a bit. There will be presumably an optimum of preference for each species, so I think ideally one has to obtain the peak of overdrinking. But there's another, very much more serious difficulty with this kind of measurement of preference, and that is this: if you take something which is not as dramatic or as glamorous as alcohol, but is just a solution of salt in water, say 0.6 per cent saline, and give the animals a choice between this saline and water, you'll find that they'll drink 10 cc of water each day. Now the funny thing about this is that you might therefore conclude that they like the 0.6 per cent salt solution much more than they do the weaker solution or the water. But this is not the case. I was able to predict that the reason for the overdrinking is the peculiar effects of the saline on the water taste finders in the rats. I found that this was not preference, but that they simply overdrank.

In my experiments, I used a maze in a box with two sides. The rat was put in and given 15 trials a day. On each side there was a little receptacle and each held ½ cc of either water or saline. You would expect that if the rat really preferred saline, he would learn to run towards the saline side. On the other hand, if he didn't prefer saline, but simply drank more of it because it wasn't satiating, because he didn't get quite so much satisfaction out of the taste—and this can be translated into neurophysiological terms—he should then prefer water, because given ½ cc he would get much more satisfaction out of ½ cc of water than from ½ cc of saline. All the animals consistently learned to run towards the water. Then you can do the experiment in other ways. You can use different strengths of saline. They always prefer, in this situation, a weak concentration of saline. So this suggests that intake experiments do not necessarily give you an index of preference. It simply gives you an index of overdrinking. This overdrinking might be because the animal does actually like it. It might, on the other hand, be that the animal is drinking more of it because it's not actually so satisfying.

Now, put yourself in the animal's situation. If you're given either a meal of lettuce or a meal of steak, you'll eat more of the lettuce—you have to, in order to keep yourself alive. This doesn't mean to say that you prefer the lettuce, because given a choice of equal amounts of lettuce and equal amounts of steak, you'll take the steak. I tried to do this experiment with alcohol, and I got a significant result showing that if the animal is given a choice between water and alcohol, he will tend to prefer the water. Then I modified the apparatus a bit, because I wasn't quite satisfied with certain aspects of it, and I got a significant result in the opposite direction. At this point I simply gave up.

Dr. Forsander But if you had no choice at all, if you had only an alcohol solution, I think you could get some idea how they drink on one day and another. On a control experiment, using only water, you could measure the total amount of water consumed. Then, if you give them alcohol and water, if they don't like alcohol they should drink a little less than before.

Dr. Deutsch In the case of saline, it's not that they like saline any more or less than water. In fact, if you give the animals two bottles, one containing saline and the other water, you'll find that the intake of the saline fluctuated from one day to another and the intake of the water also fluctuated from one day to the other.

Dr. Forsander Yes, but if you compare the amounts of saline and water consumed, but not in the same experiment—

Dr. Deutsch They'll still drink more saline, much more saline than water. The animal will start drinking from one side, it prefers one side, of the container. It will go to that side and drink and simply keep on drinking from the saline side. If you do the same experiment, putting sucrose on one side, which is something the animal really likes, and water on the other side, you don't get anything like this. Instead of sticking to the same side, the animal will then follow the sweet tasting bottle around. I don't think the amount of overdrinking can be taken as an indication of a choice situation or can necessarily be taken as indicating a preference.

From the Floor Well, isn't that the reason for the higher intake of saline, because they have to have a greater quantity in order to satisfy their thirst? This taking of salt then promotes excretion of water.

Dr. Deutsch But the way we do it is to give the animals saline for half an hour only, and then we give them water for a full hour afterwards. Now, this is of course a very important point. Most people who do these experiments do not usually try to separate the short-term factors from the long-term factors. I think even a half hour isn't long enough, so now we're using a technique for overcoming any postdigestional factors in order to study this phenomenon further.

It's difficult to know whether the animals overdrink because their taste apparatus isn't functioning so well, or is being fooled in some way, or whether they prefer the taste, or whether there's some modification of their physiological state as a result of the drinking. All these things unfortunately are very difficult to disentangle in the experiments.

Dr. Forsander Therefore you have to make many assumptions.

From the Floor Dr. Forsander, do you think that your hamsters have a real tissue demand for alcohol? Is this an inborn error of metabolism?

Dr. Forsander I don't think so. I think it's only food for them. The rat is not drinking because for him it's not good—that is why he drinks only small amounts of alcohol. But why it is that the hamsters drink so much, I don't know. It must not be a metabolic fault, because it's common for all hamsters. However, when the hamster is pregnant, she starts to drink water.

From the Floor How about the alcohol effect? If they drink enough to give an effect, how noticeable is the effect?

Dr. Forsander They don't get drunk. The alcohol is metabolized before they get drunk; you can never find alcohol in their blood.

From the Floor The hamster drinks even less than the rat, doesn't it?

Dr. Deutsch Yes. But here is an interesting thing, something which I think would be of interest to you, Dr. Forsander. There's a doctor in Berkeley working on genetic differences in strains of rats and their choice of alcohol.[3] He found that some strains of rats will drink very much more alcohol than others. He has found one strain of rats, for instance, which will drink a 10 per cent alcohol solution, and other strains which will completely avoid it. Even if the animals are deprived of food, so that there is dietary insufficiency, one strain will drink alcohol and make up its body weight that way, the other

[3] G. E. McClearn and D. A. Rodgers, Differences in Alcohol Preference among Inbred Strains of Mice, *Quart. J. Studies Alc.*, 20:691–695, 1959.

G. E. McClearn and D. A. Rodgers, Genetic Factors in Alcohol Preferences of Laboratory Mice, *J. Comp. and Physiol. Psychol.*, 54:116–119, 1961.

D. A. Rodgers and G. E. McClearn, Mouse Strain Differences in Preference for Various Concentrations of Alcohol, *Quart. J. Studies Alc.*, 23:26–33, 1962.

one apparently is incapable of doing so. Apparently this correlates with an ability of one strain to metabolize alcohol and another strain of being incapable to do so.

Dr. Forsander   Yes, I've heard of it.

We are trying to study the drinking habits in rats in free-choice experiments. We have also run fat-tolerance tests. In these, we gave the rats a large amount of fat and measured the ketone bodies which appeared in the urine. If the fat metabolism is very good, then the ketone level is very low. Here, of course, is another correlation between how rats are drinking and how they can tolerate fats. The rats that drink large amounts of alcohol have a good fat tolerance, and those that drink small amounts have a very low tolerance. You can correlate this with a metabolic factor, and I think that this metabolic factor holds for people, too. Some people have this low tolerance for alcohol, which means that they can't drink alcohol at all.

Dr. Deutsch   That's very interesting. Do you know of any specific factor which would account for this inability to metabolize alcohol, and why it should correlate with the ability to tolerate fat?

Dr. Forsander   There may be a correlation between human drinking and fat tolerance, because usually adults who are drinking have a high fat tolerance, whereas children, who have a very low fat tolerance, are not drinking alcohol. Also, women have a much lower fat tolerance than men, and they usually drink much less alcohol than men.

From the Floor   This is not true in all countries, in all cultures, though, is it, Doctor? In the Latin countries the children are practically weaned on wine.

Dr. Deutsch   Of course, you did your work in Finland, so there may be differences.

Dr. Forsander   Yes. I think the main reason why children do not drink in my country is because of moralistic reasons. But it would be very interesting to know if there could be a physiological reason too.

From the Floor   Do the hamsters have a high fat tolerance?

Dr. Forsander   We have not studied the fat tolerance in the hamster.

From the Floor   Oh, but they have a high tolerance for alcohol?

Dr. Forsander   Yes, if they have a free choice, they drink mostly alcohol.

From the Floor   What happens there physiologically?

Dr. Forsander Nothing at all. They can drink it for years without any effect.

Some animals, for example the rat, can tolerate big, big amounts of alcohol. You can keep a rat for more than a year on alcohol, and it's not affected in any way.

From the Floor Provided you give other food?

Dr. Forsander Yes, but a year is very long for a rat.

From the Floor When you're feeding the animals, you're not giving them just alcohol?

Dr. Forsander They have other food, but if they are drinking large amounts of alcohol, they do not eat much food, because alcohol is a food.

From the Floor In other words, it doesn't affect the liver?

Dr. Forsander No. Rats can be kept their whole life span so drunk that they can hardly walk, and you still can't get a cirrhotic liver with alcohol, but you can on other diets. You can produce cirrhotic livers, but not with alcohol.

From the Floor Only 5 per cent of the general public is alcoholic, yet the percentage of cirrhosis is very much higher.

Dr. Forsander That is very important.

Dr. Deutsch This could be a secondary effect, presumably.

From the Floor The problem is not only eating, but what they're eating and how they're eating, how they live the rest of their life; their whole life is very complicated, and this causes a great deal of cirrhosis, just as much and more than alcohol. That's my opinion. We don't know the answer, but in the animals it's been definitely shown that they don't have cirrhotic livers from alcohol.

Dr. Deutsch Of course the animal experiments can only be done over a relatively short time; rats will live for 2½ years if you look after them very well.

From the Floor The rat doesn't say, "Let's go out and drink and have a party," so you don't have an alcoholic rat, whereas a man lives his life differently. There are a lot of psychological factors that enter into the way he lives, and this may be one of the reasons why we do have cirrhosis.

From the Floor Have you done any work on alcohol tolerance in rats?

Dr. Forsander How high the level can be? Yes, it can be over twice that in man, about 0.9 per cent.

From the Floor It can go up to 0.9 per cent before you get death?

Dr. Forsander Yes. In the human, it's about 0.5 per cent. So the rat's tolerance to alcohol is about twice as much as the human's.

ALCOHOLICS AND ALCOHOLISM

From the Floor If I may change the subject, I should like to ask this question: In a hospital setting, where you have a schizophrenic patient and also an alcoholic, is the alcoholic patient a help to the schizoid patient?

Dr. Deutsch I suppose one could answer with another question. Who would be of help to the schizophrenic patient?

From the Floor Well, if you mix schizophrenics with other patients, can you mix them with alcoholics?

Dr. Deutsch I don't know. I suppose anything is worth trying with schizophrenia.

From the Floor It seems to me that most psychiatrists will take alcoholic patients and mix them in with psychotics. Many other therapists in alcoholism don't like to mix their patients with the mental cases at all. Personally, in my work, I found that I don't care to mix the patients. The alcoholic will not like it, and of course the Alcoholics Anonymous, the lay therapists, and other forms of therapists are absolutely opposed to it. In large institutions there are alcoholic patients, but they segregate themselves pretty well, as far as I know. They'll help each other a great deal, the same as diabetics help each other. Tuberculosis patients help each other, and cancer patients help each other—there's sort of a common bond, you can't get away from that. But when you ask the question whether a schizo will benefit from an alcoholic, that's another story. The alcoholic can be a schizo, too, you know; you can look at it that way. How many alcoholics are schizo; what percentage? That's another factor.

Dr. Deutsch Well, are there any further questions?

From the Floor Tell us something about your work with alcoholism.

Dr. Deutsch I don't work with alcoholism.

From the Floor You work with alcohol in your experiments?

Dr. Deutsch I do the same sort of thing as Dr. Forsander. I treat alcohol as a substance with a certain taste and try to discover the factors which lead to overdrinking, which also includes the drinking of ordinary substances. People talk a great deal about over-drinking of spirituous things like beer and whiskey, but if you ask what regulates ordinary drinking, drinking water, or what regulates ordinary eating, people will give you all sorts of answers which are obviously wrong. I don't think anybody knows how people maintain their body weight, or maintain themselves in good health for many years, within very close limits of tolerance. One's work is extra-ordinarily well regulated; most people do not shift very much year in and year out, and this is a very important mechanism to keep you on a certain line. A similar mechanism applies to drinking and to eating. This constitutes a puzzle if you are a physiological psy-chologist, if you want to find out how the behavior which you observe in eating and drinking is related to physiological processes, or how physiological processes give rise to this sort of behavior. Now, I turned to the study of drinking because it's easier to manipulate than the study of eating, for various reasons. For one thing, you can dispense the stuff out of a bottle; you don't have to worry about wasted food, and it's much easier to manage.

It becomes very clear that what regulates drinking or eating is some very immediate effect of the food or water. It seems that with water, the thing which regulates how much you will drink is the taste of what you are drinking. One seems to be able to assess the amount of water one is drinking by getting a certain amount of taste which is fed back to the central nervous system. For instance, in the saline experiments I told you about, you can show that the amount of water message, per unit volume for saline, is much lower than for water alone. This is why the animal won't keep on drinking it for longer. You can show this physiologically. Now similarly, the thing that interests me about alcohol is the immediate effects of alcohol on a thirsty person or a thirsty rat. If you give him an alcohol solution, as opposed to just plain water, what effect has this on the mechanism of water intake—that is, does it fool the taste buds in the same way that saline seems to do? Some of the work that I've done seems to suggest this. When you had two bottles set up so that the rats could drink as much as they wanted out of each, then if you limited the amount they could drink from either nozzle by making them work a lever in order to get some more, they would, in fact, prefer the water. Fortunately, I never published anything until I repeated the experiments at least twice. The second time I did, it came out absolutely the other way, with the same animals.

At present, therefore, I can't make any statements except that the matter is up in the air. I still believe that there is an effect of alcohol which does in fact affect the drinking process.

From the Floor Then you're working with the drinking process, and how alcohol affects the drinking process. You're not working with alcoholics.

Dr. Deutsch That's right.

From the Floor I wondered where this would apply in an alcoholism program and what information you have to offer to us who are working with alcoholics. You, as an experimental psychologist, should perhaps have something to offer us who are not specialists.

Dr. Deutsch Yes, I think the whole thing is tied up with the basic question of why people drink as much as they do even when they're perfectly sane and in perfectly normal health. This is a problem which has not been solved, and I submit that you will not solve any of the problems of pathology until you get some good idea, at least, of normal function.

Dr. Forsander Some people think that the different tastes of various alcoholic beverages affect their drinking.

From the Floor It's very likely.

Dr. Forsander But the alcohol is drunk mainly because of its effect. So, if they can't get one alcoholic beverage, they will take another.

Dr. Deutsch Professor Drew said that it's been found that if alcoholics are put on a tranquilizer in order to get them off their alcohol, you'll find that these patients will then start hoarding pills so that they can go on a tranquilizer jag. Instead of getting addicted to alcohol, they get addicted to some tranquilizer. They seem to be the kind of people who must become addicted.

From the Floor There is no question that alcoholics are that way. This is our big problem.

From the Floor Of course, the fact of addiction is a different one from the problem of ingestion of alcohol, but it's obvious that if you have a substance which leads to overdrinking and which has addictive properties also—this is an absolutely fatal combination.

PSYCHIATRY, NUTRITION, PHYSIOLOGY, AND LITERATURE

Moderator Dr. Karl M. Bowman
Participants Dr. Claudia Balboni, Dr. Leon A. Greenberg, Mr. Berton Roueché

Dr. Bowman I thought we would start by giving each person about ten minutes to discuss any particular points of the whole alcohol problem, and he can take it from any attitude in any way he likes.

Dr. Balboni From the multidisciplinary point of view, which I share, the most important factors in this alcohol problem are the physiological, metabolic aspects, the psychological aspects, the social aspects, and the psychiatric aspects. The Center of Psychodietetics which we have set up has for its purpose to link the sciences together through the cooperation of research workers from the different professions. We have nutritionists, dieticians, psychiatrists and psychiatric nurses, social scientists, and physiologists, in order to make the approach to the alcohol problem as complete as possible.

You have heard in my previous report that we have tackled several problems dealing with the specific use of alcohol in various conditions. Our inquiries have focused on drinking and eating habits linked together, because we think that these normal eating and drinking habits linked together should give a clue to the occurrence of deviations such as obesity, alcoholism, and so on.

Our research work has dealt with normal subjects and also those affected by some kind of metabolic disorder, such as diabetes or coronary disease. All this is just a beginning but it leads to one consideration, that is, the importance of linking the alcohol problem to the more extensive study of eating habits from a multiple point of view.

Dr. Bowman Thank you for that interesting account. I take it that you are checking the old problem of which symptoms, alleged to be due to alcohol, may be really dietary deficiencies?

Dr. Balboni Not only that. We also study the problem from the nutritional point of view. We know very well that there is a definite nutritional aspect in alcoholism related to the intake of calories. Alcohol gives a certain number of calories in the diet, and these calories exclude the intake of other food which would be more beneficial to the organism. We are studying such nutrition disorders as stem from the overuse of alcohol, but this is only one of the aspects that we are dealing with, and there are many others that could be considered together with this one.

Dr. Bowman Dr. Greenberg, would you like to say a few words on this subject?

Dr. Greenberg I suppose that perhaps the best way to present a picture of the area in which I have been interested is to describe the development of our center of alcohol studies.

Originally we were a physiology laboratory, a unit at the University. We were interested in noxious materials, particularly noxious gases, vapors, and in the course of our work we studied alcohol, which has a noxious vapor. We hoped to answer such questions as how alcohol gets into the body (and I am referring of course to ethyl alcohol, the drinking kind of alcohol), how it distributes in the body, what happens to it in the body, how it is eliminated, and what its effects are. As you can well imagine, it was a very short time before we recognized that the drinking of alcoholic beverages was more than a very simple phenomenon, that it had many, many ramifications, and we realized that there were questions that could not be answered in the test tube or in the animal, that there were problems that involved a great many disciplines.

They had to be viewed from many points of view, from the psychological, from the physiological, from the psychiatric, from the nutritional, the legal, the moral, and the social point of view, and in recognition of this, our staff began to expand, began to interest people from other sections of the University, from other departments, and then people from outside who were also interested.

I might add that at no time do we like to look upon ourselves or to be considered as, shall I call it, alcohologists. No, quite on the contrary. We became interested and have remained interested in the study of alcohol and its use mainly because it is a wonderful vehicle for studying typical problems in human behavior. Alcohol has a world-wide use; it has a very old use, and the areas of inquiry from many directions have an impact on this question, so we are not alcohologists. We never have been interested in alcohol solely for the sake of alcohol. If anything, I should say we have not been married to alcohol; we are sort of carrying on an affair with it. It is a good vehicle for studying certain basic principles that might lead to deeper insights and better understanding of typical problems in human behavior.

As I have indicated, our group has consisted of people from the widest variety of disciplines. I happen to be a physiologist and in some ways a pharmacologist or biochemist, so that my interest has been in that direction, but—and I think this is the advantage of working in a kind of multi-, poly-, or interdisciplinary center or institute—all of us have always had a significant impact on each other.

It is really surprising how much the social scientists, for example, have learned about certain basic principles, ways of thinking, of the nutritionist and the biochemist and the physiologist, and how, for example, I have learned much about certain basic principles in the social sciences. They have had an impact on my thinking and on the direction of my thinking in my own field. We have done a great deal of work on the physiological effects, the metabolism, the biochemistry, and many of the psychological effects—effects upon behavior—of different amounts of alcohol. I think, with this for background, these people have some clue as to what kind of questions they might want to direct to me.

Dr. Bowman Mr. Roueché, would you care to spend about ten minutes on your background of interests?

Mr. Roueché Dr. Bowman, I think I ought to start by re-identifying myself. I am, I suppose, the only one here who doesn't represent any discipline. I am an author and a reporter, which means that I am not necessarily an originator of ideas but an accumulator and a collector, so there is very little that I can say on my own.

I came to the field of alcohol simply for my own information. It seemed to me that the subject was full of legend and myth and of violent opinions, and my intention was to see what facts, if any, there were on the subject of alcohol—its physiology, its effects on the mind and on the body, exactly the sort of thing that Dr. Greenberg has been discussing. I was surprised to find that there was a great deal of accurate information, only a small part of which had been made available to the mass of people, but it was well known to people in the field and was well known to people in medicine.

For example, I imagine anyone attending this symposium has

learned by now that alcohol is the thing that intoxicates, not the form in which it is served. Beer is not less intoxicating than whiskey; it is only less intoxicating because there is less alcohol in it. Still, many, many people persist in believing that the martini is a particularly potent drink, that there is some magic quality there that somehow enhances the intoxicating power of alcohol when it is mixed with vermouth. Of course, that isn't true, but this information isn't known.

Many people continue to believe that the effects of alcohol can be readily eliminated by going to a Turkish bath or by playing a set of tennis. But, as has been brought out here, alcohol is oxidized at a constant rate. And so the questions that I can answer can only be secondhand.

Dr. Bowman Thank you. I might just add a word about myself, in case you don't know. I became interested in alcoholism when I was at Bellevue Hospital in 1936 to 1941. At that time a group of us organized a research council on problems of alcohol, and Dr. Howard W. Haggard founded the *Quarterly Journal of Studies on Alcohol.* First, we managed to get a $25,000 grant to study what was and was not known about alcohol. Dr. E. M. Jellinek and I worked nearly two years on that. Then Dr. Jellinek went to Yale to join Dr. Haggard and set up a program for studies on alcohol, in the center of which Dr. Greenberg has told you.[1] I have been following alcohol problems ever since, doing some research and teaching, writing some articles, and so forth, and I am very interested in all of this work.

We are going to devote our time now to finding out something about alcohol, and the direction of our discussion will depend on the wishes of the audience. Later on we are going to let all of you ask questions, so if there are certain things we have not talked about, which you feel frustrated about, you will have your chance.

PHYSIOLOGICAL BASIS OF ALCOHOLISM

I shall start out by asking a point or two about the physiological basis of alcoholism. Within the last year or so there have been a number of articles about thyroid function in alcoholics and the use

[1] Originally the Yale Center of Alcohol Studies, now the Rutgers University Center of Alcohol Studies.

of thyroid substances in the treatment of both alcohol addiction and alcohol intoxication, and even delirium tremens. Therefore I thought I would just mention this very briefly to see if you wish to make any observations along this line, whether you agree that here is something that may be of great interest to us, or whether you feel that it is probably going to be just a flash in the pan, as have so many of the wonder cures.

This has to do with some work that comes from Harvard, so if we have Yale people here and they criticize, we shall assume that they are not too influenced by the feelings of the two groups for each other. As a matter of fact, they fight bitterly (I was at Harvard for fourteen years), but they sort of each agree that the other fellow is right next to the top, so they both have great respect for the other.

A Dr. Goldberg, not the one that you have been hearing at this symposium but one who is in Boston, stated that in a study of thyroid function in thirty-three alcoholic patients he found that twenty-one, or 64 per cent of them, were definitely thyroid-deficient.[2] He treated them with either desiccated thyroid extract or L-tri-iodothyronine and found great improvement. He referred to the work of Curt Richter at Johns Hopkins in 1936, which suggested that thyroid deficiency might be a cause of alcoholism and its presence might cause a continuance of this symptom.

In a personal communication that I had from Dr. Goldberg, he stated that he had now added more cases to this series and they had examined one hundred alcoholics and found forty-seven of them to be unequivocally hypothyroid.

In a second article,[3] he tells of the treatment of twelve cases of alcohol intoxication by intravenous L-triiodothyronine, using eight untreated acute intoxications as controls. He found that the mean rate of metabolism of alcohol in the blood was apparently twice as rapid in those treated with iodothyronine as in the untreated, and that therefore this was a very excellent treatment for patients in acute intoxication, the "ordinary drunk," if you prefer; he reports the treatment of one patient with delirium tremens and a low blood alcohol, only 0.025 per cent, with auditory and visual hallucina-

[2] M. Goldberg, The Occurrence and Treatment of Hypothyroidism among Alcoholics, *J. Clin. Endocrinol. and Metabolism*, 20:609–621, 1960.
[3] M. Goldberg, R. Hehir, and M. Hurowitz, Intravenous Tri-iodothyronine in Acute Intoxication, *New Engl. J. Med.*, 263:1336–1339, 1960.

tions which disappeared within one hour after intravenous L-tri-iodothyronine and did not reappear.

Now we have, as so often happens, somebody who has opposite results to report. Mardones had rats on a stock diet and a choice between water and alcohol.[4] If he gave them a thyroid extract, they immediately drank a lot more alcohol, and then when he discontinued the thyroid extract, inside of two weeks they were back to their previous level. This is the sort of thing, he pointed out in his findings, that is exactly the opposite of what Curt Richter had found.[5]

These are the problems—somebody gets wonderful results with one thing, and somebody else gets just the contrary findings. I wonder if any of the group here are familiar with these findings, or have had any experience along these lines, and if they would care to comment on it?

Dr. Greenberg Yes, I have. I might start by saying that I am going to express some degree of skepticism and, in doing so, as a Yale man, I certainly shall not be in an untraditional position with respect to a Harvard man.

There are several parts to the general question that you brought up, Dr. Bowman, and let me deal with them separately. First, with respect to Richter's work on self-selection of alcohol versus water, and Mardones's work on the use of L-triiodothyronine, or some other thyroid extract, what I want to talk about is just what is the relationship between this self-selection phenomenon and alcoholism?

I think this has been very much misused; I think it has been abused. The basic observations are correct. They have been repeated many times; namely, if you take some animals and put them in a cage where they have a choice of drinking fluid, a choice between water alone or water with alcohol in it, they will exhibit a choice in terms of the proportion of water they drink and the proportion of water containing alcohol. It was Mardones, as a matter of fact, who was the very first, I think, to point out that if these animals are put

[4] R. Prieto, A. Varela, and J. Mardones, Influence of Oral Administration of Thyroid Powder on the Voluntary Alcohol Intake by Rats, *Acta Physiol. Latinoam.*, 8:203, 1958.

[5] C. P. Richter, Loss of Appetite for Alcohol and Alcoholic Beverages Produced in Rats by Treatment with Thyroid Preparations, *Endocrinology*, 59:472–478, 1956.

on a deficient diet, they will show a greater preference for alcohol.[6]

Prior to this, Richter had made some studies of the same kind and at that time his interest was mainly not alcoholism at all. He was interested in the phenomenon of taste and how taste changes preference.[7] He did this not only with alcohol; he used many other materials, but he did observe this same phenomenon so far as alcohol is concerned, and whether or not he actually said that this was an expression of alcoholism, I don't know. Do you know did he say this?

Dr. Bowman   I think he said it might be.

Dr. Greenberg   He suggested that possibly this was so. Then along came Dr. Roger Williams, and he also made the same observations.[8] He found, furthermore, that when he restored vitamins to the diet of the animals that were on the deficient diet, they now lost their increased preference for alcohol. He hypothesized that this was an expression of a need for alcohol and that therefore this was alcoholism. This was all built into what he described as the genetotrophic theory of the cause of alcoholism. This theory postulated that, while we do have a value that represents the average normal daily requirement of vitamins, no two people are the same in their requirements for each of the vitamins as well as for other nutrients. In addition, there were some people whose genetic make-up caused them to require extraordinarily large amounts of some vitamins, and these were the potential alcoholics; they would have a craving for alcohol. This was generalized from this observation in animal experiments.

The thought occurred to us—not too brilliant an idea, but it was different from what anybody else had done—to give the animals a third choice. We did this because we felt that perhaps those ob-

[6] R. J. Mardones and B. E. Onfray, Influencia de una substancia de la levadura (elemento del complejo vitaminico B?) sobre el consumo de alcohol en ratas en experimentos de autoselección (Influence of a Substance in Yeast [an Element of the Vitamin B Complex?] on the Consumption of Alcohol by Rats in Experiments with Autoselection), *Rev. chilena hig. y med. prevent.*, 4:293–297, 1942.

[7] C. P. Richter, Alcohol as a Food, *Quart. J. Studies Alc.*, 1:650–662, 1941.

[8] R. J. Williams, L. J. Berry, and E. Beerstecher, Jr., Individual Metabolic Patterns, Alcoholism, Genetotrophic Diseases, *Proc. Nat. Acad. Sci.*, Washington, 35:265–271, 1949.

servations were not really an expression of alcoholism. And what led us to believe that alcoholism was not involved is the fact that these animals, when they showed a higher preference for alcohol, nevertheless never drank alcohol in amounts even to approach showing any effects of being under the influence of alcohol. Our image of alcoholism is that when an alcoholic drinks he wants to get drunk, or at least to feel the effects. Well, the animals don't get drunk when they drink; they don't come even close. So we thought, well, this can't be alcoholism—there is no reason to assume that it is, and perhaps the reason for their drinking alcohol is that because of the deficiency of some factor in their diet, they are unable to utilize metabolically the foodstuffs in their ordinary diet, and therefore they were hungry. We know that alcohol is a rich source of calories, and maybe they now prefer alcohol because they can utilize the alcohol and can't utilize, let's say, the fat or the carbohydrate. Whatever it was we don't know, but we decided to give them a third choice, sugar or fat, to see whether they would rather take that than alcohol. We did just that; we gave them a third choice, sugar; they could choose among water, an alcohol solution, and a sugar solution. And sure enough the supposed craving for alcohol disappeared, because they now had a craving for sugar—they wouldn't touch the alcohol as long as the sugar was available. Of course, we were just too smart alecky, and we spoiled our own theory, because we decided to give them a still different choice, and we gave them saccharin. And this they liked better than anything else. So that is where we left them, but we were convinced that the alcohol-preference experiments were not demonstrations of alcoholism.[9]

I think this was rather disturbing to Dr. Williams, and his criticism of our research was that we just muddied up the waters— and that we sure did.

RATE OF ALCOHOL METABOLISM

Now we come to the other question, a drug; let's say L-triiodothyronine. It is said to increase the metabolism, the disappearance, of alcohol so rapidly that a person who is in a stuporous state

[9] D. Lester and L. A. Greenberg, Nutrition and the Etiology of Alcoholism. The Effect of Sucrose, Saccharin and Fat on the Self-selection of Ethyl Alcohol by Rats, *Quart. J. Studies Alc.*, 13:553–560, 1952.

of alcohol intoxication was reported to have recovered within an hour to the extent that he was not able to answer questions, give his case history, brush off his clothes, and go home.

During the past fifteen of the twenty-five years we have been investigating the effects of alcohol, I don't think a year has gone by when there have not come to our laboratory, from all over, at least two or three sure-fire cures for alcoholism and for drunkenness. None of them has panned out.

I remember, Dr. Bowman, long years ago in Bellevue, there was a Dr. Walter Goldfarb, who worked with you. I recall that he published a paper which at the time was very exciting, in which he described the administration of sugar and insulin to produce rapid sobriety.[10] What was particularly interesting to me was the very rapid disappearance of alcohol—presumably the alcohol was metabolized manyfold the normal rate. I recall my first reaction—I sat down and did a little calculation on the thermodynamics of this increased burning of alcohol. In consideration of the fact that the first two steps of that burning occur mainly in the liver, the total energy exchange there would have to be such that one should be able to smell frying liver—it was an incredible energy exchange that would have had to take place.

These things happen, and this is why things have to be repeated over and over again and confirmed by other researchers. The fact of the matter is that this was a very exciting thing at the time, and like many other reported works which have just naturally faded away, one does not hear of them any more.

Now this is one of the very recent reports, on this L-triiodothyronine. Henry Newman, shortly after Goldberg published his first findings on this, carried out some studies with this drug, and he couldn't find any difference in the rate of disappearance of alcohol.[11]

About a year ago we did some preliminary experiments with some smaller animals using this same drug, and we found no changes in the alcohol content of the blood in animals that had been given a substantial dose of alcohol. Also, we were not able to find any change in their sleeping time or wake-up time after a dose of alcohol. In other words, it didn't work for us.

[10] W. Goldfarb, K. M. Bowman, and S. Parker, The Treatment of Acute Alcoholism with Glucose and Insulin, *J. Clin. Invest.*, 18:581–584, 1939.
[11] H. W. Newman and M. E. Smith, Triiodothyronine in Acute Alcoholic Intoxication, *Nature*, London, 183:689–690, 1959.

I cannot comment on the effects on delirium tremens; this has not been within my experience. I don't know whether this has been tried or tested by others, but I would say of Dr. Goldberg's observation, and of the drug, that one must never be so skeptical as to write things off immediately. I think one should be willing to have the patience to wait. Other people will try it; clinicians will try it, and in due time we will know the answer.

Dr. Bowman Thank you. Would you care to comment on this at all, Dr. Balboni?

Dr. Balboni I have no direct experience with this type of therapy. The treatment of alcoholism is not quite in line with what we are doing, but I have read the papers and I feel, as Dr. Greenberg says, that time will tell.

Dr. Bowman Mr. Roueché.

Mr. Roueché All the information I have on the metabolism of alcohol I learned from Dr. Greenberg.

Dr. Greenberg You have a prejudiced view.

Mr. Roueché I spent a lot of time at Yale absorbing that information.

TREATMENT OF ALCOHOL INTOXICATION

From the Floor Do you distinguish between the people who are hypothyroid to begin with and then get treatment as against a person who is in an alcoholic state, uninvestigated with respect to their thyroid condition, whom you then treat with the thyronine? You might get very different results, depending on what kind of an alcoholic you have.

Dr. Bowman In this study, they have treated both groups and report their best results with the hypothyroid patients, but some good results and lowering of the blood alcohol occurred both in the hypothyroid patients and the ones who were not hypothyroid.

Dr. Greenberg I might add something, Dr. Bowman. Quite a few years ago, we were interested in some possible means by which the rate of alcohol metabolism could be increased. Naturally, one of the things that would suggest itself immediately was to increase the general metabolism of the body. At that time, we tested the effect of a whole variety of metabolic stimulants on the rate of alcohol disappearance, including thyroid extract, thyroxine, and there just was no appreciable effect. This was the general conclusion that we came to, and since then it has been generally accepted that alcohol disappears from the body essentially at a constant rate. There is nothing we know of yet, including running around the block ten times and two cups of hot black coffee, that will sober you up. Now I think this is what we must bear in mind when we try to pass some judgments or evaluate clinical reports.

There is, of course, a very common belief that by increasing the rate of energy expenditure, by exercising, one can work off a state of drunkenness, or that hot black coffee will sober people up. I think that very often these beliefs are reached because of a kind of a fuzziness in our definition of what we are talking about. Of course, you know, when people are drunk they tend to fall asleep. Now if you run them around the block twenty times and give them two cups of hot coffee, they behave quite differently—you have a wide awake drunk, as compared to a sleepy drunk. One can very easily fall into the error of thinking, "Look, this man has been sobered up," but actually there is no evidence that this happens. It has been said many times that if you are drunk, you might just as well relax and enjoy yourself, because it takes about an hour for the alcohol in an ounce of whiskey to disappear. I have yet to see any authenticated material in the literature demonstrating that this alcohol loss from the body can be greatly increased. Nothing has yet been brought forth that stands up.

Dr. Bowman   In your work, Dr. Balboni, with dietetics and so forth, would you feel that you would agree with this, or have you anything that makes you feel that there are ways that could increase the elimination of alcohol?

Dr. Balboni   I think there is only a protective metabolic device: drinking alcohol with a full stomach, because in that case there are other mechanisms which come into account, such as slower absorption, and also the metabolic activity of the liver is somehow awakened by the digestive processes.

Mr. Roueché   You don't mean that feeding a man who is drunk will sober him up?

Dr. Balboni   I am not talking of treatment of intoxication, just a metabolic device to protect the organism.

Mr. Roueché   Does food have any effect some hours after drinking? Does eating have any effect on hangovers? Does a hearty breakfast, if you can stomach it?

Dr. Greenberg   If you can hold it down, yes.

Dr. Balboni Low blood sugar levels have been reported in hangover, and probably, if the person can eat, the ingestion of food might bring up the blood sugar to a level that would make him more comfortable. But I don't think it has anything to do with going back to sobriety.

Mr. Roueché After a man was sober but suffering from the symptoms?

Dr. Greenberg I think perhaps you could substitute indigestion for the hangover, to take your mind off the hangover and have a bellyache.

Dr. Bowman If you can keep down the food you have taken into your stomach, it probably would result in improvement, because if you could start absorbing carbohydrates and get the sugar back up, this would perhaps affect the acid-base equilibrium.

ETIOLOGY OF ALCOHOLISM

I wonder if we have anything to offer now as to the cause of alcoholism that has not been gone over in previous meetings. Does anybody have some special theories on alcoholism? You have heard of Roger Williams's viewpoint, and many others. We heard the psychoanalytical view from Dr. Alexander, but have we any other views that you think should be brought up and discussed as to why people become alcoholics—psychological, genetic, physiological—anything you want?

Dr. Greenberg I have something, perhaps. Naturally, we are always thinking about, and have for many years thought about, possible explanations of the cause of alcoholism. It has always been felt by many people in the field that it would be a real jewel in the crown of any person or any group that could come up with the answer. So there have been very strong motivations to find it. The motivations have been so strong that we have had the most bizarre explanations. The theories fall into a variety of categories, the psychological, psychiatric, personality theories, and the theories that our social scientists hold that the cause arises mainly from certain social distortions and deviations, and there have been some who have attempted to answer the question in terms of biochemical or physiological deviations.

In some ways and to some people, a physiological or biochemical explanation would be most satisfying. This has been most apparent to the alcoholic himself, and even to the recovered alcoholic, because certainly a mental-state explanation as the cause of alcoholism has, for many years, carried with it the stigma of any kind of mental deviation. So we have had a whole variety of theories. One was that it was due to a vitamin deficiency—that was the Williams theory. Another rather well-known theory was that it was due to a malfunction of the adrenal gland, and I think this theory was postulated by J. J. Smith in New York. Still another theory was that alcoholism was an allergy sort of response. There were all kinds of theories, and you could take your choice, and none of them has stood up very well. In fact, as of today, I think that the psychological-psychiatric-personality theories, or perhaps even the social science theories, are easier to take than any of the physiological and biochemical ones so far suggested.

One idea that I have been thinking about for some time came to me by kind of reversing the question. The usual way of asking the question is, "What is there about the body, or some organ or some chemistry in the body, that causes certain people to become alcoholics?" One could put the question the other way, "May there not be some biochemical difference between people that, in most people, keeps them from becoming alcoholics?" We do know that when certain things are not handled well in the body metabolically, the body rejects them; the person doesn't select them, and he avoids taking them.

We do know that except for the first two steps of the oxidation of alcohol, the oxidation of alcohol thereafter is very similar to the oxidation of fat in the body. We also know that there are wide differences in people in their fat tolerance and that those people with a metabolically lower fat tolerance just don't like fat, and those with a higher tolerance do like fat.

If you will, the hypothesis I shall suggest and which I hope some day in the not too far future to explore is this: that perhaps people who have a high alcohol metabolic tolerance, which may be parallel to the high fat tolerance, do not find quantities of alcohol distasteful. Others find large amounts of alcohol disagreeable because they have a lower metabolic tolerance for alcohol. In other words, then, it is the people who don't become alcoholics who are different, not the people who do become alcoholics. If no one had this metabolic limitation, or if all people had a very high tolerance to alcohol, they would all be candidates for alcoholism. But there is some biochemical difference in people so that certain people, perhaps a majority of people, even though they are exposed to factors which would encourage the excessive use of alcohol, have a metabolic limitation which blocks the excessive use of alcohol.

If it has no other virtue, I think this has the novelty of approaching the problem in a sort of backward way and asking, "Why don't over 90 per cent of the people who drink become alcoholics?" rather than asking, "Why do a small percentage of the people who drink become alcoholics?" This is, to me, an appealing hypothesis.

Dr. Balboni Going further in your hypothesis, what would you suggest as a possible field to explore to get to this?

Dr. Greenberg Well, I can't give you an exact blueprint, since this is just in a formative state in my own mind, but I should certainly look for some measurable dimensions that would give you some index of differences in the threshold of tolerance in individuals, or experimental animals, if you will, in terms of the type of metabolites you get, ketone bodies.

Dr. Balboni Intermediate metabolites?

Dr. Greenberg Or even final metabolites. How do we know that some people have a high fat tolerance or a low fat tolerance? We know because when we give a test meal of fat to a person with low fat tolerance, we find a much greater excretion of ketone bodies than in a person who has high fat tolerance. This is the sort of thing that might be investigated with the underlying thought in mind that this may be the answer, rather than to look for something positive that makes people alcoholics.

Dr. Balboni The minority.

Dr. Greenberg All things being equal, we would all be candidates for it, but we know we are not.

Mr. Roueché You would couple that with some form of emotional disability?

Dr. Greenberg I can't draw you any detailed pictures, but I would say that emotional and personality disabilities are also part of the requirements for the development of alcoholism, that it will develop only in fertile soil.

Mr. Roueché The two have to coincide.

Dr. Greenberg After all, we have .heard expressions like this: Alcoholism is a condition which prevails in people who are poorly integrated, in poorly developed personalities; they have emotional problems, all kinds of things, and always the annoying question comes up, "Well, do all people who are poorly integrated or who are emotionally immature, or this or that, become alcoholics?" We know that all those people don't become alcoholics, but we don't know why. They just express their peculiarity in some other way, and what I am suggesting is a possible answer to the question, "Why don't they become alcoholics?"

Dr. Balboni   Would you explore the area of the central nervous system, the cell tissue?

Dr. Greenberg   I don't know. I suppose that if a study were to develop from such a focal point, a vast variety of areas could be studied.

Dr. Bowman   You have to think of the fact that you have five times as many men alcoholics as women, and whatever this quality is that is present or lacking, it would vary to some degree according to sex.

Dr. Greenberg   Well, Dr. Bowman, this may be just a coincidence, but a high fat tolerance is much more frequent in women than in men. This may be purely coincidental, as Dr. Masserman said about his cats, but we must also keep this in mind—that socially, psychologically, and in many ways, women play a different role, occupy a different position in relationship to factors in the social environment. These, too, are variables as between men and women. My thought is that it isn't just this factor which causes the alcoholism, but that this is the kind of fertile soil or isn't the kind of fertile soil in which, given other conditions, chronic excessive drinking may develop. Other conditions may be different between men and women, that is, the social, and the psychological factors.

MOOD AND EFFECT OF ALCOHOL

Mr. Roueché   The one certainty is that alcohol has an agreeable effect on mood.

Dr. Greenberg   You mean an agreeable effect on the mood of the drinker or upon the mood of his companion?

Mr. Roueché   For most people, a drink increases self-esteem, increases confidence, increases satisfaction with one's situation.

Dr. Bowman   I should say that this is probably so in the majority of cases, but some individuals get weepy and maudlin as soon as they have a drink or two; some get very irritable and pugnacious, a habit pattern that they bring out with alcohol, and then we find that the same individual does not always get the same reaction.

A distant relative of mine was always the life of the party, and he enjoyed alcohol so much that it was just a pleasure to see him take a drink; this was the sort of person he was. His wife died, and when I saw him, I offered him a drink and he said, "No. Since my wife died, every time I take a drink I just get into a horrible depression." It is the same person, maybe he is mildly depressed anyway, but certainly there was a very different reaction to the alcohol. You find plenty of people who will say, "Well, last night I just had the usual amount of drink and the first thing I knew I woke up in bed; it just knocked me out cold, yet I didn't have a bit more than what I had dozens of times without it affecting me." So I think you find that there are all sorts of variations with the same person; the reaction is dependent, perhaps, upon his particular mood, state of fatigue, and any number of things that would produce variations in the response. But I would agree that if you took a thousand people and gave them a drink of alcohol, you would find that a large percentage of them would feel better, and relaxed, and more at ease.

Mr. Roueché I wonder if many people really do become belligerent or melancholy on a couple of drinks?

Dr. Bowman There are some people who habitually are this way. When you were in college, you may have heard of somebody, "Don't ever take him on a drinking party; he gets about two drinks and just goes wild and wants to fight with everybody"—so you never take him along.

Dr. Greenberg Not even to a cocktail party.

Mr. Roueché Such a man would not be a likely candidate for alcoholism. It would be such a depressing experience for him that he would choose not to drink.

Dr. Greenberg Now I think you made a switch there. He is depressing to everybody else, but you don't know that he is depressing to himself.

Mr. Roueché I think the man whose spirits drop to bottom and who cries after a couple of drinks, unless he finds some perverse pleasure in this, must be depressed.

Dr. Greenberg I think there are some wonderful rewards that some people get out of crying.

Mr. Roueché   Well, then I will reverse myself again. He would get the release he wanted.

Dr. Bowman   The man who gets very belligerent, you can say that maybe he gets a lot of pleasure out of letting go and fighting everybody, I don't know, but he doesn't seem happy; he seems very irritated, and he is just fighting drunk, as we say. He gets that way on a couple of drinks. I have seen people who have habitually been that way.

Mr. Roueché   Alcohol, then, evokes a desired mood change, whether it's melancholia or something else.

Dr. Bowman   I don't see how we can say that he desires it. I don't get the impression that this man who has these outbreaks desires them.

Dr. Greenberg   I would say, if I may say so, I do like my theory because it is a departure from the monolithic concept. Everybody would like to feel that the explanation lies in his discipline, and I think this presents at least a kind of a design for an understanding of the cause of alcoholism, not in terms of any one single discipline but as the result of the impact of a number of forces.

Dr. Bowman   I should personally go further and say, as I have indicated, that there may be quite different reasons causing alcoholism in different persons, that it is not necessarily a single cause, and that it is not necessarily the same set of causes in every person, and certainly we don't know very much about them.

From the Floor   Dr. Bowman, could we perhaps say that alcoholism is a homeostatic agent, that it helps man bring himself into a state of homeostasis, whether it is psychologically, or chemically, or physiologically, or what?

Dr. Greenberg   I will say this with respect to the biochemical —you included that—this much is certain: when a man gets drunk, he is not biochemically in homeostasis. He is as disrupted a man as can be, biochemically. There is a shift of electrolytes to very abnormal distribution; there is a water shift in his body; there is really a biochemical upheaval in his body, and, as a matter of fact, the so-called hangover is in large part a process of restoring the biochemical wreckage that is left over from the period of drunkenness, the biochemical disruption that has occurred.

From the Floor   Maybe the biochemistry has to be on one end of the teetertotter and some psychological factor at the other end.

Dr. Greenberg I don't know where you want to place them; I am just answering the question. Biochemically, getting drunk is not a homeostasis-producing condition. Quite on the contrary, it is a homeostasis-disturbing condition.

From the Floor And yet many people seem to need it, don't they?

Dr. Bowman The question is whether they need it or not. Sometimes they get drunk and yet realize that they don't really want to. I doubt if we can simplify it as easily as that.

TYPOLOGY AND CLASSIFICATION OF ALCOHOLICS

From the Floor I wonder if you or Dr. Greenberg are familiar with the study being done by some doctors in Canada in which they found that the alcoholic has a deficiency of some substances which help the body burn up adrenochrome,[12] which is supposed to contribute towards their need for excessive alcohol?

Dr. Greenberg There has been a lot of screening done of alcoholics versus nonalcoholics, and you do find some biochemical differences in certain things. Our problem is to discover, if we can, whether these differences occur as a result of long excessive drinking or whether they preceded the alcoholism and may therefore be the cause of it. You find differences, but you can't tell whether this is the horse or the cart. For this reason one has to think ultimately about doing some kind of longitudinal studies. I think right here in California this is being projected, that is, where you start with a population of young people that you have fairly good prospects of being able to contact periodically for the next twenty years of their lives, and develop a series of tests that you can subject them to. You can expect that, some ten or fifteen years hence, a certain proportion will have become alcoholics, and you hope to see whether there is any correlation with any of the components that you measured before.

Dr. Bowman At the University of California, over forty years ago, they started a study to follow a group of very young children to see what happened to them. They can't get the money now for the

[12] A. Hoffer and H. Osmond, Concerning an Etiological Factor in Alcoholism. The Possible Role of Adrenochrome Metabolism, *Quart. J. Studies Alc.*, **20**:750–756, 1959.

study of children, but the geriatrics group is planning to give them some money because these people are getting along to the age where they are eligible for a geriatric study.

Actually, I believe this does form a unique set of cases where you have taken very small children and followed them over this long period of time to see what happens to them to try to find out why.

I have not checked with them recently, and I don't know whether they have any alcoholics in this group or not, but if they did, here you would have a whole series of psychological and physiological tests done since childhood, and you might find something worthwhile. They are trying to do the same sort of thing for cases of essential hypertension. This started ten or fifteen years ago, picking out in the freshman class of the University of California persons who showed a high blood pressure on their initial physical examination; they didn't have arteriosclerosis or anything. Then they matched a group of these with persons of the same age, sex, race, and so forth, and as far as possible alike in every way except they didn't show high blood pressure. The question is, Are those persons going to be the ones who are going to show the hypertension and arteriosclerosis fifteen or twenty or thirty years from now?

This is the type of study which is becoming very popular now, getting the individual and then following him pretty much through his life and then seeing what happens to him and trying to find out what may be the cause of this or that or the other type of thing, and I think that, if applied to alcoholics, it would give us some clue, if you took enough individuals and tested them every possible way.

From the Floor   Dr. Bowman, I wonder if we are not being fooled a bit by using the generic term of alcoholic as just alcoholic? It seems to me that Dr. Jellinek recently, in one of his books,[13] made nine different classifications and subdivisions of those nine classifications—I have forgotten whether it is twenty-seven or twenty-eight. Don't you do somewhat of a disservice in trying to classify this whole field as one?

Dr. Bowman   The question is whether we are really dealing with this problem adequately and properly when we use the term "alcoholic" as a unitary term, and with reference to Dr. Jellinek's

---

[13] E. M. Jellinek, *The Disease Concept of Alcoholism*, New Haven, Conn., College and University Press, 1960.

work. I think in the first article of a work we wrote together,[14] in 1940 or 1941—I have forgotten how many types we had—there were twelve or thirteen there—and you can go on and get an almost endless number of terms; there are very possibly very great differences between some of these different cases. The causes may be different, and their symptoms are different, and yet they all have in common the misuse of alcohol. Whether they belong in different groups, and whether you find different causes and different factors, I think many of us feel, just as we do in mental disease generally, that these are highly individual things and that you are doing a little something wrong when you toss them all together. Yet I don't know that any of these divisions we have made of the alcoholics in themselves are really basic or intrinsic, and I don't know whether we are not doing just as great an injustice by tossing them into ten or twenty or thirty different groups and expecting them to be different, as we are in leaving them together.

Would you have anything to say about that?

Dr. Greenberg No, just that I think Dr. Jellinek is right, and you are right. Certainly there are certain behavioral differences. I think perhaps the best way to resolve this problem for one's self is what I do, just look upon all of them as people who lack control of their drinking and therefore drink excessively, and this is a manifestation of dependence on the alcohol. Of course I don't believe that the cause is the same in all cases, or that they all are are like peas in a pod. But one thing common to all of them is that they drink in such a way as to give us every reason to believe that they lack any control of their drinking and therefore are dependent on it, and this is a very simple rule that I follow.

Mr. Roueché What is the advantage of cataloguing types of abusers of alcohol?

Dr. Bowman I think, just as in medicine generally, when you have sick people you start finding different symptoms, and you wonder whether they fall into different groups and may really be different types of illness. So, with regard to the alcoholics, I think this same point arises. Are there really very definite types of al-

[14] K. M. Bowman and E. M. Jellinek, Alcohol Addiction and Its Treatment, in E. M. Jellinek (ed.), *Effects of Alcohol on the Individual*, vol. 1, *Alcohol Addiction and Chronic Alcoholism*, New Haven, Yale University Press, 1941, chap. 1.

coholism? For example, the periodic drinker that we speak of as opposed to the steady drinker, there is a difference there. Here is a man who goes sober for a month or more, goes on a binge for a week, and then is sober for another month or longer. Here is another man who is drinking steadily all week and then on Saturday night he gets dead drunk. On Monday morning he comes to and goes back to drinking again. There are differences. I think we always try to note those differences to see if this gives us any clue as to different causes or different ways of treating them. We are always on the lookout for it, but I don't think we have gotten very far with all of those different attempts, which we have changed constantly. I think we shall continue to classify drinkers and alcoholics to try to see differences and whether certain groups fall together and have a possible common type of picture, and then a common cause, and then a common way of treatment. That would be the sort of thing we are doing in medicine all the time, but we have not gotten anywhere with it in alcoholism, as far as I can see.

Mr. Roueché Those are certainly two different manifestations, but further refinement down to twenty-six, or twenty-seven, or twenty-eight seems to me to be a little paradox.

Dr. Bowman I confess that I couldn't follow some of those types along in the way it was done; I didn't find it useful.

Dr. Greenberg I don't think that Dr. Jellinek would necessarily hold that today. I think this merely represents the kind of effort that you were talking about, Dr. Bowman. The researcher tries to systematize things; he tries to classify things, because classifying and systematizing is sometimes helpful in clarifying the rules that govern the occurrences.

Mr. Roueché I have gotten the impression that in mental disease, generally, there is a tendency away from strict categorizing —"this is a schizophrenic," "this is a manic-depressive,"—that has become more accurate than useful.

Dr. Bowman I think we have two schools of thought, and this would depend on the group you talk with. If you talk with someone from the orthodox psychoanalytic group, you will find a classifying which would be different from that of a follower of Adolph Meyer. If you are running an institution of any sort, you have to make these classifications, and you refer to your Standard Nomenclature of Disease. And you find variations throughout the world in the way that they classify them, and yet the term "schizophrenia" applies to a particular set of symptoms which generally mean a pretty serious prognosis, and it is helpful to have that term. Now whether schizophrenia is a single disease or not, all of that is still being very much argued. But many people find it rather necessary to have some shorthand term in the discussion of syndromes. If you don't want to use the word "disease," you can use, like Adolph Meyer, reaction types. They don't believe they are actual disease entities; they are just reaction types, and then you go ahead and use a term for that reaction type, which is just the same as if you call it a disease and call it schizophrenia.

From the Floor This morning a distinction was made between the alcoholic and the skid rower who drinks to excess, and as I remember the definition of the alcoholic, it was the man who drinks in order to seek oblivion. This is a pretty stringent type of thing and the skid rower merely wants to change his environment so so that it becomes tolerable to him, so he keeps at this level of unreality.

Dr. Bowman The question is about the use of the term "skid rower" as different from the term "alcoholic." The alcoholic is one who seeks oblivion in alcohol whereas the skid rower is one who is just drinking enough to sort of cut the edge off and give a certain degree of comfort, and then, as was said, puts the bottle back in his pocket and an hour or two later might pull it out again and hit that stage.

Now I think there is that type of skid row drinking; it occurs. But as I remember, when questions were asked, it was agreed that some of these so-called skid row people were true alcoholics and others were not; the group that are living together on skid row are not all just the same. I think that was conceded by the speaker.

From the Floor Part of my question is, do you agree with a definition of the alcoholic as a person who seeks oblivion? There are many people who are not skid rowers who drink not to seek oblivion but for many other reasons. It may be because they are on business trips and are in contact with many people and find themselves drinking much more than necessary because of individual relationships and so forth. Are these people not finally alcoholics when it gets out of hand, even though they are not seeking oblivion?

Dr. Bowman I would say yes. There is a whole group of people that I personally would call alcoholics who don't commonly go on to complete oblivion, and that again brings up that we have a very wide range.

Dr. Greenberg This comment was made by Judge Murtagh, and I know Judge Murtagh's thinking; I think he was just trying to indicate that there are some people on skid row who drink because for some reason or another they are dependent upon drinking, and there are others on skid row who drink because they are just trying to escape from unpleasantness, or because this is part of the custom in the subsociety in which they live.

Dr. Bowman He said there are also some on skid row who don't drink at all.

From the Floor You would say that there are excessive drinkers who continually drink excessively who could not be classified as alcoholics?

Dr. Greenberg You want to draw some pretty sharp lines.

Dr. Bowman The question is whether people may be excessive drinkers and yet not alcoholics, and I believe your feeling is that—and mine certainly is—we don't get anywhere by trying to make all these sharp distinctions.

DEFINITION OF ALCOHOLISM

From the Floor I may have been absent when the question was asked, but if the question was asked and answered, I have not yet heard a definition of alcoholic, nor a definition of alcoholism.

Dr. Greenberg You will get as many definitions, I am afraid, as the number of people you ask, but I will give you the one I like. This working definition of an alcoholic was developed at our center of alcohol studies.[15] If a person drinks so much and so frequently that he gets into trouble, health-wise, economically or socially, and still continues the drinking, this man has no control of his drinking; to me this man is now suffering from alcoholism.

Dr. Bowman And you wouldn't make a distinction between an alcoholic or alcoholism or alcohol addiction?

Dr. Greenberg No.

Dr. Bowman These distinctions have been made. Jellinek was always great for definitions, but you notice in this last volume of his, *The Disease Concept of Alcoholism*, after a few chapters he finally

[15] M. Keller, Definition of Alcoholism, *Quart. J. Studies Alc.*, 21:125–134, 1960.

ends up by saying, "Well, if the doctors call it a disease, anything the doctors call a disease must be a disease, and so alcoholism is a disease."

Dr. Greenberg Trying to define alcoholism has become in itself a disease.

From the Floor Dr. Greenberg, by your definition, if a man has the constitution of a horse, a tolerant wife, and a private income, he will never be an alcoholic?

Dr. Greenberg Yes, he will end up with cirrhosis of the liver, probably, or polyneuropathy, or central nervous system deterioration, and all of his horses and all of his wives and all of his wealth—

From the Floor I didn't say "horses," the constitution of a horse.

Dr. Greenberg I very carefully included damage to his health, and to his economic or social well-being. If he loses his job, if he loses his family, or if he loses his health, and still continues to drink, this man presumably has lost control, because it is not normal for people to want to continue to hit themselves on the head with a hammer.

From the Floor Dr. Bowman, I wonder if the discussions in the conference so far seem to indicate that a reasonable community goal regarding alcohol would be to turn these disrupted uses into moderate uses. What approaches might you recommend to stimulate a community toward that goal?

Dr. Bowman The question is, in what way can we turn the disruptive forces, the disruptive uses, to moderate uses, which would not be disruptive?

Dr. Greenberg I would not suggest community cocktail parties.

Dr. Bowman I think this becomes a highly individual question with every patient that I see, and what would be good treatment for one man wouldn't be with another.

Now, I know a great many people who have gone to Alcoholics Anonymous and they are adjusting well. I know a number of other persons who have gone to Alcoholics Anonymous and couldn't stand it and started drinking again, and then in some other way they found some solution to it and they are not drinking. One thing didn't work with them; something else did.

I think the great danger is in trying to make generalizations that are going to fit all persons, and the idea that we would all be happy and contented and well adjusted and satisfied with the same set of circumstances. Some of us would be very unhappy with those circumstances, other people would be very happy. So if the alcoholic is a person who is maladjusted to his environment and has all sorts of problems going on, the thing that will satisfy him and get him adjusted might be the very thing that might make somebody else so upset that he would become an alcoholic. I think that is the danger of laying down "You do this, and this, and this," and then people won't drink any more, because as the old saying goes, "What is one man's meat is another man's poison." I think that individual treatment is the one thing that we in psychiatry are insisting on all the time, and we are objecting to this laying down of rigid rules which will apply to everyone. That would be my own view.

ADDICTIVENESS OF ALCOHOL

From the Floor I am thinking in terms now of the compulsive drinker, which has been one definition given of the alcoholic, and I rather gathered there was some discrepancy of feeling here. Can the so-called compulsive drinker, once he has been so-called cured, ever take a drink?

Dr. Bowman The question is whether the so-called compulsive drinker, once he has been cured, can ever take a drink.

I don't know whether anyone else would want to answer that.

Mr. Roueché It has been my experience as a reporter that there is no cure for alcohol addiction, that a cure, to use that word, would imply that he would be able to drink normally. It is my understanding there is no evidence that anyone properly classified as an alcoholic has ever been able to retrace his steps and start out again as a moderate social drinker.

Dr. Bowman I wouldn't agree with that. I think I can point right away to three or four persons, individuals who were alcoholics in every sense of the word. I know one of them who was in Alcoholics Anonymous for a number of years and is now a very well-adjusted individual with a very important position, and I have known him for at least fifteen years. He will take a few drinks with the group and seems to have very good control.

I think, however, these are pretty much museum specimens, and that by and large most of us would say to the individual, "You have got to stop drinking altogether. You are not going to solve your problem and become a moderate drinker." I think that by and large this will be true nine times out of ten, maybe ninety-five out of a hundred, maybe ninety-nine times out of a hundred. There are a few rare exceptions, but this is so seldom that for practical purposes I should say your compulsive drinker cannot drink moderately.

Dr. Greenberg It would be a bad thing to bet on.

From the Floor I wonder if this problem is so different from that of the smoker? There are very few smokers, also, who can restrict themselves and become moderate smokers after having given up smoking, and I wonder if there are not more parallels between the alcoholic and what I call the nicotinic?

Dr. Bowman I should agree there are, from what I have seen —and I am not a smoker—but I know a number of persons who have been both alcoholics and excessive smokers. They have told me that it was much harder for them to quit smoking than it was for them to quit drinking, and I think you do get a certain type of physiological dependency probably from any of these things.

Now a very large percentage of us have a dependency on caffeine. How many people say, "Don't talk to me until I have had my cup of coffee," and they get their caffeine. It is a drug addiction, in one sense, but we don't worry about it particularly, because we don't go out and ruin ourselves or commit antisocial acts because of an extra bit of caffeine. But get some of the amphetamines and you are likely to go out and do that sort of thing—see if you can't race the car at 90 or 100 mph and smash up the car. You get this dependence on these various types of drugs.

I think alcohol really belongs with all these other habit-forming drugs and is probably responsible for more trouble and difficulty than any of the other drugs that we have, and I don't leave opium out of that, either.

Dr. Greenberg I think that is a particularly good question, and it is exactly the question that has driven people in the field of alcohol studies to add an appendage to their definition—I am referring to the definition that was finally agreed upon just a few years back by Dr. Jellinek and others in the World Health Organization. They said, "Look. If it is an addictive drug, then we should include as a necessary part of the definition that there will be withdrawal symptoms when the drug is discontinued," and now this has raised some questions.

There has been some experimental work done. Dr. Isbell, in Kentucky, has definitely produced very severe, very dramatic withdrawal symptoms in human subjects that he exposed to long periods of continuous alcohol intoxication.[16] Now this is a very extreme case, and I think one can certainly say that people who drink to the extent to which he exposed his subjects will constitute a real case of withdrawal symptoms and a real case of addiction.

It has been difficult so far to establish in the more moderate degrees of alcoholism, if you will, to define and really put your finger on something which may be identified as withdrawal symptoms, but maybe in time this will be clarified. This does not apparently occur with cigarettes, if you want to make a difference between the two.

Dr. Bowman There are a group at the present time who are insisting that alcoholism is an addiction in exactly the same way that morphine is. They would like to consider delirium tremens and the convulsions which occur at times with the withdrawal of alcohol as direct withdrawal symptoms of alcohol in the same way that you get symptoms from the morphine addict, and you can bring the barbiturates into this, if you like. You know, if you have a case of barbiturate addiction and you suddenly withdraw a barbiturate, you are likely to throw the patient into a status epilepticus, and he may die. We are very much more cautious in treating our barbiturate addicts and our morphine addicts than we are our alcoholic addicts. There we have another type of true physiological addiction, but we are still arguing this point about alcohol.

From the Floor I postulate, Doctor, that we take 100 people at random and expose them and overexpose them to alcohol, and take another 100 people and expose and overexpose them to any derivative of the poppy. I imagine that when the alcohol is withdrawn, you will find 16 out of the 100 who were addicted; but I imagine that when the derivative of the poppy is withdrawn, you will find probably 99 hooked. In other words, there are a few million alcoholics in 70 or 80 million people who drink. If the substance is addictive, why aren't all of the people who drink hooked?

Dr. Greenberg This comes back to my theory—

Dr. Bowman Will you let me repeat the question. If you exposed 100 people to opium over a long period of time and 100 people to alcohol over a long period of time would you not find that about

[16] H. Isbell, H. J. Fraser, A. Wikler, R. E. Belleville, and A. J. Eisenman, An Experimental Study of the Etiology of "Rum Fits" and Delirium Tremens, *Quart. J. Studies Alc.*, 16:1–33, 1955.

99 per cent of the people exposed to the opium would have a true physiological addiction, whereas a much smaller percentage, the figure mentioned was 16 per cent, would be alcoholics, and therefore are the two strictly comparable?

Dr. Greenberg No, we have no reason to assume, just because we use the same word to describe both addictions, that we have the same phenomenon going on. I started to say, a few moments ago, that this goes back to something like the theory I proposed, that maybe there are not that many people who are liable to become alcoholics.

Dr. Bowman I think we would all agree that it is easier to produce physiological addiction to opium than to alcohol, and this seems pretty well established.

MEDICINE, PHYSIOLOGY, AND LAW

Moderator Dr. Salvatore P. Lucia
Participants Dr. Leonard Goldberg
The Honorable John M. Murtagh

From the Floor It has been said that if a child has a parent who is an alcoholic, his chances of becoming an alcoholic are increased. May we have a discussion on the inheritance of alcoholism?

FAMILIAL ASPECTS OF ALCOHOLISM

Dr. Lucia There are many conditions of unknown etiology which have been conditioned by close proximity with an afflicted person in the very important formative weeks, or possibly months, of a child's contact with its family. Alcoholism may be one of them. A pertinent example of this is the case of schizophrenia, in which a perfectly magnificent study has demonstrated that if you allow a child to remain in an emotionally disturbed atmosphere or in a family in which there is a schizophrenic, the child may grow up to be a schizophrenic, and it will have the same pattern of schizophrenia as its predecessor, its parent or model. But if you take it out of this environment, you now have a child who is not exposed to the pattern and may avoid it—but this has to begin very early, extremely early.

In England, they're doing some very interesting studies on the conditioning of children in the first few weeks of life and have found that the pattern of autistic thinking that leads to schizophrenia is already set at the second week of life. This is fantastic. At an orphanage in Mexico City, where children are seen by one nurse, who covers quite a population, they are picked up, given a bottle, and dropped down again. Now, these youngsters have completely flattened out personalities. They are no problem at all. They are quiet. It does them no good to do anything. This is really conditioning and brainwashing at a very, very important early level. Here's another situation. Right here in this institution not so long ago, a child was born who needed to remain in the hospital, and it was fed by tube for two weeks. The tube was put down four times a day for three days, and then it was eased off. To the sixth month after the child left the hospital, it had great difficulty with the rate of flow of milk through a rubber nipple. This is hard to believe, but this is true. These things begin at a very early age, much earlier than we want to admit, or that we would admit, but in the face of evidence, you cannot deny them. The question comes up about the legality of disrupting this family tie, because I think some of these people have good intentions, but out of ignorance, they don't know what harm they do to the offspring. This means re-education of the entire society; this is a big job.

Judge Murtagh Do I gather that I am to address myself to the question? If I am, I should introduce a modified dissent. Dr. Goldberg has said that the emphasis in Sweden is on society, while in the United States it is on the individual. That is a very pithy way of expressing the truth, and I hope it remains that way in the United States. I'm sure most of us in this room grew up in families that left a little to be desired on the basis of social standards; many of us had to react to traumatic experiences, traceable to the comparative inadequacy of our parents. Notwithstanding that fact, many of us not only survived, but somehow we and our other siblings are, by conventional standards, pretty useful and decent citizens in the community. If we begin an experimentation by reaching into individual families, assessing their inadequacies and so forth, where do we draw the line? The next thing you know, if the father ever drank and went on a bender, for example, we might feel that the state had the right to move in, take Johnny and Jimmy and all the others, and put them in foster homes. It would be a pretty ambitious and expensive program and I don't think a very feasible or practical one. We have in New York a focus on the so-called multi-problem families——a very commendable thing——on a sort of voluntary basis whereby the health authorities move in and try to shore up if you will the families that are manifestly breeding delinquency. Dr. Lucia's basic thesis is eminently sound, I suspect. Notwithstanding that, in a realistic way you can't transform that thesis into action without invading the civil liberties and the rights of many countless families who would be better off left alone and who have every right in the world to be left alone.

SOCIAL AND MEDICAL MANAGEMENT OF
ALCOHOLICS:

Dr. Goldberg   May I add to something you said a moment ago,
Judge. If we accept, as a working hypothesis, that the definition
of the different attitudes towards alcoholism in Sweden and the
United States is right, I think what we are trying to do on both
sides of the Atlantic is to come to some common denominator. You
have adopted one part of our philosophy, and I guess we're adopt-
ing some of yours. For instance, we have begun to respect the life
of the individual. However, we think that there are instances where
you have to commit a patient to treatment because he cannot judge
for himself. With regard to mental patients, I think we could have
agreed. But I'm not so sure that we do agree on it now, because
we now know that there are quite a few mental diseases which can
be treated with chemical aids, so you don't have to have them in a
closed institution any longer. You can have them in an open institution. This is one field where the darkness is no more, and this has
told us that we don't have to commit so many patients as before.

There's another basic idea of how we feel with regard to civil
commitment. We would like the judge, as the neutral individual
in this procedure, to help protect the individual from the doctor
who would have him treated. This is why we like the court procedure
in certain cases of commitment—in order to have the law behind
us, not only the wish of the doctor. We think this procedure protects the rights of the individual more than if commitment is left
solely up to the doctor.

From the Floor   This goes back to the basic system which we
have here in the United States—the system of checks and balances.
When we can get two opinions, nobody is going to get railroaded,
so to speak. On the other hand, when you have a tubercular person, whether he wants to be treated or not, he has to be removed
from society to be treated, so he won't infect other people. This
may pertain to the question we were considering before, about dope
addicts or alcoholics—how can a man who's sick both mentally and
physically make a rational judgment as to whether he needs treatment or not? This is something that society has to do.

Dr. Goldberg   We have used civil commitments of alcoholics,
and with the years, fewer and fewer are committed by this law. We
have nothing of this kind in existence with regard to narcotic ad-

dicts, because up to a few years ago, we had only a very few narcotic addicts. Shall we force them into treatment? Should we adopt some kind of provisional civil commitment for a few years and see how it works? Or shall we only confine certain cases?

Dr. Lucia I think there's a point that ought to be brought out here, since it was asked. In presenting our approach to tuberculosis on the one hand, and leprosy on the other, someone said that we have this built-in clause in the public health law that enables us to invoke commitment when necessary. But it's a very difficult thing, under the guise of public health, to condemn someone to a lazaret without this thing being aired and his civil rights protected. Now, the better way, and the way the health officers of this state have found works, is to discuss and educate the person who needs to retire himself from the community. We would have a lot of difficulty if you came in with an arm of the law and made something mandatory in this respect, although it is incorporated in our so-called public health law, but I don't think our public health law is involved with the civil law.

Dr. Goldberg May I just add one thing? According to our rules for commitment of alcoholics, any doctor according to law had to report his case to a council, but it is understood that his right to keep it secret remains. He doesn't have to report the case, if it helps him keep in contact with his patients. This is one of the new factors in treatment—people now know that doctors do not necessarily report them, and therefore they can seek the help of a doctor at an earlier stage in their illness.

From the Floor Dr. Lucia, are you suggesting that we have voluntary commitment for alcoholics?

Dr. Lucia No—I don't know. I must admit that I haven't spent too much time on alcoholism, and so my opinion would be of no value to you.

From the Floor I think it's a pretty sad commentary, really, perhaps on this whole conference, and maybe on your profession in general, that you're not aware of even the fact of what kind of proceedings can take place for a person with this sort of problem, what sort of facilities are available, and what sort of public relations could be done in this field.

Dr. Lucia It isn't that I am ignorant of this thing, or that I am unaware—it is that I feel that a great deal of harm might be done by the opinion of someone who is not an expert on this aspect of the problem. And I feel very strongly about anything that has to do with a person's approach to living, or with his health, which is his most important asset. I think you can accomplish a great deal in our society by educational means. Now sometimes you call it indoctrination, but I feel that in certain areas we can't come down with the full mallet of the law.

I would rather take a person who comes to me with poor eyesight and make sure that he gets into the hand of a topnotch ophthalmologist, and I feel the same way about these other problems. It isn't a matter of ignorance; it's a matter of exercising careful judgment, that you do no harm, and that you do not estrange, or produce a defense reaction, a hostile reaction, in a person with whom you have to deal. This is extremely important.

From the Floor   I have two points: first of all, I think that the position in which the medical profession puts itself, in this culture, requires that the doctors should be well versed in the particular techniques of how to treat someone with this sort of problem. It's incumbent upon them to know how to do this, because they are the people who are going to be meeting the alcoholic and his problems.

Dr. Lucia   I don't want to argue with you, but frankly, I think they do a fairly good job.

From the Floor   I was trying to envision the person who was tuberculous who would voluntarily put himself away, recognizing the contagiousness of his disease, also the necessity for prolonged respite somewhere, and trying to correlate this with the problem of the alcoholic who cannot envision himself going away to be treated.

Dr. Lucia   When it comes to the question of tuberculosis, you are dealing with a totally different psychic pattern. And still, I think that you wouldn't get anywhere if you went up to a person and said, "Look, boy, you're a tuberculous individual, and you're a menace to the community." That is not the way to handle it. And it's been proven over and over again that that is not the way to handle it. I hope that I have transmitted to you the kind of delicate relationships which the doctor involves himself in and indulges in, referable to tuberculosis, and that he might be able to apply this pattern to alcoholism if that is the way we wish to develop it.

From the Floor   I was more interested in public information, so that the alcoholic will know that there is some way he can find help.

Dr. Lucia You've hit on something that's very near to my heart. Very often, I've told a person, "You know, you could get a great deal from Christian Science." I was afraid to recommend a psychiatrist, but I knew that a Christian Scientist might be able to give him some help. Often a person who realizes there is a defect in his ability to handle imbibed alcohol will search out help among his friends, or go to Alcoholics Anonymous, which offers a much better program than orthodox medicine has been able to develop. But when you ask a person from Alcoholics Anonymous, as I've done on many an occasion, How do you regard a drink? What is your program for tomorrow and after tomorrow? They'd say, "Doctor, we're not worried about that at all. We're worried about the present only, today. We don't stop to philosophize." Is that your experience?

From the Floor Yes.

From the Floor Dr. Goldberg, you stated that in Sweden you are able to treat alcoholics under court order. Is that correct? Do they remain with you?

Dr. Goldberg Under the old law, before 1955, the only ones who could be committed for treatment were very severe cases. Now this law has expanded, and it means treatment as such, and only a very little part of it refers to civil commitment. But there are two points. It is not uncommon today for the courts to suspend a sentence if the person agrees to undergo treatment. We refer them for treatment under a suspended sentence. And here is a queer thing—if you look at a homogeneous population of alcoholics and try to find out what happens to them after five years, you will find that those who were committed for treatment had even a better chance than those who asked for treatment voluntarily. This is very interesting. This shows that the element of commitment might have, for some cases at least, some value, but may I add something else?

There was a definite reason why earlier today I brought in the word "epidemiology." It means the scientific study of how diseases spread in society, and I think this is the scientific approach to the problem of alcoholism in society which has not been tried very widely. This is point one: we should apply new scientific methods to see how alcoholism spreads in society, and whether this has a bearing on the problem, because if we know something about how it spreads, we will know where to begin prevention and teaching.

The other point is that epidemiology is part of public health, and if alcoholism is a public health problem, you can look at it in a detached way; it doesn't involve morality or teetotalers on one side, or Alcoholics Anonymous on the other. This is a public health problem, which has a bearing on every one of us. This is one way of trying to understand how alcoholism can be treated in a purely detached way, as we do with other diseases. It is odd, but if we can find the proper word for something, people suddenly realize maybe it *is* like that, although we thought it was quite different, and this is why we put in the term epidemiology.

From the Floor   May I ask you if you consider alcoholism to be a chronic disease?

Dr. Goldberg   I know that people speak of acute and chronic alcoholism, but I should think that the word alcoholism means something which is chronic, which has a long history. This history can be thirty days or it can be eleven years—but it usually is a long history.

EDUCATION ABOUT ALCOHOL

From the Floor   Dr. Goldberg, in general, do you have in your country a special place in your curriculum for education on alcoholism?

Dr. Goldberg   Yes, we have, and you remember that Dr. Bruun said that in Finland, the education in children's schools is mostly done by the temperance movement. We have a semigovernmental agency for the spreading of information, which started out as part of a temperance movement, sixty years ago, and then became governmental. One of its purposes is to provide material for objective teaching in schools. The teaching in schools is, if possible, not based on any moralistic view at all but is an attempt to teach the basic facts. Therefore, alcohol has to be dealt with at various stages in school, in biology, in social history.

From the Floor   At what age?

Dr. Goldberg   Oh, it should start somewhere at the age of ten, in a very simple way, and then it should go up, all the way up through the grades. Of course, the type of information given should all the time apply to the educational level of the child, but it should be objective, very definitely objective. We tried in all those courses to inform the teachers that they should never forget that when they speak about alcohol, the child's parents can be alcoholics, and this child has to go on in his class. The subject of alcoholism must be put in such a way that this child can still be an integral part of his class. This is very difficult for a teacher to undertake, and I agree they don't know what to say about it.

From the Floor Here in California it's required to teach about alcohol in the junior high school curriculum.

Dr. Goldberg I can tell how I think some of the teachers go about this. I think a few of them take a biological problem, say the central nervous system, and spend five minutes out of sixty indicating the effects of alcohol on certain functions. Also, I think it's very good to tell children that drinking and driving is one example where alcohol interferes with the body, because this is such a simple fact to state.

From the Floor Has a study been made on the ratio of teenagers who become alcoholics, or those who start to become alcoholics by drinking before the age of twenty-one, compared with those who start afterwards?

Dr. Goldberg No. We have the figures, actually, but we have not had time to analyze them yet, and I wouldn't even dare to make any kind of a prediction of what we might find. But I can tell you one thing, and this is that the teen-agers' habits have changed very definitely in the last few years. I don't know whether we discussed in this group what happened after the abolition of our rationing system. We had a decrease in intake of alcohol by the moderate drinkers, but we have a definite increase in the drinking by teenagers. This is something to be concerned about, and we don't know what to do about it right now.

From the Floor Is that because of the accessibility?

Dr. Goldberg Yes, we think so. There are many other things involved. All the factors involved in juvenile delinquency, and so on, go into it. But I can only tell you one thing; when we made a study on drunken drivers back in 1949, the drunken drivers were not the teen-agers. This was the time when the black leather jackets and gangs and so on were in vogue, but the money they had went on the bike, on the motorcycle. Today, all these youngsters have a salary. They don't have bikes any longer; they have cars and they have girls, and they drink alcohol. So the teen-agers have changed, definitely changed, not only their attitude, but their whole behavior. This is all I can tell you.

From the Floor   Have any studies been made on the attitude of the general population towards the consumption of alcohol, as, for example, the Kinsey sex studies?

Dr. Goldberg   We are starting.

From the Floor   Wouldn't it be wise to investigate why some people don't become alcoholics and why others do?

Dr. Goldberg   You have, in those few words, put the label on the study we are trying to conduct. And the first one started was the study to which Dr. Bruun referred, a comparative study of teen-age drinking—I mean, not abuse, but attitudes and drinking experience in the four capitals, Copenhagen, Helsinki, Oslo, Stockholm, at the same time. What we are thinking of doing is a special study in the four capitals, and of course, to start long-term studies on drinking behavior.

TREATMENT OF ALCOHOLICS

From the Floor   Could I ask if your laboratory treats alcoholism in a kind of detached sort of way, as you would treat other diseases?

Dr. Goldberg   Yes, but I'm afraid that my answer is how I would wish alcoholics to be treated. You see, we have an old social system in existence in Sweden which started in 1917 and stopped in 1955. This system had one aim—this is why civil commitment was in this system—to protect society against the alcoholic. You, in this country, have no backlog of such social implications. So when you started in 1944 with the Yale Plan clinic, you started with a medical approach to the problem. This what we have adopted today. Our new laws, and our attitude today, are adapted to a medical approach. We're trying to get away from the social approach, with civil commitment. This is why I am saying that we are trying to come near to the American pattern. Maybe you will adopt some of our other attitudes, I don't know. But in essence this new approach means that alcoholism can be looked upon as a disease, which means that alcoholics should be able to go to a doctor without having to be reported.

When Antabuse was introduced, it became popular not so much because it might cure people but because there were so many who perhaps thought, "This is one way of going to a doctor, getting a pill, and nobody will know that I am being treated." This made a large number of patients come to doctors at an early stage.

Then, of course, you all realize it doesn't matter so much whether you give medicine or what you do—it's the personality of the person who treats which, I think, is one of the most important things— much more than any medicine. Are you with me, Dr. Lucia?

Dr. Lucia I'm with you 100 per cent.

Dr. Goldberg I think this is very important. In essence what you can do is to go to a doctor. Very few doctors know what to do, but they will refer cases to a few psychiatrists and internal medicine men who are trying to specialize in this field, who have some knowledge about it. We are setting up outpatient clinics. One of these is located next to the cancer clinic. This pattern is taken from Richmond, Virginia, where they have a ward of this kind right in the middle of a general hospital. You see, we get our ideas from different places. In the outpatient clinic we take care of people at an early stage. We are trying to educate, and we have a combined attack on industry through the labor unions, through our employers' association, and through the doctors. All these three go together in an attempt to tell industry about the man in industry who drinks excessively—not to fire him but to treat him. We got this program from Consolidated Edison and other places. For severe cases, we can resort to the possibility of civil commitment, and 2,000 out of 100,000 are committed in this way. I don't think this is good at all. Very few of us think it's good, and this is the fight between the medical man today and those engaged in the social agencies. I think that the alcoholic farm institution isn't good at all, because they just stay there. We have tried to get group therapy started, and we have a few groups of this kind which we have patterned after yours. You know, things always taste better when they come from a foreign country. This is why I don't think that we can tell you very many new things, because we have learned them from over here.

From the Floor Are the Alcoholics Anonymous active in Sweden?

Dr. Goldberg We have a very small group of Alcoholics Anonymous, but we have a society with about twenty-five thousand members, with a similar program, who don't call themselves Alcoholics Anonymous, and they don't have the religious part so strong. And the fact which might startle you is that they are state supported. They get state support, which means that the government has realized that they play an integral part in the program of helping alcoholics. This cannot be too strongly emphasized.

From the Floor   Do you recommend it?

Dr. Goldberg   For some people, yes.

From the Floor   Would you recommend that this country have these state supported organizations?

Dr. Goldberg   Oh, this is not my part to discuss, definitely not. You know, we have different philosophies about state support.

From the Floor   Judge Murtagh, in your lecture you spoke of the law pertaining to alcoholics. How can something be done about the law if it is a bad law?

Judge Murtagh   It's rather hard. There was a decision of the Supreme Court of the United States as recently as the year 1960 that I think gives thorough support to my thinking. It concerned an individual in Louisville, Kentucky, who was arrested on a so-called vagrancy and disorderly conduct charge. He was essentially a derelict, and the Supreme Court of the United States reversed the conviction in a unanimous opinion, and implicit in the decision is a concern about the widespread use of the police technique to curb human drunkenness and to curb human inadequacy. The decision, incidentally, is eloquently written about in the November, 1961 issue of *Reader's Digest*. But for the court to rule that in an individual case, and for the court to implement it into the police administration of the various states, is a little difficult.

In 1925, the Supreme Court of the United States showed a similar wisdom with regard to the problem of drug addiction, and yet notwithstanding the fact that it so ruled, the Treasury Department of the United States continues an administration of our laws which I think is in violation of the laws, but in any event it constitutes to all intents and purposes the practice and the law of the United States. It's difficult to make a reality of special thinking, whether it's correct or otherwise. It's one thing for the court to rule and it's another thing for that to become police practice and government practice.

From the Floor   I'd like to ask: Isn't it strange that alcoholics prepare their own beverages?

Judge Murtagh   Alcoholics do not prepare their own beverages to any substantial extent. Some of the more deprived areas, because of extreme tax regulation, have a problem of illicit liquor. Some of your skid row areas seek their alcohol in rather devious means, but the use of illegal liquor by alcoholics is a minor aspect of the entire problem.

From the Floor   Would a person who prepared his own liquor be violating the law?

Judge Murtagh   Yes, undoubtedly, he would be violating Federal law.

From the Floor   But he could manufacture a certain amount of his own wine?

Judge Murtagh   I think he could probably do that legally. But that isn't a part of the problem.

Dr. Lucia   Any other questions? Then I'm going to ask Judge Murtagh to give us a summary and a send-off into the future of the solution of some of our problems.

Judge Murtagh   Oh, I wouldn't attempt a summary. Needless to say, I would congratulate the University on an excellent symposium. I would congratulate each and every one of you on your dedication, these several days, to trying to learn something about the problem, and suggest to you that doubtless you feel as I did when I attended the school at Yale in 1953, that the main thing that we learn at a session of this kind is not so much specifics with regard to the social problem under study but rather a bit of a scientific approach to all problems of human behavior. Even though some of those who held forth today might seem opinionated, I would suggest that the one virtue of a session such as this is that we tend to get less opinionated. We become aware of the necessity of employing the knowledge of all disciplines and to question and requestion constantly those things that we accept as facts.

PHARMACOLOGY, MEDICINE, AND PSYCHOLOGY

Moderator   Dr. Chauncey D. Leake
Participants   Dr. Giorgio Lolli and Dr. Karl H. Pribram

Dr. Leake   Maybe you have some specific questions to start our discussion.

THRESHOLD EFFECTS OF ALCOHOL

From the Floor   This question of threshold, which has been discussed previously, I should like somebody to take up on the basis of the various aspects. I have been told that threshold varies with different states and different levels. I'm thinking about individuals, let's say the driver of an automobile.

Dr. Leake   All right, that's a very practical problem. I think I would say right away that even the smallest amount of alcohol, any drink, a cocktail, a glass of beer, or a glass of wine, can have in itself a measurable effect in producing some degree of altered reflex activity, some degree of slight incoordination.

From the Floor   All right. Now, where does that become material in respect to vision or audition—in respect to perception and responses?

Dr. Leake   At much higher levels than that of which I just spoke. You can have many types of measurement. For example, you can measure the speed of reflex reaction to a given stimulus. That was discussed in one of our papers yesterday, and it was said that at the 0.05 per cent blood alcohol level and lower you get speeding up of the activity of the central reflexes, but the higher and more complicated activities begin to show some effect only at a much higher level. I would expect you to have some threshold effect at, say, 0.2 per cent. Now you asked about visual or auditory responses. They are probably affected at a higher level.

From the Floor   That wasn't true according to the Drew studies. Even at 0.02 per cent I thought he had some narrowing of the visual field.

Dr. Leake   Oh yes, narrowing down. OK. All right, then, that's it.

Dr. Lolli   We have seen some changes of flicker frequency at 0.03 per cent on an empty stomach; however, the changes did not appear if the individuals were fat, for instance. After a meal of 1500 calories with the same blood alcohol concentration, those changes did not appear.

From the Floor   How about personality shift?

Dr. Lolli   Well, I think that it's very difficult to speak in terms of individuals. You have to speak more or less in terms of statistics. We can only repeat what has to a certain extent already been stated.

Dr. Leake   Supposing we take the average personality picture of an individual, as measured by average blood pressure, pulse, respiration, muscle tension, and all the things that make up personality. Now, if the individual is at a higher level of activity, as a result of anxiety, or fear, or other emotional factor, stress of any sort—this produces a level which you might call excitement. You will get one level of response to alcohol. But if the individual goes progressively downwards, as a result of drugs or otherwise, the base level is one of depression, and these various functions that are correlated with personality are reduced. You could also get another level of response to alcohol, then. Next comes the picture of delirium; then, a picture of anesthesia, and then comes the level of coma. Now, alcohol always lowers the overall biological activity of the individual; it depends on where you're starting.

You can start with the person at the lowest level—the threshold value—the amount of alcohol that will produce that effect. If you're dealing with a statistically average person, then that's the average effect. But in real life you're never dealing with an average person. They may be depressed to begin with, in which case the same dose of alcohol will produce a considerable tendency toward delirium. Or they may be excited, and when you give the same dose of alcohol here, what do you do? You don't do much. You don't even bring them down to an average normal.

From the Floor   Perhaps it would help you if I clarify my position. I'm a police officer; I make arrests.

Dr. Leake   All right, you're dealing with that level, and you want to know what alcohol does.

Police Officer   I want to know where the boundary lines can come into play. I want to have a better conception of what you mean when you say threshold. A threshold could be a threshold of visual impairment, a threshold of manual dexterity impairment, or some other threshold. Alcohol affects people differently at different alcohol levels. What I was hoping to get was a feedback of discussion on these different levels, where these impairments occurred, and what we might expect to find in the way of a level in a particular individual.

Dr. Leake Well, I think that would depend largely on the individual that you are examining, because I'm quite confident that the threshold might vary with regard to the different criteria that you have used.

Dr. Pribram At different times in the individual's history, also, and the situation will make a difference. I refer you to Professor Drew's paper for the actual statistics in a very tightly controlled laboratory situation in which driving an automobile-like instrument was used.[1] I think for legal purposes this is your best evidence. Actually, I think his paper is going to be a classic in its field. I think it will be referred to over and over again, because here you have the best kind of study possible.

Dr. Lolli I should like to add that the rules, by and large, are given. The instructions given to the police officers in the several states about concentrations of 0.15 per cent alcohol in the blood as a definite indication of intoxication still stand. I mean there is a valid correlation between the degree of impairment and concentrations above 0.15 per cent. Between 0.05 per cent and 0.15 per cent the correlations are less clear. There is the broad area which you call "under the influence," where in some individuals you see impairment, in other individuals you see nothing, and in some individuals you see also some improvement, sometimes.

Police Officer The thing that I have noticed is that I find individuals who are remarkably normal in their appearance but when tested have abnormal amounts of alcohol in them.

Dr. Pribram Did you hear Drew's paper?

Police Officer Yes, I did.

Dr. Pribram Do you remember the slowed-down person who did everything a little more deliberately and actually functioned very

---

[1] See above, pp. 102–105. See also G. C. Drew, W. P. Colquhoun, and H. A. Long, Effect of Small Doses of Alcohol on a Skill Resembling Driving, *Brit. Med. J.*, 2:993–999, 1958.

well, provided he was allowed to go at his own pace? But as soon as he was pushed, then he began to disintegrate. All kinds of things happen, not just slowing down but this very careful controlling of self, and these people look very good. You can't see the control; you see, they're a little overcontrolled.

Dr. Lolli Going back to Drew, and trying to answer your question of threshold, I think that what Drew points out is that there is no such detectable threshold at this stage of our knowledge and with the method that we use for testing individuals. He has not been able to find a threshold. As soon as even the tiniest amount of alcohol appears in the blood, some individuals are affected, which doesn't mean affected in the sense of impairment. Some are affected in the sense of some improvement of their functions. But even the tiniest amount of alcohol might cause some changes.

Dr. Leake It seems to me there is a psychological factor involved, too. I would expect a police officer, or any authority who is called upon to administer a law, to seek an absolute figure, a precise figure. Unfortunately, with regard to alcohol, the scientific information does not justify that exactly. It's quite as Dr. Lolli said; there's a long area where you can say "they're under the influence," but what influence? When you come up to 0.15 per cent blood alcohol, then everyone is in agreement.

EXCESSES IN EATING AND DRINKING

From the Floor Dr. Lolli, would you speak on the relative concern for nutrition as compared to alcohol. Maybe in your studies you wondered sometimes if we shouldn't think of "foodism" like "alcoholism."

Dr. Lolli In that case, I should be sick of that illness.

From the Floor Well, it seems to me that we make a great fuss about this. Perhaps we should concern ourselves with these people as well as with those who show indiscretions with alcohol.

Dr. Lolli I think we do concern ourselves a good deal with our indiscretions with food.

From the Floor But overeating is not as socially unacceptable as overdrinking.

Dr. Lolli No, because we do damage mostly only to ourselves with overeating.

From the Floor   When Dr. Balboni spoke, she indicated that this has some direct bearing on our emotional well-being, which of course may affect other individuals in the way that alcohol does.

Dr. Lolli   Yes, but it is not so direct. Unquestionably, anyone who has worked with alcoholics, or addicted drinkers, knows that the antisocial type of behavior which you observe after the ingestion of large amounts of alcohol is not comparable with what happens when an individual eats too much. We deal with two different sets of phenomena. I would say the social impact is far greater. There is a difference.

Dr. Leake   There is a point of interest on which I know Dr. Pribram will correct me, if I misstate it. You see, we always like to try to explain things in terms of physics and chemistry in one way or another, and in part you're dealing with a psychological factor that we haven't explored as yet in this manner. This is the factor of satisfaction. And in connection with appetite, which is the drive, in part, for self-preservation—seeking food enough to keep ourselves going—there seems to be not only a center in the brain stem that provides that drive, but there is also another center that may give the sense of satiety, or satisfaction, and the drive ceases. You see, if there are two centers this way, either one can be stimulated or inhibited. Now, you may stimulate the appetite center and the individual eats more. If you cut out the inhibitory center, which you can do in experimental animals, they just eat and eat and eat and get enormously fat, because they have nothing to stop them. On the other hand, you may either stimulate the satiety center or inhibit it. And you see, you have the reciprocal effects then. Now insofar as alcohol is concerned, it may operate in much the same way that food itself operates, or blood sugar, probably, in stimulating the satiety center, which then cuts down the desire, or appetite. That seems to be something of a factor in alcohol. I don't know. But the point you are raising, you see, has ramifications perhaps beyond what you thought.

Dr. Pribram   May I make an emendation here, that the satiety center isn't the same thing as the glucostat, for instance, which regulates it. It may be a much more diffuse mechanism. I shouldn't even use the word "center," which receives input from a lot of different sources and which then shuts off the feeding mechanism.

Dr. Leake   And some of those may be from the cortex, and learnable, or conditioned.

Dr. Pribram I should say most of them. I think most of them are quite diffuse ramifications of neural mass which are programmed by experience

Dr. Leake But you see, this point of satisfaction comes into the whole picture of alcohol very significantly, I think, as in the skid row people of whom we heard, who take enough alcohol to get a satisfying plateau of relief from whatever is bothering them, their loneliness or anything else.

From the Floor Dr. Lolli's interest here is psychodietetics. To me this term has neither a denotation nor a connotation, but I would be very interested, Dr. Lolli, to know how these two got together.

Dr. Lolli Well, it means just the psychological and social aspects of nutrition. It includes a variety of things, treatment approaches, prevention approaches, methods of research. Going specifically back to your question about similarities or differences between excessive eating and excessive drinking, which I think is what you asked, I concur with what has been said about the possibility of neurological causes for this trouble, which, however, do not rule out a variety of social factors which might interplay with them. For instance, it's just enough to look up the telephone directory of New York City and see how many Italian or Jewish or German restaurants operate in New York. Then you look up and see how many English restaurants or Irish restaurants operate. You find very few of them. Then you try to establish some correlations between incidence of obesity among the Jews, the Italians, and, say, the Irish and the English, and you see some very substantial differences. Then you go and look at literature, or the English novel, or the history of England, and look at the pictures of the English kings of two or three centuries ago, at the time they were having those long, drawn-out banquets which are so well described in some beautiful English prose. And you compare the English kings of that time with Queen Elizabeth, and with her father, who was skinny. It seems that at a certain time of history the English lost the pleasure of having Italian or French cooks, and of getting fat.

Dr. Pribram I want to say simply that it's not so bad as all that today. I went to London the summer before last and for the first time I could enjoy food there.

Dr. Leake Social acceptance is the important point, too, when you consider, for example, that in Hawaii it is the mark of distinction for the native Hawaiian to be very fat, and they eat plenty to get that way.

Dr. Lolli The first time I landed in New Haven, Connecticut, the landlady made me sit on a chair, which was of this width [very wide]—and said, "You should feel privileged to sit here, because here President Taft sat." Well, he was President of the United States. But I don't think that any President of the United States would be allowed to be fat any more.

CONDITIONAL FUNCTIONS OF ALCOHOL

From the Floor Dr. Leake, I just want to clarify something in my mind. It's a different subject. Yesterday, someone said that things such as judgment were the first to be depressed; in other words the higher centers of the mind were depressed first. And then there was a movie of the cat, if you recall, and there was an indication at that point that the most recently acquired skills and knowledge were the first to leave the individual. Now, were these the same things they were talking about, or is this now something different?

Dr. Pribram Remember, I asked that question of Dr. Masserman, because he kept talking as if the most recently acquired were also the most complex. And he finally admitted in the panel that he was talking about the most recently acquired rather than the most complex. So he made the distinction later, in the panel, and suggested that it was the most recently acquired and not necessarily the most complex behaviors which were depressed in his experiments. I'm not sure, if you went over this with him, that he'd stick to that, but that was his answer in the panel. I don't think we know; I don't think that question has been clearly answered in the laboratory, but so far it seems to depress the most recently acquired skill. The only thing that I would add to that is this, that most of us are constantly making judgments, and guiding our behavior, on the basis of choices of already learned material. As adults, we are not acquiring very primitive, new memory tracings, and I think, therefore, it is usually a matter of choice rather than a matter of learning.

Dr. Leake And yet, in connection with alcohol, no matter how old we get, I think it is important to remember that we can become conditioned, even as we go along in age, and we also can become deconditioned, or reconditioned. But we don't know as much, certainly, as we should know about the conditional process.

Dr. Pribram Reconditioned, but I'm not so sure about the deconditioned.

Dr. Leake Well, all right, reconditioned then. No, I agree with you. I'm not so sure about it. But in regard to alcohol, conditioning is a very strong factor in the responses to alcohol, whether in subjective mood on the part of the individual, or the behavior he exhibits on the social level. Wouldn't you agree with me on that? Alcohol is a powerful factor in the conditioning process in individuals who experiment with it.

Dr. Pribram Well, let's put this in another way, perhaps without using the word conditioning which in itself is not completely defined; there are various types of so-called conditioning. Let's just talk about the situational impact and the effect of drugs, of which alcohol is one. We're finding out that not only with alcohol but with drugs such as adrenalin, benzedrine, the tranquilizers, and so on, that with all of them it is extremely important to specify the conditions under which they're given. Take, for instance, adrenalin, which has the physiological effect of causing excitement, of getting the organism stirred up. Now, if you put a group of people in an examination situation, and make it a difficult affair, mentioning that whatever they do on the test is going to go in the files, why the people become very anxious while taking the test, and afterwards may be quite depressed and feel that they have done miserably, and maybe even have some paranoid feelings towards the tester. On the other hand, if you place the same group of people, or another group but with the same drugs and controls, in a test situation like this, and surround them with other people saying, "well, this is just a joke, you know; it isn't a very hard test anyway," and "isn't this a ball," and "isn't it fun to play games like this," and "you'd think that the guys would have better sense than to spend their time doing this, but we might as well play along; we're getting well paid," and so on and so forth. If you get this mood going, then the people with adrenalin, as compared with the controls who had saline injections, come out very euphoric; they've done well, and feel it was a good way to spend their time and earn money. So, depending on the situational determinants in this test, an entirely different sort of behavior and psychology will come out of it.

Dr. Leake Now how about the results of the test itself?

Dr. Pribram The results of the test I don't know. I don't even know whether they were graded.

Dr. Leake Well, now this is important, again, because we speak commonly about the behavior under alcohol, and I think that is always something that really, at least in judgment, is expressed at a social level; whereas mood is the individual's feeling. And the individual, of course, knows how he behaves, but the character of his behavior may be totally different to him from the way in which society judges it.

Dr. Lolli I should like to add a word in reference to judgment and ask a question of Dr. Pribram. Don't you think that this word judgment is a little dangerous? I mean, we tested a number of subjects in different ways—for example, judging how much time they spent in driving a car, judging how many beats a second a metronome plays, and you see sometimes opposite results with the same concentration of alcohol. One judgment test improves; another is impaired. However, we often say that judgment is affected at this or that blood alcohol level. Don't you think it would be—I know you wouldn't do it as a trained psychologist, but you still read it in textbooks—an abstract concept, to speak of judgment, instead of speaking of the concrete realities of how people behave in a given situation, and what a given test does? I think this is fundamental in this field.

Dr. Pribram This is *so* important. You can't say threshold; you can't say judgment; you've got to say—what?

From the Floor In line with what the *Chronicle* attributed to you, if I am not mistaken, Dr. Lolli, perhaps one should be advised professionally about his own judgment about his own use of alcohol. Is this in relationship with what you're talking about? Yesterday I think you called it inefficiency, didn't you?

Dr. Pribram It's perfectly all right to be inefficient, for some. For instance, let me give you an example. I had gone, when I was dead tired, to give a talk, and someone who knows me very well, said afterwards, "Gee, that was a good talk; for once you were slow enough so people could understand you." You see? Inefficient, I wasn't ahead; I wasn't jumping, and this was good for the audience. And so a little bit of fatigue, a little bit of inefficiency, was just the thing we wanted.

From the Floor I think Dr. Lolli, though, is primarily concerned, at least in part, with the effect of alcohol insofar as we want to be efficient. Isn't that correct, Dr. Lolli?

STANDARDIZATION OF RESEARCH TOOLS

Dr. Lolli   Yes. My remark, the very last remark, dealt with something a little different. I do feel that in this field of alcohol many of us speak very often in terms of abstract generalities instead of going down to concrete, real facts as they occur, and from a few experiments they then draw conclusions as to whether speed is affected, judgment is affected, moral controls, the ability to distinguish right from wrong, and so on and so forth. On the other hand, the only thing that we can say at this stage is how a tiny little facet of our personality is affected or is tested in a given specific manner. I also think that there is a tremendous job to be done by all of us to standardize some tests to be used on a kind of national-international basis, a simple psychological and physiological test, which we would all stick to for a year, for two years, for three years, until we get some operable type of material. After all, we do this for blood sugars; we do it for other biological constants; why shouldn't we do it for behavior tests? And it is possible to do it.

Dr. Pribram   It is certainly possible. The only thing is that it takes a fair amount of money. I think this probably is what has held the thing back. You see, to set up a decent behavioral laboratory, let's say to do some psychophysical judgments, to do operant-conditioning techniques and a few motor-skill problems, such as an automatic trainer, Link-type or some modification, would take a fair amount of money. It's much easier to set up a biochemical laboratory. Or let me put it this way—money is more easily available for an atomic reactor today than to set up a behavioral laboratory.

Dr. Lolli   Yes, Doctor, but there are still—and I'm not going to tell you this, because you know this much better than I do—there are still some very simple psychological tests, like tapping, like a Toulouse-Lautrec correction of errors. I mean, tests which carry universal value because they are known all over the world. Some intelligence tests which could be set up at the price of very little money—not more than standardizing blood alcohol determinations. It is a matter of getting together and agreeing to work for a year with some specific tools—I mean even at the cost of getting rid of them after a year.

Dr. Leake   Well, in the field of clinical psychology there are batteries of tests, including the Rorschach and the thematic apperception, or a dozen others, that can be brought together as a unit for estimating the personality characteristics of the individual, in particular to indicate the emotional loads that that individual may be carrying, consciously or unconsciously—and they're getting to be quite precise. Now as far as I know, they have been used only in certain instances, sporadically, for particular patients. There is as yet no systematic study using these methods on alcoholics, or on people who use alcohol, or to find out perhaps why it is that they find alcohol useful for suppressing their particular emotional load or what difference may be induced by alcohol in individuals who carry a serious emotional load.

Dr. Pribram   I would beg to differ there. These tests are *not* standardized. These tests are always dependent upon verbal report of introspective data, and those are the very things that are changed by the alcohol. An instrumental test is better.

Dr. Leake   Oh no, I agree with you that they are not standardized. You see, I placed here certain physiological correlates associated with the personality picture of an individual, if you wish to put it on the basis of depression or excitement.

Dr. Pribram   Tapping, tapping is better than the Rorschach and all the other things put together.

Dr. Leake   All right—blood pressure, pulse, and respiration.

From the Floor   The more complex measurements of our behavior, whether or not we can standardize them, are important, and I think really that the problem of getting a test that we can use internationally is one of personal pride. Now I get into this in my own business of education. We can go right down the street and get an excellent instrument to use, but no, we must fabricate our own and put our name on it.

Dr. Lolli   I dare say that with a metronome in front of you, with a pencil, with a tapping instrumentation—these are three things that you can buy for thirty dollars, and with them you can do a lot of testing and start with the fundamentals.

From the Floor   That would be testing purely physical skills, wouldn't it?

Dr. Lolli   Physical, as well as mental, if you want to call them mental; none of these skills is strictly physical or strictly mental.

From the Floor   Would you talk on the nature of the ramifications of intoxication between 0.05 per cent and 0.15 per cent. Now we say that in one person the results will come much sooner than in another, so we have this wide range. Can we be absolute about any-thing?

Dr. Lolli I think that we have to think also in terms of statistical truths. Won't you agree on this? Let's go back for a minute to the tapping. We have evidence that some healthy individuals, age twenty-five, students of medicine, more or less of the same weight, and of the same height, without alcohol in their system, tap a given number of times a minute when prodded to tap at a faster speed. We also have evidence that if you build up in the blood stream a certain concentration of alcohol, the same individuals tap at a faster speed. You give the statistician both sets of data. He tells you whether the difference is, or is not, significant. Now we have tools for answering your question, I think.

ALCOHOL IN MEDICINE AND NUTRITION

Dr. Leake You know, an interesting point about reaching agreement—we're discussing in this conference alcohol and civiliza-tion, and reaching agreement is an enormously important aspect of the civilizing process. Certainly I think experience has indicated that the judicious use of alcohol in connection with negotiations leading to an agreement can be really quite effective. This is just experience, but there's something very deep in that the alcohol itself, you see, may cut across the petty irritations or annoyances, and so on, that are involved in our aggressiveness, or our submissiveness, or other aspects of our psychological make-up—alcohol may tend to level them out for all of us. Under those circumstances, agreement is more readily achieved.

There are lots of aspects to this whole matter that I think are worth exploring. I'm interested in alcohol as a drug—I'm a pharma-cologist. I'm interested in the possibility of its rational use as a medicinal agent, and that has been explored to some extent very wittily and brilliantly by Bill Dock. But you see, there are certain social factors involved in looking at it as a medicinal agent. Now, from the standpoint of nutrition, or something of that sort, what do you think alcohol can do in this range as a medicinal agent?

Dr. Lolli Well, aren't the two things a little bit different? Is it a nutritional agent or a medicinal agent?

Dr. Leake It can be both.

Dr. Lolli It can be both. Generally people use it at different times for different purposes. For instance, let's take me. I was born in Italian culture, started to drink at the age of three, and I still do drink. I drink with my meals; in other words I use it as a food. However, the night before last I knew that I was not going to sleep because I flew here from New York and my biological time had been affected, and I had a couple of ounces of whiskey before going to bed; that was a medicinal use.

Dr. Leake A sedative effect, and a very useful one.

Dr. Lolli In my case a very useful one, because I tolerate barbiturates very poorly. They would make me feel weak and tired, and alcohol doesn't. From the nutritional angle, what I'm most interested in at this stage is this interplay of effects that we see between alcohol and food, and this kind of protective action that food seems to have.

Dr. Leake On the psychological effects of alcohol.

Dr. Lolli Exactly. What I briefly mentioned yesterday—and I don't know if I made it clear—is the following: We have been thinking all the time that drinking on a full stomach meant only one thing, that blood alcohol concentrations would be much lower, and the individual wouldn't feel the effects, just because of that. But we have found something a little bit different, that if you build up blood alcohol levels on a full stomach, exactly the same concentration as one builds with half as much alcohol on an empty stomach, the individual on a full stomach tolerates alcohol much, much better. In other words, blood alcohol at low levels is not an indication of the psychological condition of the individual.

Dr. Pribram Could this be because of the other things, such as sugar, fat, etc., in the blood along with the alcohol?

Dr. Lolli It has to do with the resistance of the central nervous system. What it is we don't know yet.

Dr. Leake We can put it in this way on a pharmacological level. Alcohol is a physical-chemical compound, and as a molecule, it does compete in a lot of enzyme systems that are ordinarily involved with maintaining our equilibrium.

Dr. Pribram Either that, or it may be adsorbed on other molecules, therefore not get through the blood-brain barrier.

Dr. Leake That's correct.

Dr. Lolli The blood alcohol curves are exactly the same, in our experiments.

ATTITUDES TOWARD ALCOHOL AND RESEARCH

Dr. Leake There was one point that we were discussing a moment ago, and that is the matter of money—on the one hand for such devices as nuclear reactors, and on the other hand, for the study of psychological aspects of alcohol. Now this is a sociological problem, and in one way I think it's more peculiar to the United States than to some other parts of the world. We are much more willing to put our money and effort and our learning into an understanding of our physical environment. We're willing to do that, but, in general, I would say that as a people, we're a little bit afraid as yet of looking hard at ourselves. We don't like to find the unpleasant things that we turn up when we study ourselves.

Dr. Pribram Not only the unpleasant things, but also we suspect that perhaps you can't do anything about them when we have full knowledge, and this turns out to be unpleasant in and of itself. Sometimes it isn't a positive unpleasant thing, but simply that things are best left alone to develop in and of themselves on the basis of the complicated factors of our culture beyond our control. This kind of thing can be just as unpleasant.

From the Floor I'm interested in this particular part very much. I'd like to hear you say something about the bottom of the scale of ecological society, starting at that end rather than at the other end. Particularly in the United States, we have a sort of societal guilt feeling about alcohol. If you mention alcohol at a talk before a Rotary club, you get a titter. Everybody's nervous, afraid of this subject; they're afraid they have it, the same as with an illness. Talking about the positive use of alcohol is all right in this room, but it's totally impractical in our society, because it's immediately red-raggish—the WCTU versus the liquor industry. We had the WCTU at one meeting and the liquor industry at another. If we had them both in the same room, the thing would be impossible. So what about all these factors?

Dr. Pribram These conditions gradually disappear with education. I mean, this was the case with tuberculosis a generation ago. I am sure Chauncey remembers that one just didn't mention TB in one's family, or anything of the kind. It just wasn't done. Then came a period in which the educational process took over, and it was found that it was a disease like all other diseases, in the sense that it was a dis-ease. Gradually, then, with the advent of drugs, which could not cure tuberculosis, mind you, in the sense that it was a specific antibacterial, but alleviated the process—all of a sudden we're emptying our tuberculosis sanitaria; and the same sort of thing I think is happening with tranquilizers and the social therapies in the state mental hospitals. Gradually we are no longer getting this vast increase in the number of people going to state hospitals, but at least a plateau has been reached and we have some evidence that somthing positive has been done.

Dr. Lolli I should like to add another point. There are still quite a few millions of people all over the world who resent the idea of relinquishing inebriety, including many scientists. They are much more willing to unload the responsibility, all the drinking problems, on the few alcoholics, or the many alcoholics, trying to manipulate statistics to prove that they are in very great numbers, and they are not willing to face the problem that a lot of people who are not "sick," who are still quite well adjusted, who still hold very important positions, feel that they have a right to get drunk once in a while. I think this is a very important point and one which is often overlooked.

Then there is another point, which I think is from the angle of psychodietetics. We deal with a drinking habit which is closely linked to an eating habit. Eating and drinking habits, nutritional habits, are linked with the very dawn of the psychological life of the individual. And they are linked with the appearance and thriving of the emotions of love and of the emotions of hatred. They're linked with the appearance of perhaps the greatest evil of our society, which is the taboo on tender feelings. This taboo is more fundamental than all the sexual inhibitions which derive from it, and this taboo on warm and tender feelings results from wrong early experiences of the child with the mother. Well, I would say that we all, as civilized men and women, and scientists, too, suffer, and very seriously, from that taboo on tenderness. And it is that taboo which forbids our looking objectively at both eating and drinking habits. We know a lot about the psychology of sex, because it is loaded with aggression. We know very little about the physiology of sex. We know a lot about the biochemistry and physiology of nutrition, because it has no aggressive implications. We know nothing about the psychology and sociology of nutrition, just because of this very same taboo on tenderness which affects practically all of us, or most all of us. I think we have to face it, because at least I see it in myself, perhaps, and in many other people who have been working with me a number of years—psychiatrists, social workers, biochemists, and so on and so forth. I don't know whether you people would agree with me.

Dr. Pribram Wholeheartedly, and I think the cocktail party, the size it has reached, is part of our reflection of this very fact that we get many people together because we want to pay our debts en masse instead of thinking of the tender relationships that we've built up.

Dr. Lolli I also think this taboo on tenderness has affected research policies, the granting of money, in this country and abroad. I know it, because of difficulty I face myself, in getting money for this type of thing.

Dr. Leake And a very important point in regard to alcohol, as you've indicated, is the inevitable association of abuse of alcohol with a mental disorder, and we haven't come to the point yet of accepting mental disorder as a disease in the same way that we accept tuberculosis now. This is a process in which we are now engaged, but it will take, I suspect, several generations before we will accept socially the fact that a mental disorder is a disease and must eventually be handled medically. This I think will be the picture with alcoholism.

Dr. Pribram And view disease as a temporary restitutive process which is often necessary; and, therefore, that a mental disorder can be a growth phenomenon, a temporary one.

THEORIES ABOUT ALCOHOLISM

From the Floor I'd like to ask the three of you about something that each of you has made a unique contribution to. We in public health education had a notion that perhaps the reason a person turns to alcohol is primarily because of a metabolic need. He may be a reasonably competent person, but sources of energy which seem to affect metabolism are found in alcohol. I have since met a fellow who has been working for a pharmaceutical house, as a Ph.D. in chemistry, who has been looking for something which would perhaps be more socially acceptable for the person who needs the metabolic effects of alcohol. How much truth is there in what I think I have heard these people say?

Dr. Leake Well, I can tell you only in part, but I would have hoped that Curt Richter had been here, or at least that his point of view might have been discussed. I mentioned it earlier this afternoon. Not only may there be biochemical factors of individuality such as Roger Williams thinks he has found in all of us, and in some instances compatible with the situation of being satisfied by alcohol, but also, Curt Richter has shown that there are also endocrine deficiencies, which may involve the adrenals or the thyroid.

Dr. Pribram   Not deficiencies, differences.

Dr. Leake   Differences, that's right. And if you use rats in whom these deficiencies are present, and if you give them a choice of water and of water with a certain amount of alcohol in it, they instinctively know that the alcohol somehow or another will balance off whatever metabolic deficiency they have, and they will take it as long as the deficiency is present. When the deficiency is corrected, they give up the alcohol. This has been shown experimentally, but whether it will apply to human beings, I don't know.

From the Floor   Are you saying, then, that chemically the deficiency will be eliminated?

Dr. Leake   We don't know.

Dr. Pribram   I think there are two problems. I think there are people, perhaps, who have a chemical affinity to alcohol, who really need alcohol in the sense that once they have been exposed to it, some kind of addiction is set up.

From the Floor   We see it in alcoholics.

Dr. Pribram   Alcoholics, that's right.

Coffee drinking is a good example. I'm sure we can all get along without coffee. On the other hand, if I don't have my cup of coffee in the morning, I get a headache by evening, and most people are really addicted to coffee in some way or other.

Dr. Leake   At least they're habituated.

Dr. Pribram   Well, I'd even use the word addicted, because you get the withdrawal symptoms, etc.

Dr. Leake   Antisocial behavior too?

Dr. Pribram   Antisocial behavior and everything. I think there is that element to a different degree in different people.

Dr. Leake   This is an awfully good point, as to how far one can make a comparison between alcoholism and any other drug addiction, and whether or not another drug can substitute for alcohol in an addict, or whether alcohol can substitute for the drug that the addict has become addicted to. Well, now, this is a very difficult thing, but it does look as though there are a significant number of people who may start their general antisocial career, if you want to put it that way, through alcohol and then turn to something else. There is a psychological factor, then, and it's usually put under the term of escape—you escape from an intolerable environment—and there are a number of chemicals that will help you do that, alcohol and most of the addictive drugs.

Dr. Pribram This is a different problem from the chemical one, and I think they should be kept separate. I mean, they're both equally important, but perhaps different with different people.

Dr. Leake Oh yes.

Dr. Lolli If I may inject a humorous remark, a German psychiatrist, twenty-five or thirty years ago, used to treat morphine addicts by getting them drunk. I certainly would not approve of that type of treatment, but I think there can be cycles and alternations between morphine addiction and alcohol addiction or amphetamine addiction, and so on.

From the Floor Now I'm going to push on this question here just for another minute. For instance, if a man has been persuaded to join Alcoholics Anonymous because alcoholism is not socially acceptable, and if chemically he needs alcohol, we can be committing a social crime, as I understand.

Dr. Pribram Oh no. Let me give you an example, just to finish off quickly that point. The days before we had insulin, we treated diabetics and kept them alive (unless they were very severe diabetics) with dietary methods, high ketone diets and high fat diets and things of this kind, and we did very well. Now, in a sense we were committing a crime by keeping them from eating and by not giving them insulin, but we didn't have the insulin, so we just kept them alive. Now the alcoholic, the severe alcoholic, is a menace to himself and to others, so if you just can in any way keep him viable, this is fine. And remember, this kind of chemical affinity I was talking about may exist only in the minority of instances anyway.

From the Floor I should like to ask a question concerning predisposition. I've heard the discussion of Roger Williams's theory, pro and con. I mean biochemical predisposition. And secondly, psychological predisposition. What is the relation between the two?

Dr. Lolli May I say a word very openly? The problem with Roger Williams is that he is a good chemist. In that field he has done a tremendous amount of good work. Whether the work he has done in the field of alcoholism is just as good as that which he has done in other fields remains to be seen.

Dr. Leake He is prejudiced himself and doesn't understand he has an unconscious built-in prejudice.

Dr. Lolli There is no evidence whatsoever that a vitamin deficiency precedes the onset of that type of an addictive pattern of drinking which is called alcoholism. As far as the so-called emotional liability—I call it so-called because we are in the year 1961, and concepts of mind and matter are changing so rapidly that we cannot talk any more in the language that we used fifteen years ago, which now is medieval. I really mean it. After a book like *The Concept of Mind*, for instance, I doubt if we can talk any more in those terms. Still we know what we mean when we speak about the emotions, at least faintly. Surely when we see 300, 500, 600 alcoholics or more, as any one of us has seen, we can according to our personal belief decide whether they have a dependence-independence complex, or any other psychological, psychopathological liability, according to the several orthodoxies or heresies that we stick to. However, we have failed to gather adequate controls and to compare notes between the various groups. More than anything else we have failed in the most fundamental thing, to define who an alcoholic is, and I dare say that we'll never be able to do it, because if we use some little tools of logic and try to apply them to what we have been saying, we will see that we are on just as sound a track as if we were trying to define a witch, I think.

Dr. Pribram Back to the problem of the psychological or chemical, let me just remind you that when we say psychological or mental or any of these things, what we're really talking about is the way in which the experience is laid down in the memory traces of the individual, plus his predispositions to it which are built in. This interaction gives rise to the behavior pattern from which we derive our psychological or mental behavior, and mental becomes verbal behavior, and psychological becomes mental behavior, and that's all. So what you're talking about, in addition to the usual physical and chemical, is the new kind of physical and chemical that's been laid down by experience, which comes from parts of the brain.

From the Floor Some of the staff of Dr. Sanford of Stanford University, are now talking about the possibility of doing research to see whether there is a so-called alcoholic personality before alcoholism, predisposing to alcoholism, and this is the kind of thing I'm thinking about.

Dr. Pribram We can almost predict what their findings will be. They will find that there is such a thing, provided that you keep the culture constant. In another culture you will find there is a different predisposing personality but the personality, mind you, is made up of whatever the organism has gained through experience embedded in his own nervous system, his own reaction patterns, plus his own chemical dispositions, and so on.

Dr. Lolli Going back to the psychopathology of the researcher, excuse me if I insist on this, even this attempt at sifting the good guys from the bad guys is an extremely dangerous trend—in science, in sociology, in morality, in anything. We read a few months ago that some very well-meaning scientist had decided on five points by which you are going to decide, at the age of five which child is going to become a thief at the age of twenty-five.

Dr. Pribram The real danger in this is a subtle one; Jerry Frank has a word for it. It's called the *self-fulfilling prophecy*. If you label something for an individual, and he knows his label, he will then go ahead and grow right into it and follow right into it as if it were a track. Now this is a well-known and well-documented psychological and psychiatric fact, so the danger that you're talking about is just this sort of thing, that in doing a study of this sort, it's just like creating an atom bomb. In a sense, you're altering the culture that you're living in by making the study, just as the atomic physicist has done, so therefore there are some moral values that immediately come forward. It's the same thing that I've come up against in my studies. I'm interested in the human brain, but I can't go about putting electrodes in and making cuts in human brains; it's morally improper; therefore, I have to use animals and get at this in various ways which will not affect the human process, per se. And I think these people will have to come to that also. They will certainly have to limit their researches in such a way that they don't alter and perhaps damage beyond all recognition the very process that they're studying.

Dr. Leake Now I'm going to take the liberty, by virtue of my age, of concluding this discussion. I want to review this conference pretty quickly and briefly.

We have had really a very remarkable time discussing lots of aspects of alcohol and civilization. We started out, you remember,

with discussing the effects of alcohol on the body, with a consideration of the metabolism of alcohol, alcohol and nutrition, the clinical
value of alcohol, and our knowledge of the physiology of alcohol.
Then we had a session on alcohol and the mind, where we discussed
alcohol and skills, alcohol as a tranquilizer, and alcohol in regard to
individual behavior, the effects of alcohol on behavior and emotion.
Then we came to the social implications of alcohol, where we discussed the antiquity of alcohol as a beverage, the use of alcohol in
human cultures, the alcohol problem or alcoholism, the cocktail
hour, and alcohol in contemporary culture. And still at the social
level we considered alcohol and the law, drinking habits and their
function, and the responsibility of the individual and the community, and we've split up for discussion of specific and interdisciplinary viewpoints.

You see, as this was built up, in a way it corresponds to a consideration of these various levels of biological organization. We start
with relatively simple things, what alcohol does in cells and then
come to individuals, but inevitably, you see, we come to the picture
of societies; the extremely important thing is, I believe, that we have
as yet very little information as to those integrating factors that
build up as we go along in this kind of a sequence. They become
increasingly complex and interact. As was pointed out, when we
do alter our own environment as we go along, we come back always, I suppose, to the old position of Heraclitus, that it is in
change that we exist, and it is in the balance of adjusting to that
change that perhaps we can exist in reasonable decency and satisfaction. I think this has been an extremely profitable and useful
conference, and I think it has brought out an amazingly wide and
significant series of viewpoints.

I want to conclude with this observation: Whereas the business
of science is to get, if we can, the truth about ourselves and our
environment, it's always wise to make sure that we balance our
science—whether in our educational procedure, or in our social discussion, or in our individual lives—with the humanistic point of
view, the humanities; science going off by itself doesn't give us all
the answers in life. The humanities, involving literature, history, art,
and music, have a function in this matter that we skirted a bit today, this matter of judgment. They're concerned with taste, and
discrimination, and propriety, or the appropriateness of fitting the
facts that we have to the purposes we want to accomplish. This does

call for judgment, and it is, I think, only in connection with the practice of the arts and the humanities or the reading of literature or history that we can sharpen our own individual tastes and judgment so that, when we're confronted with the facts that we have about a matter like alcohol, and wish to apply them, as we all do, to the welfare of ourselves and our societies, the judgments we can acquire from a humanistic background will be of help.